Minerals and Rocks 17

Editor in Chief
P.J. Wyllie, Chicago, IL

Editors
A. El Goresy, Heidelberg
W. von Engelhardt, Tübingen · T. Hahn, Aachen

F. J. Sawkins

Metal Deposits in Relation to Plate Tectonics

With 173 Figures

Springer-Verlag
Berlin Heidelberg New York Tokyo 1984

Dr. Frederick J. Sawkins
Department of Geology and Geophysics
University of Minnesota
108 Pillsbury Hall
310 Pillsbury Drive S.E.
Minneapolis, MN 55455, USA

Volumes 1 to 9 in this series appeared under the title
Minerals, Rocks and Inorganic Materials

ISBN 3-540-12752-6 Springer-Verlag Berlin Heidelberg New York Tokyo
ISBN 0-387-12752-6 Springer-Verlag New York Heidelberg Berlin Tokyo

Library of Congress Cataloging in Publication Data. Sawkins, Frederick J. Metal deposits in relation to plate tectonics. (Minerals and rocks; 17) Includes index. 1. Ore-deposits. 2. Plate tectonics. I. Title. II. Series. TN263.S27 1983 553.4 83-16890

The use of registered names, trademarks, etc. in this publication does not imply, even in the absence of a specific statement, that such names are exempt from the relevant protective laws and regulations and therefore free for general use.

Media conversion, printing and binding: Brühlsche Universitätsdruckerei, Giessen
2131/3130-543210

Preface

I attempt this volume with no small degree of trepidation, for despite the near universal acceptance of plate tectonic theory, and the undeniable sweep and power of the concepts involved, points of controversy and uncertainty still abound. This is especially true with regard to the limited extent to which many ancient geologic terrains, however well studied, lend themselves to plate tectonic interpretation. There is also considerable controversy regarding the genesis of many metal deposits, and this impacts upon the degree to which such deposits can be meaningfully related to the tectonic settings in which they occur.

It is relatively simple matter to point out that certain types of ore deposits exhibit impressive time-space associations with certain kinds of more recent plate boundary environments. It is also all too easy to possible plate tectonic-ore deposit relationships in ancient geologic terrains. What is more challenging is the recognition of the boundaries beyond which speculation is idle, but within which useful new insights regarding the relationship of certain ores to their lithologic and tectonic environments may emerge.

My interest in plate tectonic-metal deposit relationships was initially motivated by a desire to find a suitable framework within which students could be introduced to the wide variety of distinctive metal deposit types. Somewhat later it was fostered by the desire to investigate the degree to which such concepts could be used in creative planning of exploration programs. However, I have encountered a certain degree of confusion about metal deposits and their divergent types amongst students, exploration geologists, and geochemists interested in ore genesis problems. We all have much to learn regarding these matters, but an attempt as synthesis seems warranted at this time, especially in view of our increasing dependence on earth resources. I make no claim that application of plate tectonic concepts can pinpoint new metal deposits. The main tool available to the exploration geologist is that of analogy with respect to other deposits and to their lithologic settings, i.e., certain types of metal deposits occur in association with certain types of rocks. The importance of plate tectonics is simply that plate interactions spawn various types of lithologic assemblages and, thus, such concepts can considerably sharpen our perceptions and interpretations of geologic terrains. As such, they can aid the exploration geologist in his(her) evaluation of various lithologic sequences and the types of metal deposits that might have been generated within them.

The study of metal deposits has accelerated a great deal in the last two decades, in particular through geochemical study. The application of fluid inclusion, stable isotope, and various experimental techniques to the study of metal deposits has broadened our insights into the chemical and hydrodynamic aspects of ore formation. These advances have, in turn, allowed the formation of more realistic conceptual models for various types of ore generating systems. Such models are of considerable aid to the exploration and mining geologist in areas of known mineralization, but are of more limited utility in terms of the search for new mineral districts.

The problem of the geographic distribution of metal deposits must be addressed initially in terms of geologic and tectonic environments rather than the nuances of ore solution geochemistry. Endeavors in this field, it seems, have not kept pace with those of a more geochemical nature (e.g. Barnes, 1979). In part, this is because geochemical research tends to be more 'tidy' and amenable to institutional funding and publication that the rather less rigorous and more empirical aspects of regional synthesis and compilation. The latter have to be based on some combination of personal experience and literature research. An important point in this regard is that metal deposits and the systems that generate them need to be viewed not as geochemical accidents, but rather as fortunate culminations of normal geologic and geochemical processes.

No one has made this point with more eloquence than Wyllie (1981), who states that metal deposits are not "the illegitimate offspring from random couplings of rocks and fluids from intermediate sources," but "have respectable ...family lineages, with ancestors deep within the continental crust, or below it."

The extent to which ore generating systems can proceed to fruition and where they develop depends on a host of local factors, but the broad environmental controls in each case will be tectonic. It follows that if these tectonic controls result in the main from plate interactions, and if plate tectonics have operated throughout much of earth history, then a variety of environments favorable for ore generation must have repeated themselves through geologic time. A consequence of these observations, if correct, is that major irregularities in the time distribution of various metal deposit types require explanation.

Ore deposits can be broadly divided into those generated by endogenetic processes and those generated by exogenic processes. The former are invariably associated with thermal processes and, in general, can be related more readily to magnetic and tectonic events instigated by plate activity. Deposits formed by surficial processes such as weathering or shallow marine sedimentation will have relationships to their tectonic environment that are more tenuous.

This volume represents an attempt to provide a rational basis for the observed time-space distribution of metal deposits, at least those of endogenous type. Such deposits can form by a wide variety of mechanisms in a highly diverse spectrum of geologic environments, and it follows that their relationships to plate tectonics will vary from significant in some instances to more tenuous in others. In fact, it is important to realize that even in cases where an impressive association between plate tectonics and certain ore types is manifest, plate interactions merely provide the master control for the particular geologic environments within which such deposits tend to form.

What I propose to do in the chapters that follow is deal with specific plate tectonic environments and cover the ore deposits that can be associated with each. Descriptions of individual type examples for which abundant data exist are provided to add substance to the volume. Additional examples are catalogued, where feasible, but any exhaustive compilation of world metal deposits is early beyond the scope of this book. Certain of my interpretations of distant ore deposits garnered from the literature will inevitably be in error, and possibly enrage some of those with first-hand local knowledge. To such people I can only offer an advance apology and an exhortation to publish and set the record straight. The line between creative synthesis and idle speculation is an extremely fuzzy one. I have included, wherever feasible, some thoughts on how the relationship between tectonics, geologic terrains, and metal deposits can be used in the context of exploration planning. Inevitably, such thoughts will be of a speculative nature, but the literature on ore deposits is notably lacking in attempts to do this. A concerted attempt has been made to include up to date references and to avoid references pertaining to obscure sources or unpublished material, so that the interested reader with access to a good geological library can backtrack on any particular subject.

It is hoped that this book will prove useful to students at the advanced undergraduate and graduate levels, and to mining and exploration geologists. I owe no small debt of gratitude to various company geologists around the world for their willingness to share freely of their time and local expertise with an itinerant academic. Without their enormous, and sometimes unheralded, contributions, the science of economic geology would be sad shape indeed, and in recognition of this, I dedicate this volume to them. I am also indebted to the front line troops such as Richard Sillitoe, who, not only have covered vast amounts of territory, but have written lucidly and imaginatively about their observations.

Finally, it is hoped that we will be able eventually to use "fundamental ore deposit geology to elucidate plate tectonics, not (only) the reverse" (Guilbert, 1981).

Acknowledgments. The initial typescript of this book was produced by Kathy Ohler, for whose competent, patient, and always cheerful help I am most grateful. The figures were draftet by Roxann Cioper and Jim Kiehne, and I thank them for their timely aid.

I owe a special debt of gratitude to Richard Sillitoe who reviewed nearly all stages of the manuscript and corrected a number of my misconceptions. Discussions with my colleagues at the University of Minnesota were also most helpful. Finally, my thanks to Peter Wyllie for initially suggesting the project and for encouragement during its evolution.

Frederick J. Sawkins

Contents

Introduction: Plate Tectonics and Geology

Plate tectonics, as it operates in the modern earth, represents in a fundamental sense a mechanism by which excess thermal energy from the mantle is dissipated (Sclater et al., 1980). A substantial data base now exists concerning the operation of plate tectonics during Phanerozoic time, and evidence for similar tectonic activity during Proterozoic time appears to be steadily growing, both in quantity and quality. Concrete evidence for the operation of plate tectonics during Archean time is simply not available, but provocative similarities exist between certain important elements of Archean terrains and the lithologic assemblages generated by certain types of modern plate interaction.

Before we proceed further, the spectrum of tectonic activity that can be included under the rubric of plate tectonics requires clarification. In addition to large scale horizontal rotation of plates, aborted rifting, hotspot activity, and even Basin and Range-type extensional tectonics are all considered legitimate facets of plate tectonic activity. The last 200 million years of earth history can be rather rigorously interpreted in terms of plate interactions, thanks largely to interpretation and dating of seafloor magnetic anomaly patterns. Reconstructions of earlier plate interactions have to be made on the basis of the geologic record of the continents and paleomagnetic studies, but we need to remind ourselves that a considerable set of assumptions are involved in these exercises. Nevertheless, plate tectonic interpretations of more ancient continental geologic terrains appear to have met with considerable success in many instances, and exercises of this type continue apace.

There are certain fundamental principles, in addition to that of uniformitarianism, that must be adhered to in attempting such reconstructions. One of the most important is that of isostasy. Thus, thicknesses of sedimentary and/or volcanic rocks in excess of a few thousand meters cannot accumulate and be preserved in intracontinental areas unless extensional attenuation of the crust takes place. It follows that ancient accumulations of such rocks with greater thicknesses must have initially accumulated at continental edges, or in intracontinental areas subject to some sort of tensional rifting activity. By the same token, plate convergence that results in major thickening of the continental crust (e.g. Andes, Himalayas), must be followed by massive supracrustal (and possibly some subcrustal) erosion. By the time erosion has removed the topographic expression of such areas and isostatic equilibrium is re-established, ancient examples of these orogenic belts will bear little resemblance to their modern analogues. As we shall see later, this has important implications for understanding the time distribution of certain types of metal deposits.

Another important clue to ancient tectonic regimes is the petrochemistry of igneous rocks. Martin and Piwinskii (1972) pointed out that igneous rocks generated at convergent plate boundaries tend to be characterized by unimodal petrochemistry, whereas those generated in rift zones are characterized by bimodal petrochemistry. This bimodality, especially with regard to silica content of volcanics, although not as yet fully understood in petrogenetic terms, appears to provide a powerful tool in terms of recognition of ancient rifting events. The trace element chemistry of ancient igneous rocks has also been used, again by analogy with data from modern terrains, as a fingerprint for the tectonic environments of magma generation (Floyd and Winchester, 1975).

These, together with lithologic assemblages, are the main tools other than actual structures that geologists have at their disposal for tectonic interpretations of older geologic terrains. Despite the assumptions involved, they have been used with success by many, both in areas where telltale structures (e.g. normal faults, nappes) are still observable, and to some extent where metamorphism and orogenesis have blurred the structural relationships. What is pertinent here, both in terms of ancient tectonics and the distribution of ore deposits, is that certain similar lithologic assemblages have been generated and welded into the fabric of the continents repeatedly during much of earth history. Thus, various types of ore-generating environments have undoubtedly repeated themselves through time.

This is not the place for an exhaustive review of the full spectrum of geologic terrains spawned by various types of plate boundary, but certain points need to be made preparatory to the main sections of the volume that follow. Plate convergence via the process of subduction can occur entirely in oceanic areas, adjacent to continental margins, or within such margins. A preliminary consensus appears to have been reached that the bulk of the materials that build volcanoplutonic arcs in this plate setting are fluxed from the asthenospheric wedge overlying the subducting slab (Anderson et al., 1978), but there is a good deal of circumstantial evidence for a certain degree of involvement of the subducting slab in the whole process (Gill, 1981). In addition, styles of subduction can vary in terms of rates, angle of dip, thermal maturity of slab, plate vectors, and imposed stress field (Dewey, 1980; Uyeda and Nishiwaki, 1980). These variables affect the intensity of earthquake activity, and the tectonic, magmatic and sedimentation patterns of arcs at all stages of their development. Dewey (1980) defines arcs as extensional, neutral or compressional, depending on the relative motions of the overriding plate, and the degree to which rollback of the subduction hinge is occurring (Fig. 1). He also demonstrates that arc segmentation tends to correlate with breaks in the subducting plate, originally inherited from transform offsets at a spreading ridge system. Finally, Dewey draws attention to the fact that an extensional arc system will have the tendency to evolve through a neutral stage to one in which the original intraoceanic arc is welded

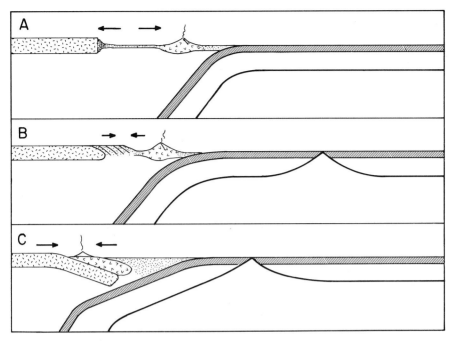

Fig. 1. Three types of arc systems. Arrows indicate vectors of relative movement of volcanic arc and continent. The typical evolutionary sequence is from A through B to C (from Dewey, 1980)

to a continental margin to become part of the forearc portion of a compressional continental margin arc. At least some of the allochthonous terrains of the western United States, Canada, and Alaska seem to provide clear examples (Coney, 1981).

The variations in style of arc development discussed above will have profound effects on the magmatic, sedimentary, and structural evolution of individual arc systems. For example, extensional arcs tend to be dominated by basaltic-andesitic volcanics and their plutonic equivalents and have subdued topographic expression. As a consequence, volcanisclastic sedimentary fans are restricted, and in composition reflect their rather mafic source terrains.

At the other end of the spectrum compressional arcs develop thick crust, and exhibit andesitic-dacitic-rhyolitic volcanic and associated granodioritic plutonic igneous rocks. As a result of isostatic uplift and consequent erosion, such arcs produce extensive and thick, more felsic sedimentary fans. These conditions are typified by the Andean arc system of Peru and Chile, although in detail the compression probably varied in intensity with time and may have been interspersed with extensional episodes. Continental margin compressional arcs of this type manifest a well defined inward younging of magmatism with time (Clarke et al., 1976), and can be divided into principal arc and inner arc seg-

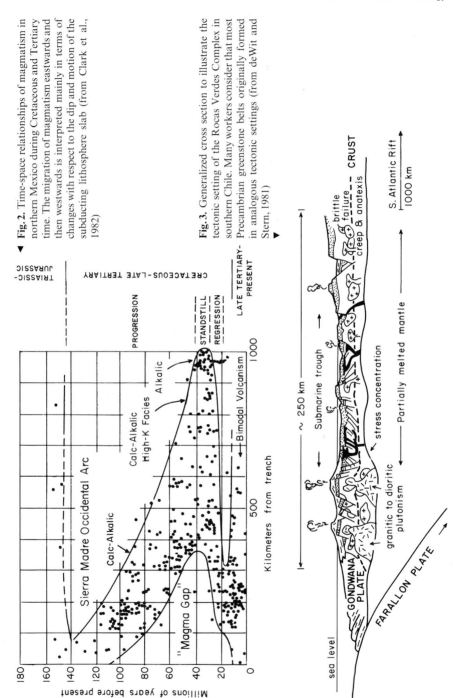

Fig. 2. Time-space relationships of magmatism in northern Mexico during Cretaceous and Tertiary time. The migration of magmatism eastwards and then westwards is interpreted mainly in terms of changes with respect to the dip and motion of the subducting lithosphere slab (from Clark et al., 1982)

Fig.3. Generalized cross section to illustrate the tectonic setting of the Rocas Verdes Complex in southern Chile. Many workers consider that most Precambrian greenstone belts originally formed in analogous tectonic settings (from deWit and Stern, 1981)

ments (Sillitoe, 1981a). Principal arcs encompass the main linear focus of volcanoplutonic magmatism, whereas inner arc zones exhibit more diffuse magmatism manifest as isolated stocks and limited volcanism. In some instances the general tendency of the angle of subduction to flatten with time will be reversed, and the locus of magmatism will swing trenchward. Such appears to be the case in the southwestern United States and northern Mexico (Fig. 2; Coney and Reynolds, 1977; Keith, 1978) during Cretaceous and Tertiary time.

The extent to which the geologic terrains present in Cenozoic arc systems are recognizable in more ancient terrains is a matter of some controversy. However, this author concurs with the arguments advanced by Burke et al. (1976) that the granite-greenstone terrains of Archean and certain younger cratons are related to ancient subduction processes. Tarney et al. (1976) have produced cogent arguments that the Rocas Verdes marginal basin in southern Chile (de Wit and Stern, 1981) represents a young example of greenstone belt formation (Fig. 3). It is important, however, to realize that the suprastructural (volcanic) portions of neutral and compressional arcs are rapidly lost to the forces of erosion and will be less likely to have preserved ancient analogues.

This brief review of the development of arc systems is admittedly sketchy, but provides a skeleton to flesh out in following chapters. It is worth noting that, as our understanding of the complexities and variations of arc environments grows in parallel with a clearer comprehension of arc metallogeny, the concept that tectonics are an important control for the formation of arc-hosted ore deposits appears to be increasingly vindicated.

Divergent plate boundary environments in the modern earth are very much dominated by sites at which seafloor spreading is taking place. However, within the fabric of the continents are many terrains related to past rifting events. Some of these occur as identifiable failed rifts, others have undergone extensive later orogenesis, at least in part due to complete revolutions of the Wilson Cycle (Burke et al., 1977), and can only be identified by careful compilation of geologic data.

The main variability exhibited by spreading ridge systems relates to spreading rates. Slow-spreading ridges tend to exhibit a well defined axial rift and greater structural and petrochemical diversity as compared to fast-spreading ridges (Fig. 4). In broad terms, magma genesis by partial melting of underlying welts of asthenosphere, and its emplacement as a layered complex of basaltic pillow lavas, sheeted dikes, and underlying gabbros is relatively well understood. Nevertheless, complexities that await further investigation do exist.

Much of the dissipation of the heat transferred from the mantle during seafloor spreading processes is achieved through the action of seawater-dominated hydrothermal convective systems at or near ridge crests (Sclater et al., 1980). Actualistic examples of such systems are currently receiving considerable research attention, especially at 21° N on the East Pacific Rise and along the Galapagos spreading system.

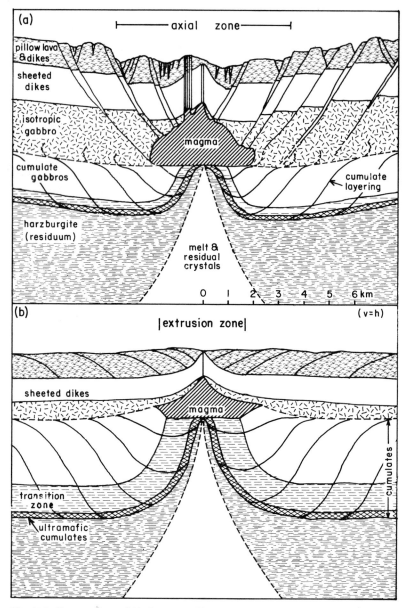

Fig. 4a, b. Cross sections of (a) slow-spreading and (b)fast-spreading ocean ridge systems. Note the more pronounced fault-induced topography associated with slow-spreading systems (from Burke and Kidd, 1980)

Only miniscule amounts of the oceanic lithosphere produced at divergent plate boundaries become incorporated into continental geologic terrains as ophiolite complexes (Coleman, 1977). In addition, only relatively small amounts of that which does escape the subduction process are not subject to intense tectonic disruption. Despite this, recognizable ophiolite complexes are known from many Cenozoic and Mesozoic orogenic belts, and they occur also in certain Paleozoic orogens (e.g., Bird et al., 1971). Unequivocal pre-Paleozoic ophiolite complexes are known only in Pan-African (1,000-500 m.y.) orogenic belts in Saudi Arabia (Nasseef et al., 1980) and Morocco (LeBlanc, 1976), and in the Baikal orogen, U.S.S.R. (Kiltin and Pavlova, 1974). As Burke and Kidd (1980) point out, however, dismembered fragments of even older oceanic crust also surely remain to be discovered in early Proterozoic orogenic belts and perhaps even in Archean terrains. The increasing scarcity of such rocks as a function of geologic age is entirely explicable in terms of erosional loss.

Hotspot activity represents an interaction of lithosphere and underlying asthenosphere and as such is considered a valid plate tectonic process. Most hotspots do little more than leave a track of basaltic lavas on the plate overriding their source regions (Fig. 5). However, in cases where hotspots impinge on overlying continental lithosphere that is more or less stationary with respect to them, the basaltic volcanism tends to be accompanied by processes that can result in continental rifting and perhaps the initiation of a new Wilson Cycle (Burke and Dewey, 1973). The sequence of events by which subcontinental hotspot activity can lead to rifting and onset of a Wilson Cycle are illustrated in Figure 6. The connection of hotspot activity, manifest as the eruption of flood basalts, with successful continental rifting is clearly demonstrated by the rifting history of the Atlantic Ocean. The Iceland and Tristan/Gough hotspots sit astride or close to active spreading systems, and are connected to continental flood basalts on neighboring continents by aseismic volcanic ridges (see Fig. 5). As noted by Burke and Kidd (1980), all major identifiable past flood basalt events were connected with continental rifting, and, except for the Columbia River basalts, the Deccan Traps, and the Siberian Traps, ocean opening events. Older examples include a number of late Proterozoic flood basalt-rifting events (Sawkins, 1976a), and possibly the 2.15 b.y. swarms adjacent to the Labrador Trough (Fahrig and Wanless, 1963). The Great Dyke, Zimbabwe (2.6 b.y.) and the Ameralik dykes in West Greenland (3.0 b.y. or older) may well be representative of this same basalt magmatism-rifting phenomenon.

The relationships between doming, rifting and continental breakup are particularly well illustrated in post-Paleozoic history of Africa (Burke and Whiteman, 1973). Crustal melting, in response to hotspot activity, can produce anorogenic alkali granites such as those of the Jos Plateau, Nigeria (Jacobson et al., 1958) prior to rifting. However, the volcanic and sedimentary rocks that fill rift basins and the broader downwarps that post-date them (see Milanovsky, 1981) are the most important products of rifting in terms of environments for metallogenesis. Such rocks and their metamorphosed equivalents have wide distribu-

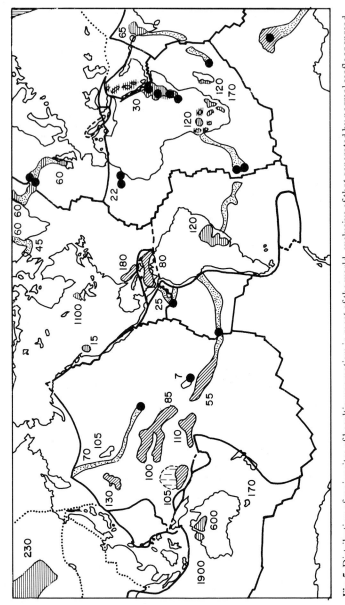

Fig. 5. Distribution of major sites of basaltic magmatism in most of the world, exclusive of that generated by normal seafloor spreading processes. Linear trends record plate motions relative to hotspots (black dots). Diagonal ruling indicates submarine equivalent of flood basalts, horizontal ruling indicates continental flood basalts. Numbers give approximate ages of flood basalts in millions of years (from Burke and Kidd, 1980)

tion on the continents and host a number of major metal deposits (Sawkins, 1976b, 1982a).

The lower portions of rift troughs are typically occupied by basalts and lesser amounts of felsic igneous rocks (bimodal volcanism). Overlying these volcanics, non-marine arkosic arenites and local conglomerates tend to accumulate.

(a)

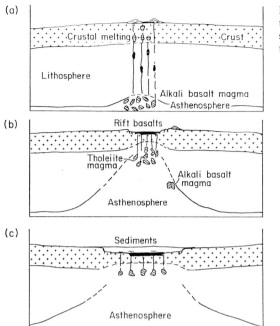

(b)

(c)

Fig. 6. Generalized cross sections to illustrate the sequence of events commonly associated with intracontinental rift formation

As rifting progresses and lithospheric attenuation continues, the rift floor drops below sea level and marine sediments, both clastic and non-clastic, will accumulate. Real world examples of this scenario (Burke and Dewey, 1973) are numerous, but inevitably each rift system contains its own set of (typically minor) variations. Many Proterozoic metamorphic terrains contain high grade cover rocks preserved in synforms between domes of reactivated basement. These cover rock assemblages typically consist of quartzofeldspathic gneisses with lesser amounts of amphibolite, marble, and minor iron formation, and at least in part must represent original rifting-related lithologies.

An inevitable result of ocean opening and closing (Wilson) cycles is continental collision. Burke et al. (1977) have attempted to demonstrate that all ancient orogenic belts can be interpreted in terms of such events. This approach has not gone unchallenged (e.g., Kroner, 1977a, b) by those who support the concept of ensialic orogeny. Space does not permit a more detailed examination of this dichotomy here, but evidence is growing that all orogenic events are preceded by a rifting episode (e.g., Martin and Porada, 1978). Thus, the crux of the matter is the amount of extension and ocean opening that need occur prior to the onset of compression and accompanying orogenesis. It is worth noting that even failed rifts tend to undergo an inversion from extensional to compressive stress regimes during their history (see Milanovsky, 1981). More careful work on ancient rifts and related mobile belts is clearly needed.

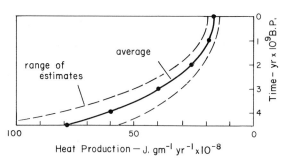

Fig. 7. Heat production-time relationships in the earth. The progressive decrease is due to decay-related reduction in the budget of heatproducing radioactive isotopes of U, Th and K (after Lee, 1967)

Both types of orogeny, if they are in fact distinct, not only follow rifting events, but tend to result in high grade metamorphic terrains, characterized by basement reactivation and emplacement of anatectic granites. Exposure of such terrains implies significant amounts of uplift and erosion. The theoretical gamut of structural, sedimentary, and magmatic events occurring at higher levels during collision events can involve awesome complexities (Dewey, 1977) and can affect large segments of the continents (e.g., Himalaya-Tibet region). It is thus no small wonder that a certain degree of controversy surrounds the tectonic interpretation of many ancient orogenic belts.

In the preceding pages we have considered various plate environments and touched on evidence suggestive of their presence during more remote geologic epochs. Much of this evidence can be integrated into a comprehensive theory of plate tectonic-controlled continental growth, for it seems abundantly clear that the subduction process builds new continental-type crust in intraoceanic areas, and probably adds to the volume of the continents at continental margin subduction sites.

During Archean time the capacity of the mantle to produce heat was considerably greater due to larger budgets of radioactive elements (Fig. 7), and thus the requirement for some type of heat-dissipating convective activity was more pronounced. This fact, taken in conjunction with other persuasive similarities of the Archean rock record to certain younger terrains, and Hoffman's (1980) compelling evidence for the operation of Wilson Cycle tectonics in northwest Canada two billion years ago, supports the notion that plate-like activity and attendant continental growth have been features of earth evolution since early Archean times. Moorbath (1980) has reviewed the implications of the geochronologic data base for the oldest continental rocks, and argues cogently for progressive continental growth from those times onward. The requirements for greater rates of mantle heat dissipation at that time can be accommodated merely by increasing the number of plates, and/or their rates of rotation, without the necessity for greatly increased geothermal gradients. Opposing concepts of a very early permobile sialic crust (e.g., Hargraves, 1978; Fyfe, 1980) seem not only at odds with much of the geologic and isotopic evidence, but run aground on available P-T estimates derived from Archean granulites and related rocks (see Tarney and Windley, 1978; Wells, 1979).

This very brief review of the role plate tectonics is believed to have played in the evolution of the continents represents a mere skeleton on which to hang the various geologic environments we will encounter in the chapters that follow, and is an indication of the writer's own conceptual baggage. Readers who feel a need for more substance are strongly encouraged to avail themselves of 'The Evolving Continents' (Windley, 1978).

Part I
Convergent Plate Boundary Environments

Chapter 1 Principal Arcs
and Their Associated Metal Deposits

Principal arcs are relatively narrow, well defined zones of volcanic and plutonic igneous activity that occur above intermediate to steeply dipping subduction zones. These important metallogenic elements are characterized by the formation of Cu, Fe, Mo, Au, and Ag deposits that exhibit a close time-space association with calc-alkaline magmatism.

1.1 Porphyry-Type Deposits

Porphyry-type deposits can be defined as low grade, large disseminated deposits emplaced either in shallow porphyritic intrusives, and/or in the country rocks adjacent to such intrusives. Diagnostic features are an intimate fracturing of the host rock and pervasive wall-rock alteration. An important corollary is that such deposits are amenable to bulk mining techniques.

Porphyry copper deposits, the major type of porphyry deposit, range in size from about 10 million tons to several billion tons and exhibit grades of hypogene mineralization that range from 0.2% to about 2% Cu. In many instances, especially in continental margin deposits, supergene enrichment is an important facet of orebody formation. Porphyry-type mineralization with grades of less than 0.2% copper also tends to be widespread in porphyry copper belts, but in most instances supergene enrichment cannot create viable orebodies from protore that lean.

Porphyry-type deposits, especially those of copper, occur predominantly along linear, calc-alkaline volcanoplutonic arcs related to the subduction process. The spatial association of porphyry copper deposits and volcanoplutonic arcs formed above current or former subduction zones (Fig. 1.1) was first detailed by Sillitoe (1972a). More recently, Uyeda and Nishiwaki (1980) have demonstrated that porphyry copper deposits tend to form in compressional arc systems, and appear to be notably scarce in extensional arcs. Thus, the volcanoplutonic arcs along the western margins of North and South America are well endowed with porphyry copper deposits (Hollister, 1978; Sutherland Brown, 1976; Sillitoe, 1976, 1981a,b), whereas arc systems that have undergone considerable back-arc spreading (e.g., Japan) appear to be devoid of porphyry copper deposits.

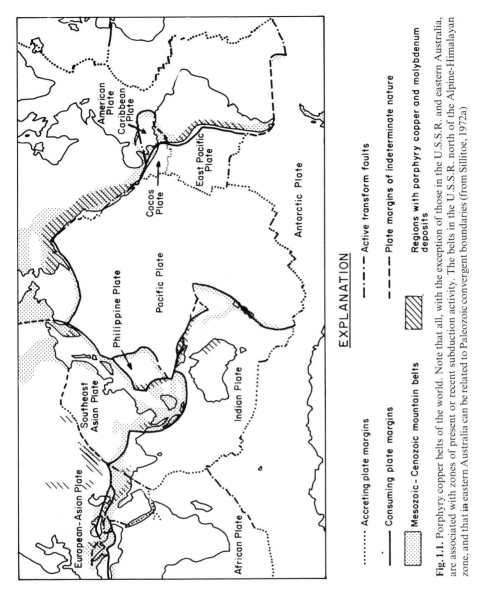

Fig. 1.1. Porphyry copper belts of the world. Note that all, with the exception of those in the U.S.S.R. and eastern Australia, are associated with zones of present or recent subduction activity. The belts in the U.S.S.R. north of the Alpine-Himalayan zone, and that in eastern Australia can be related to Paleozoic convergent boundaries (from Sillitoe, 1972a)

EXPLANATION

.... Accreting plate margins

——— Consuming plate margins

▨ Mesozoic–Cenozoic mountain belts

—·—·— Active transform faults

———— Plate margins of indeterminate nature

▨ Regions with porphyry copper and molybdenum deposits

Around the Pacific rim the age distribution of porphyry copper deposits is distinctly episodic, and basically reflects a similar time variation in the intensity of calc-alkaline magmatism along this belt. An important episode of porphyry copper generation took place, for example, from 74 to 48 m.y. ago in the Cordilleras of North America, but this was followed by a lean period between 48 and 40 m.y. ago. The main episode of such metallization in the western Pacific occurred during Miocene and Pliocene time (Titley and Beane, 1981, p. 228–229), although it should be noted that mony western Pacific arcs are themselves no older than mid-Tertiary.

The plate tectonic history of the Pacific is complex, but the flourish of porphyry metallization represented by the Laramide deposits of Arizona and surrounding areas coincided with a change from oblique to normal subduction of the Farallon Plate beneath southwestern North America, and a marked increase in convergence rate (Coney, 1972). The strong pulse of magmatism and related porphyry copper (and other) metallization around the Pacific rim during Miocene time probably coincided with an increase in spreading rates along the East Pacific Rise.

1.1.1 Associated Igneous Rocks

The igneous rocks most closely associated with porphyry copper deposits occupy a spectrum from quartz diorites to adamellites. In island arc settings, calcalkalic hornblende, hornblende-biotite, and quartz diorites predominate, whereas in continental margin settings the ore-associated intrusives tend to be more alkalic granodiorites and quartz monzonites (Burnham, 1981). In the Galore Creek area of British Columbia, a group of Triassic age porphyry copper deposits is associated with a suite of silica-deficient alkaline-rich intrusives (Barr et al., 1976). The igneous systems that generate porphyry copper deposits commonly manifest multiple intrusive events that constitute an igneous center embracing a variety of intermediate rock types. The metallization event can, however, generally be shown to be primarily associated with a single member of the intrusive suite.

The host rocks to these intrusives include a wide variety of lithologies, from coeval volcanics in some instances through older clastic or even crystalline basement rocks in others, although the most common situation involves volcanic rocks of approximately similar age to the intrusives. Although the composition of the country rocks tends to influence the nature and extent of the hydrothermal alteration associated with such deposits, the ores themselves seem to display a striking disregard for the character of their surrounding, older country rocks.

In essentially all cases, the igneous rocks fall within the I-type grouping of the granitoid classification scheme of Chappell and White (1974), and the magnetite-series of Ishihara's (1977) system. Their source is most probably the subjacent mantle, and their generation is unquestionably closely tied to operation of the subduction process, although complex, multistage processes must operate in the genesis of arc magmas (Wyllie, 1981). This complexity is mirrored by the range of initial strontium ratios of ore-associated intrusives, which range from less than 0.703 to greater than 0.709 (Titley and Beane, 1981).

Sillitoe (1973) contends that the formation of porphyry copper deposits occurs within the subvolcanic environment below andesitic-dacitic stratovolcanoes (Fig. 1.2). Whether all porphyry systems develop below actual volcanoes

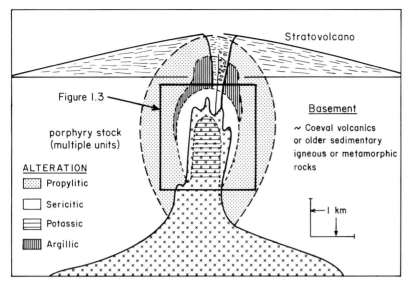

Fig. 1.2. Generalized model for porphyry copper formation. The salient feature of this model is the development of porphyry copper mineralization in the subvolcanic zone below a stratavolcano and above an intrusive body of some magnitude at depth. Within this critical zone geometries of individual intrusions can vary considerably, as can the geometries of the various alteration envelopes (modified from Sillitoe, 1973)

is not clear, for in most instances erosion has removed the critical evidence. It does seem possible, nevertheless, that porphyry copper deposits could also develop in the apical portions of stocks that protrude above larger igneous bodies, but that do not connect to overlying volcanics. The critical point, however, is that porphyry systems form at depths of approximately 2–8 km, although the shallower end of this spectrum is probably most common.

Kesler (1973) has demonstrated that porphyry copper deposits can be divided into either molybdenum- or gold-bearing subclasses, and gold-enriched examples tend to be more prominent in island arc settings. There are, however, some important exceptions to this rule, and the occurrence of porphyry molybdenum mineralization in the Philippines principal arc has been reported (Sillitoe, 1980a). A more thorough investigation of precious metal contents of porphyry copper deposits in western Canada has been recently carried out by Sinclair et al. (1982), who demonstrate that silver tends to be most enriched in alkaline-type porphyries, whereas gold is higher in volcanic as opposed to plutonic porphyry settings.

1.1.2 Mineralization and Alteration Patterns

The mineralization and alteration patterns manifest in porphyry copper deposits are closely interrelated (Lowell and Guilbert, 1970; Beane and Titley,

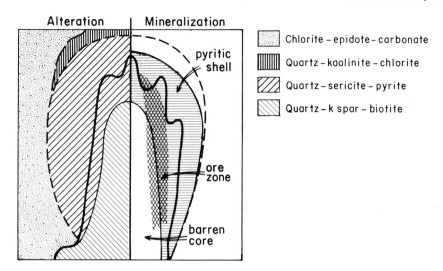

Fig. 1.3. Diagrammatic illustration of mineralization and alteration envelopes that develop in a typical porphyry copper system (from Beane and Titley, 1981)

1981). In general terms, the central deeper portions of porphyry copper deposits are characterized by disseminated or microveinlet mineralization and potassic (Qtz-biotite $\pm$ K-feldspar-anhydrite) alteration. Copper-iron ratios are high, and a low grade core zone of low total sulfide content may be present (Fig. 1.3). The deep zones of porphyry systems tend to contain magnetite, actinolite, epidote, chlorite and perhaps albite as additional alteration phases. Outward and upwards from this zone the copper-iron ratios in the total sulfide assemblage decrease and potassic alteration gives way to phyllic assemblages (Qtz-sericite-pyrite). In such zones, mineralization is exclusively of veinlet type and total sulfide content tends to reach a maximum. These zones are inevitably surrounded by a broad zone of diffuse porphylitic alteration (chlorite-epidote-carbonate) that may be interrupted locally by zones of intense argillic alteration (Qtz-kaolinite-chlorite; see Fig. 1.3). Mineralization, where present in these outer zones, occurs as sporadic discrete veins that in may instances contain minor lead, zinc, and precious metals in addition to copper.

1.1.3 Fluid Inclusions and Stable Isotopes

The fluid inclusion data base for porphyry systems has expanded considerably since the pioneering studies of Roedder (1971). The temperature and salinity patterns obtained from fluid inclusions mimic the zonal alteration-mineralization patterns. The highest temperature (up to 700 °C) and salinity (up to 60 wt% alkali chlorides) inclusions characterize the central portions of porphyry systems (e.g. Chivas and Wilkins, 1977; Eastoe, 1978). Fluid inclusion tempera-

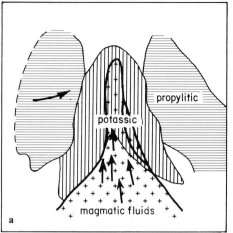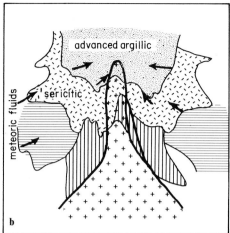

Fig. 1.4. Simplified cross-sectional illustration of the (**a**) early and (**b**) later stages of alteration and fluid movement deduced by Gustafson and Hunt (1975) from their study of the El Salvador porphyry copper deposit, Chile

tures and salinities decrease both as a function of distance from the core zone, and of time during the mineralization process. Another important observation is that evidence for boiling tends to be virtually ubiquitous during the higher temperature (> 400 °C) phase of hydrothermal activity.

Stable isotope studies of porphyry systems (Sheppard et al., 1971; Sheppard and Gustafson, 1976) indicate that potassic alteration and initial emplacement of copper sulfides is effected by hydrothermal fluids of magmatic provenance, whereas the phyllic alteration, and a certain amount of redistribution of metals, involves the participation of non-magmatic waters. The involvement of non-magmatic fluids in porphyry systems is clearly a complex matter and varies in degree from one deposit to another. However, where careful studies have been carried out (Gustafson and Hunt, 1975; Eastoe, 1978), the evidence supports a genetic model in which a magmatic-hydrothermal system is surrounded by a cooler meteoric-hydrothermal system that collapses inward and downward as the magmatic-hydrothermal system dies down (Fig. 1.4).

1.1.4 The El Salvador Porphyry Copper Deposit, Chile

The most complete study of a porphyry copper system undertaken to date is that of the El Salvador deposit in northern Chile (Gustafson and Hunt, 1975). Here, Cretaceous andesitic volcanics and sedimentary rocks, overlain uncomformably by lower Tertiary volcanics, were subjected to a series of intrusive events from 50–41 m.y. ago. Early rhyolite domes were followed by subvolcanic intrusives of quartz rhyolite and quartz porphyry 46 m.y. ago. The main mineralization and alteration events were associated with emplacement of a steep-walled granodioritic porphyry complex, dated at 41 m.y. (Fig. 1.4). A number of separate porphyry intrusive events occurred at this time, the latest of which post-date the major metallization event. Wide ranges of textural variation occur in these intrusives, including obliteration of porphyry textures locally. Compositional trends are obscured by hydrothermal events, but the ore-associated intrusives are definitely less felsic than earlier, unrelated siliceous extrusives and domes. Initial $^{87}Sr/^{86}Sr$ ratios throughout the igneous-hydrothermal complex exhibit consistent values of 0.704.

Early mineralization accounts for the bulk of the copper in the system, and occurs either in quartz veinlets or disseminated in alkali feldspar-biotite-anhydrite-chalcopyrite-bornite (potassic) alteration assemblages. Biotitization of andesitic volcanics and development of an outer halo of propylitic alteration apparently accompanied this event. Outward from the central zone of potassic alteration and mineralization, bornite decreases and is supplanted by pyrite, which increases outward until decreasing in the propylitic zone. The pyrite is closely associated with sericite or sericite plus chlorite, and pyrite-sericite-chlorite veins definitely post-date potassic and propylitic alteration assemblages.

This feldspar-destructive phyllic alteration is characterized by abundant pyrite and exhibits strong fracture control. These late sulfide veins and veinlets cut all earlier mineralized rock and contain minor, but upward-increasing amounts of chalcopyrite, bornite, tennantite, enargite, sphalerite or galena, plus quartz and anhydrite as gangue minerals. At high levels, advanced argillic assemblages containing pyrophyllite, diaspore, alunite, amorphous material, and local corundum are strongly developed.

Fluid inclusion assemblages associated with main stage mineralization contain both high salinity and vapor-dominant types, both of which homogenize in the range 360° to >600 °C. Low-salinity two-phase inclusions are the only type found in late pyritic veins, but also occur as inclusions of probable secondary origin in earlier veins. These low salinity inclusions homogenize at less than 360 °C. Stable isotope studies of the El Salvador deposit (Sheppard and Gustafson, 1976; Field and Gustafson, 1976) indicate that the sulfur involved in main stage mineralization was of magmatic origin ($\delta^{34}Ss = +1.6\%$), and that water involved in the hydrothermal events was initially of magmatic origin but became increasingly meteoric after main stage metallization. The water involved in advanced argillic alteration was enriched in deuterium and ^{18}O, presumably by near-surface evaporation processes.

The considerable body of data available for the El Salvador deposit is entirely consistent with an initial metallization event of magmatic-hydrothermal origin at a depth of approximately 2 km. This main-stage mineralization underwent subsequent modification due to the effects of deeply circulating meteoric waters driven by heat from underlying cooling intrusives. The actual ore body was formed by later supergene enrichment that produced a secondary enrichment blanket containing approximately 300 million tons of 1.6% Cu.

1.1.5 Genetic Models for Porphyry Copper Deposits

The extent to which the El Salvador model, and the more general models of mineralization and alteration of porphyry systems discussed earlier, can be applied to all porphyry copper deposits is unclear. Sillitoe (1973) offers evidence that some entire porphyry copper systems may have considerable vertical extent (up to 8 km) and "effectively span the boundary between the plutonic and volcanic environments." Burnham (1981) has considered the physicochemical constraints on porphyry copper genesis. These include the H_2O content of porphyry magma (~ 2–3 wt%), which must be such that it can reach depths of between 2 and 6 km without solidifying, crystallize hornblende and biotite as phenocryst phases, and release sufficient energy from exsolved aqueous fluids to fracture large volumes of rock. Magma temperatures must be sufficiently high ($> 800\ °C$) to allow melts to reach about 4 km in a largely liquid state. In addition, the metal, sulfur, and chlorine contents of such magmas must be sufficient to allow the extraction, transport, and deposition of large amounts of copper sulfides. Finally, the oxidation state of the magmas must be relatively high to permit transport of large quantities of sulfur, together with metal chlorides. Clearly, only some of the subvolcanic complexes in principal arcs will meet this set of requirements.

One of the unresolved problems of porphyry copper genesis is the extent to which superimposed meteoric-hydrothermal activity is a necessary and integral part of orebody formation (e.g., Norton, 1978; Henley and McNabb, 1978), or merely a likely consequence of the cooling history of mineralized subvolcanic igneous complexes. As pointed out by Burnham (1981), the main impetus for the formation of phyllic alteration zones in porphyry systems may be the HCl released by deposition of metal sulfides from metal chloride-rich brines. This observation, taken in conjunction with experimental results (e.g., Montoya and Hemley, 1975), suggests that typical porphyry copper zonal alteration patterns could develop without incursion of meteoric fluids. The stable isotope data base, however, indicates that this condition is probably rare in the evolution of porphyry systems. An extreme case of the redistribution of primary porphyry copper mineralization and alteration patterns is provided by the important vein deposits at Butte, Montana (Brimhall, 1979). Here, a combination of permeable volcanics surrounding the Butte Quartz Monzonite (~ 70 m.y.), later magmatic events, and the development of an extensive fracture system resulted in major modification of the previously formed low-grade copper mineralization, and emplacement of the extensive system of high-grade veins, now termed Main-Stage mineralization. Stable isotope data (Sheppard and Taylor, 1974) indicate a meteoric origin for the fluids involved in this vein-forming event, which occurred over a temperature range of 200–350 °C (Roedder, 1971).

1.1.6 Suggestions for Exploration

In terms of exploration for porphyry copper deposits, intermediate to felsic sub-volcanic complexes characterized by multiple igneous events and pervasive wall rock alteration obviously merit closer investigation. Erosion levels are of major significance, for compressive arcs tend to form thick crustal roots and stand high, and their uppermost few kilometers, where porphyry deposits form, are susceptible to removal. Few of the porphyry deposits of the Andes or those of the Philippines, for example, would survive 20 million years into the future, given continuation of current uplift and erosion rates in these areas.

The initial location of occurrences of porphyry copper-type mineralization, especially in vegetated areas, is best accomplished by geochemical prospecting techniques (Chafee, 1982). Once such sites have been found, recognition of zonal or distal alteration patterns is important, but it must be borne in mind that such patterns can exhibit a wide variety of geometries. The ability to interpret leached cappings (Anderson, 1982) and to 'see through' supergene overprinting of hypogene alteration assemblages is a valuable skill in this regard. In the evaluation of oxidized surface showings and geophysical data (e.g., induced potential results), it is also important to bear in mind that maximum sulfide and maximum copper contents seldom coincide. Generally, a combination of rock geochemistry, careful alteration mapping, and application of suitable geophysical techniques will provide sufficient basis for meaningful exploratory drilling.

The spacing of porphyry copper deposits along principal arc systems is of interest in exploration, and Sawkins (1980) has attempted to show that average spacings of porphyry copper deposits exhibit a relationship to the average spacing of volcanoes along volcanoplutonic arc systems. Clearly, any regularities in this parameter within a specific arc system will have major implications for exploration, especially where gaps in an otherwise regular spacing pattern are apparent.

1.2. Copper-Bearing Breccia Pipes

Mineralized breccia pipes are of relatively minor economic importance compared to the huge tonnages of many porphyry copper deposits, but are attractive in that they tend to be higher grade targets that require less capital investment to develop. In addition, they represent significant components of many porphyry copper deposits, and present some intriguing problems with respect to their genesis.

1.2.1 Distribution and Associated Igneous Rocks

In general terms, the igneous rock associations discussed under the preceding section on porphyry deposits in principal arcs apply equally to copper-bearing breccia pipe deposits. Breccia pipes occur, either singly or in clusters of up to one hundred or more, in the roofs of intermediate composition batholiths or stocks, and in their volcanic roof rocks. Their most common occurrence is in granodioritic plutons that represent typical products of volcanoplutonic arc formation (e.g., Sillitoe and Sawkins, 1971). Many porphyry copper deposits contain breccia bodies. In some instances these are clearly fluidization breccias formed relatively late in the mineralization sequence (Gustafson and Hunt, 1975), but, in others, irregular bodies of brecciated rock occur whose origin is enigmatic.

Mineralized breccia pipes that are not integral parts of porphyry copper deposits occur widely in Chile (Sillitoe and Sawkins, 1971), northern Mexico (Sillitoe, 1976), and the southwestern U.S. (Johnston and Lowell, 1961; Kuhn, 1941), but examples are also known from Peru (Carlson and Sawkins, 1980), Korea (Fletcher, 1977), and northern Australia (Knutson et al., 1979).

1.2.2 Mineralization and Alteration

Although volumes of brecciated and mineralized rock can display a variety of geometries, the majority occur as steeply inclined circular or elliptical pipes. In areas where nests of pipes are found, the intensity of mineralization and the grades of metal they contain are highly variable. Typically, a few pipes will contain ore grade material, whereas the majority will contain hydrothermal gangue minerals, but have low metal values.

Two distinct end member types of breccia pipe can be identified, one that contains highly rounded fragments of various sizes set in a matrix of rock flour, and another characterized by highly angular fragments and an absence of rock flour. Intermediate types are also known, but are less common. Ore grade mineralization is more common in the pipes that contain angular fragments, presumably because of their enhanced porosity-permeability characteristics.

Copper and molybdenum sulfides are the principal economic minerals in the breccia pipes found in principal arcs, but some pipes contain significant amounts of tungsten, typically as scheelite. A large array of other minerals are also present in some pipes, including pyrite, magnetite, specular hematite, arsenopyrite, sphalerite, tetrahedrite, bismuthinite, fluorite, apatite, and gold, although the quantities of these are generally minor. Quartz is ubiquitous as a gangue mineral, and tourmaline is an important constituent of many pipes, especially those in the Andes. Additional gangue minerals that may be present are carbonates, actinolite, K-feldspar, biotite, anhydrite, sericite, and chlorite.

In pipes that are not integral parts of porphyry copper systems, alteration tends to be rather localized, and in only a few instances extends more than a few meters beyond pipe margins (see Sillitoe and Sawkins, 1971). The majority of pipes exhibit phyllic alteration (sericite + quartz + pyrite), but this tends to give way to potassic alteration at depth (Sillitoe, 1976).

Mineral zoning is strongly developed in some breccia pipes and is less prominent in others. In the Washington pipe, Sonora (Simmons and Sawkins, 1983)

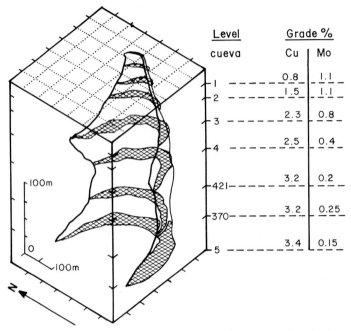

Level	Grade %	
cueva	Cu	Mo
1	0.8	1.1
2	1.5	1.1
3	2.3	0.8
4	2.5	0.4
421	3.2	0.2
370	3.2	0.25
5	3.4	0.15

Fig. 1.5. Illustration of the ore-bearing margin of the Turmalina breccia pipe, northern Peru, showing the marked vertical zoning with respect to copper and molybdenum values (from Carlson and Sawkins, 1980)

there is heavy development of pyrite, accompanied by quartz, sericite, and tourmaline at near surface levels. Downward, pyrite and tourmaline decrease, whereas chalcopyrite and scheelite increase. At the deepest levels the assemblage chalcopyrite-chlorite-calcite is dominant, although numerous patches of potassic alteration are found. The molybdenite content of the pipe increases downward. In the Cumobabi area, about 12 kilometers to the east, metal zoning patterns are irregular, but tourmaline only occurs in outlying pipes that outcrop at high elevations and lack obvious mineralization (Scherkenbach and Sawkins, 1983). The Turmalina pipe in Peru (Carlson and Sawkins, 1980) is strongly zoned with respect to copper-molybdenum values and, surprisingly, changes from high molybdenum values near surface to high copper values at depth (Fig. 1.5).

1.2.3 Formation and Mineralization of Breccia Pipes

Available fluid inclusion data on breccia pipe mineralization (Sillitoe and Sawkins, 1971; Sawkins, 1979; Fletcher, 1977; Carlson and Sawkins, 1980; Sawkins and Scherkenbach, 1981) indicate temperatures in the range 300–475 °C and a wide range of salinities (5–45 wt% alkali chlorides). Broad distribution of vapor-dominated inclusions indicates that boiling of hydrothermal fluids was com-

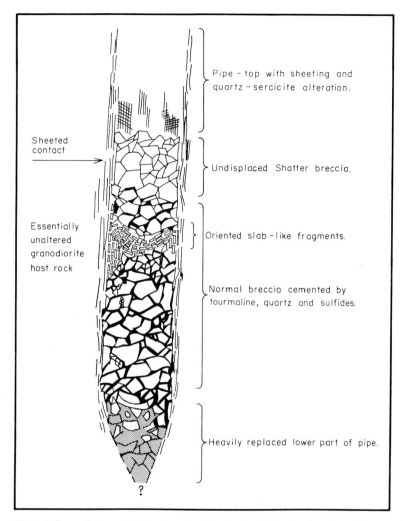

Pipe - top with sheeting and
quartz - sericite alteration.

Sheeted
contact

Undisplaced Shatter breccia.

Essentially
unaltered
granodiorite
host rock

Oriented slab - like fragments.

Normal breccia cemented by
tourmaline, quartz and sulfides.

Heavily replaced lower part of pipe.

?

Fig. 1.6. Generalized model of a mineralized breccia pipe inferred to have formed by a mechanism of
solution collapse. Note that pipe structure passes upward into unbrecciated altered rock (from
Sillitoe and Sawkins, 1971)

mon. To date, no comprehensive stable isotope studies have been carried out
on this type of deposit, but the few measurements available indicate a magmatic
origin for the sulfur and fluids involved in mainstage mineralization.

The close time-space association of mineralized breccia pipes in principal
arcs with felsic magmatism and/or porphyry copper emplacement indicates that
important aspects of their genesis must be essentially similar to those of porphyry copper deposits. The mode(s) of formation of breccia bodies and pipes

is, however, more equivocal. Breccia columns that contain rounded fragments and abundant rock flour are presumed to have vented at the surface and, if so, can be readily understood as products of phreatic eruptions. However, some demonstrably did not and this mode of formation is truly puzzling. Breccia columns that contain angular fragments, lack rock flour and exhibit evidence of collapse are also problematic, for some mechanism is required for the initiation of collapse and the creation of void space that collapse implies. The various mechanisms suggested include magma withdrawal (Perry, 1961), hydrous magmatic bubbles (Norton and Cathles, 1973), mineralization sloping (Locke, 1926), and host rock solution (Sillitoe and Sawkins, 1971).

Any hypothesis that attempts to explain this latter distinctive group of ore deposits must address their common features. These include similarities of mineralogy and paragenesis, degree of angularity of fragments, general absence of rock flour, and monolithologic nature of breccia fragments and host rock. In addition, many such pipes exhibit regular, near vertical form, enclosure by zones of vertical sheeting, and local zones of inward-dipping or flat-lying tabular fragments (Fig. 1.6). In at least one instance pipes have been observed to pass upward into altered, but unbrecciated rock (Sillitoe and Sawkins, 1971). Although much of the actual brecciation may result from phreatic explosions of superheated hydrothermal fluids, solution-corrosion of host rocks along paths of solution flow is envisaged as a necessary antecedent to breccia formation. Once formed, permeable breccia columns act as ideal sites for metal deposition by ascending postmagmatic ore fluids.

1.2.4 The Cumobabi Breccia Pipe Deposits, Mexico

The molybdenum and copper-bearing breccia pipes at Cumobabi, Mexico (Fig. 1.7) provide a good example of the fascinating enigmas presented by breccia pipe deposits (Scherkenbach and Sawkins, 1983). The country rocks in the Cumobabi area are shallow-dipping volcanics of calc-alkaline affinity. Thick basal andesites (up to 200 m) are overlain by intermediate to highly silicic flows and pyroclastics with an aggregate thickness of approximately 400 m, that were probably deposited close to feeder vents. This sequence is intruded by a quartz monzonite of irregular shape that is centered on the main area of mineralization. Cutting this unit and volcanics are a number of small apophyses of diorite porphyry. The youngest intrusion in the area is a microgranite that from drill core observations coarsens in grain size with depth and grades into granodiorite. High-angle faulting is pronounced in the area, with dominant trends in N-S and E-W directions, and much of this fault activity appears to have preceded mineralization and alteration.

There are at least 35 breccia bodies or pipes in the area and they are crudely centered about the San Judas-Transvaal area. Included in this array of breccia

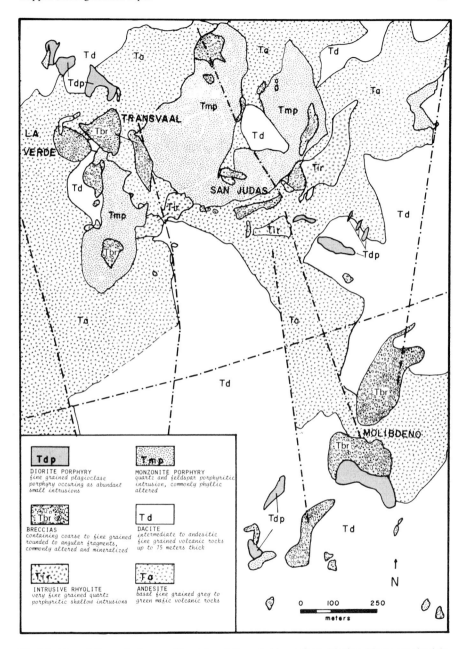

Fig. 1.7. Map of the central zone of breccias at Cumobabi, northern Mexico. Numerous breccia bodies beyond this zone are known, but most are unmineralized at current exposure levels (from Scherkenbach and Sawkins, in press)

bodies are obvious fault breccias, fluidization or explosion breccias, and collapse breccias. The explosion breccias (e.g., La Verde) are more tightly packed, contain rounded fragments, and are not strongly mineralized. The collapse breccias are characterized by angular and tabular fragments, substantial void space, and, in general, strong hydrothermal mineralization, at least in the central part of the Cumobabi area. Outlying breccias crop out mainly at higher elevations and are characterized by strong development of tourmaline, but little or no economic sulfides, at least at the surface. The more central breccias may have experienced more than one episode of brecciation and these episodes must have occurred prior to mineralization, for no evidence of brecciated ore has been noted.

Alteration patterns at Cumobabi are complex. An early tourmalinization may have permeated the area, but now survives in any abundance only in the outlying breccias. The initial mineralization of the area produced fingers of strong potassic alteration accompanied by considerable anhydrite deposition in the central breccias, surrounded by a broad diffuse zone of propylitization, characterized by chlorite, pyrite, and local epidote. Zones that underwent potassic alteration contain orthoclase, biotite, quartz, anhydrite, apatite, and very minor chlorite and/or sericite. Sericitic alteration appears in large part to postdate and overprint earlier alteration events, and to have been at least in part controlled by fractures or permeable breccias. However, some sericitic alteration may have formed as a marginal phase of potassic alteration. Sericite, anhydrite, chlorite, calcite, pyrite, and clay are the most common phases in zones of sericitic alteration.

Breccia mineralization associated with the potassic alteration event comprises molybdenite, and lesser chalcopyrite, whereas accompanying gangue minerals are quartz, orthoclase, biotite, anhydrite, and minor apatite and fluorite. Adjacent to some of the pipes, disseminated chalcopyrite mineralization of porphyry type is present. In general terms, molybdenite deposition is early and closely associated with strong potassic alteration, whereas sphalerite and tetrahedrite deposition postdate chalcopyrite, and are more closely associated with sericitic alteration.

Euhedral quartz crystals up to several centimeters in length occur in vugs within many of the central breccias, especially the San Judas and Transvaal pipes. These crystals contain excellent fluid inclusion assemblages from which a considerable body of data are now available (Scherkenbach and Sawkins, 1983; Sawkins and Scherkenbach, 1981). Temperature and salinity measurements from these inclusions (Fig. 1.8) indicate the presence of hot (340–410 °C) boiling fluids during mineralization.

Many of the high salinity inclusions and a number of vapor-dominated inclusions contain opaque tetrahedra as daughter minerals. These have been identified with a scanning electron microscope as chalcopyrite, and volumetric calculations indicate that the trapped fluids must have contained up to 16,000 ppm copper. Quantitative chemical analysis of inclusion-rich quartz crystals from the San Judas and Transvaal breccias have indicated mean contents of trapped

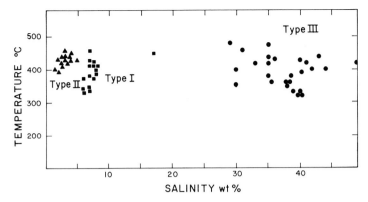

Fig. 1.8. Plot of temperature and salinity data obtained from fluid inclusions in quartz from the central zone of mineralized breccia at Cumobabi, northern Mexico. Note three types of fluid inclusion populations that can be differentiated on the basis of salinity and liquid-vapor ratios (from Scherkenbach and Sawkins, in press)

fluids of 2,150 ppm copper and 1,160 ppm zinc in addition to considerable amounts of sodium, calcium, potassium, and chlorine.

The similarity of these fluid inclusion assemblages to those reported from porphyry copper deposits (see preceding section) suggests that the chemistry of porphyry copper ore fluids is analogous to that responsible for ore deposition at Cumobabi. In both cases it seems clear that subjacent cooling intrusives were the principal source of such fluids.

1.2.5 Suggestions for Exploration

Pipes and bodies of broken rock formed in the vicinity of cooling igneous intrusives are obviously highly favorable loci for mineralization by metal sulfides. However, inasmuch as such pipes only intersect the erosion surface at a single point or may be blind, they present an interesting challenge to the exploration geologist.

Many pipes, especially those that contain considerable amounts of quartz, outcrop boldly relative to their immediate host rocks. Such pipes are easy to locate and recognize, but typically any metal sulfides they may contain have been leached and oxidized. In addition, the vertical zoning present in many pipes can create situations where pipes are essentially barren at the extant erosion surface, but contain ore grade material at depth.

In areas where arrays of pipes occur, careful attention should be paid to the occurrence of limonite types, breccia textures, interstitial material, and the alteration characteristics and geochemistry of each pipe exposure. Geophysical techniques aimed at assessing the content of metal sulfides below the zone of oxidation should also be considered. Ultimately diamond drilling is required to evaluate those pipes whose surface characteristics are most favorable. There is a tendency for many pipes to be most heavily mineralized along their margins and cognizance of this should be made in planning drilling programs.

1.3 Skarn Deposits

An excellent and extensive review of skarn deposits by Einaudi et al. (1981) has been published recently, and has provided an indispensable source for this and later sections on skarn deposits. The term skarn has been applied to a variety of coarse-grained assemblages of metamorphogenic silicates developed primarily in carbonate-bearing rocks, but is used here to categorize assemblages formed as the result of metasomatic and hydrothermal processes related in time and space to the cooling of intermediate to felsic igneous bodies. It is worth noting, however, that some very mafic intrusives can be associated with Fe skarns, and that in certain instances skarns can form from hostrocks that are essentially lacking in carbonate components.

Einaudi et al. (1981) divide skarns on the basis of primary metal type, but point out that skarns can also be classified by their dominant calc-silicate mineral assemblages. The purpose of this book, however, is to explore the degree to which plate tectonic environments can be utilized to understand diversity within various ore deposit types, and, more importantly perhaps, their geographic distribution.

1.3.1 Distribution and Associated Igneous Rocks

Mineralized contact metasomatic skarns are developed in continental margin and oceanic principal arcs, mainly where intrusives encounter carbonate-rich country rocks. Along continental margin arcs such lithologies are more common, having resulted from sedimentation in earlier miogeoclinal environments. In true oceanic arc systems, however, carbonate rocks are less common, and tend to be limited to local development of reef limestones.

Principal arc terrains that contain this type of mineralization include the batholiths of the Sierra Nevada (Kerrick, 1970), Aconchi, Sonora (Newberry and Einaudi, 1981), and less deeply eroded terrains in Japan (Shimazaki, 1980), the Philippines (Bryner, 1969), Indonesia (Djumhani, 1981), and Iran Jaya (Sillitoe, pers. comm.). Although porphyry copper-associated skarns represent an important sub-group, such deposits also occur prominently in inner arc environments where carbonate country rocks tend to be more widespread (see later).

The majority of skarn deposits are associated with magnetite series, I-type granitoids, but in Japan a number of skarn deposits are associated with ilmenite-series granitoids (Shimazaki, 1980), especially those that contain tin-wolframite mineralization. Unfortunately, the late Mesozoic and Cenozoic patterns of granitoid magmatism in Japan are particularly complex, and the extent to which the ilmenite-series intrusives can be assigned to subduction-related principal arc magmatism is unclear.

The literature on Russian ore deposits is replete with descriptions of skarn ores of all types, but apart from those that occur in late Paleozoic arcs accreted to the southern margin of the Siberian craton (Laznicka, 1976), and those within the Urals, assignment of these deposits to specific plate tectonic categories is deemed premature, at least in terms of the author's knowledge.

1.3.2. Mineralization

Magnetite skarn deposits can be divided into calcic types that form in island arc settings, and magnesium types found in Cordilleran arcs and on their inner margins (Einaudi et al., 1981). Calcic, island arc-related magnetite skarns are typically associated with dioritic or even gabbroic intrusives. They are characterized by formation of significant amounts of skarn from igneous rocks, widespread sodium metasomatism, and anomalous cobalt, and, in some instances, nickel concentrations. Examples include Larap, Phillips (Frost, 1965), Diaquiri, Cuba (Lindgren and Ross, 1916), the Empire Mine, Vancouver (Sangster, 1969; Haug, 1976), and some large (> 100 million tons) deposits in the Urals (Sokolov and Grigorev, 1977) (see Einaudi et al., 1981, Table 3).

Magnesian magnetite skarn deposits in Cordilleran settings are associated with more felsic intrusives such as quartz monzonites and tend to form only in dolomitic country rocks. Skarn silicate minerals in these deposits are magnesium-rich, leaving the iron available for magnetite formation. Examples that can be placed with any confidence into a principal arc setting are limited, but include the Eagle Mountain mine, California (> 50 million tons) (Dubois and Brummett, 1968). Two large deposits in Russia appear to belong to this class, based on mineral associations (see Einaudi et al., 1981, Table 4), but their assignment to a principal arc setting would involve pure conjecture. The well known Fierro deposit, Central Mining district, New Mexico (Hernon and Jones, 1968) represents another example, but occurs in what may be more appropriately designated as an inner arc setting.

Tungsten skarns associated with coarse grained granodioritic stocks and batholiths are widespread in the principal arc terrains of the western U.S. and northern Mexico. Based on stratigraphic reconstructions, prograde skarn mineralogy, and the nature of the associated intrusives, Newberry and Einaudi (1981) suggest that most North American scheelite-bearing skarns develop at depths of 5 km or more. Furthermore, they hypothesize that areal concentrations of such deposits reflect the coincidence of suitable intrusive and country rocks and appropriately deep erosion levels, rather than discrete tungsten-rich geochemical provinces (Fig. 1.9).

Studies of typical skarns associated with roof pendants in the Sierra Nevada batholith (Morgan, 1975; Nokleberg, 1981) indicate that, although the geometry of individual skarn bodies tends to be complex, they can be subdivided into distinctive zones, based on mineralogy. The distal zone adjacent to the marble is typically represented by wollastonite skarn with lesser grossularite, idocrase, and diopside. Progressively closer to the intrusive contact are zones of garnet skarn with andradite-grossularite, diopside-hedenbergite, and scheelite, and, finally, adjacent to intrusive, hornblende skarn containing mainly hornblende, plagioclase, microcline, magnetite, and scheelite. The whole sequence, which can vary markedly in thickness along igneous contacts, can be viewed as a layered metasomatic front between intrusive and marble in which CaO and CO_2 are progressively removed by metasomatizing fluids, and SiO_2, total Fe, MgO, MnO, Al_2O_3, and Na_2O, K_2O, and WO_3 added. Variability in these types of skarns from one deposit to another is probably controlled more by hostrock lithologies and fluid flow patterns than fundamental differences in the chemistry of the aqueous fluids emanating from the adjacent intrusives.

Only one major (> 10 million tons) deposit occurs in this Sierra Nevadan principal arc terrain, the Pine Creek Mine (Gray et al., 1968). Other world-class tungsten skarns are the Sangdong deposit, Korea (John, 1978), King Island, Tasmania (Kwak, 1978), and the MacMillan Pass (Dick, 1976) and Canada Tungsten deposits (Zaw, 1976) in N.W. Territories, Canada. Sillitoe (1981a) has suggested an inner arc setting for the MacMillan Pass and Canada Tungsten deposits and this appears more appropriate to their locale (see later). The same may also be true for the Sangdong deposit. Of these deposits all except the King Island deposit belong to Einaudi et al.'s (1981, Table 7) grouping of reduced tungsten skarns. Such reduced skarns are characterized by hedenbergitic pyroxene, almandine-rich garnet, Fe-rich biotite and hornblende, minor magnetite, and low sulfidation states. Late-stage crosscutting zones of hydrous minerals containing hornblende, biotite, actinolite, and epidote are present locally in these skarns and tend to contain enhanced tungsten grades, and assorted sulfide minerals.

The other main group of skarn deposits formed in principal arc settings are base metal ores, primarily of copper. A few such deposits are known from island arc terrains (see Einaudi et al., 1981, p. 340), where they occur adjacent to quartz diorite or granodiorite plutons, but most occur in continental margin environments. Skarn copper deposits along such arcs can be divided into those associated with porphyry copper deposits and those associated with unmineralized intrusives. The former tend to be finer grained and exhibit more marked retrograde hydrothermal alteration than the latter. In many instances zinc mineralization is significant, but many large base metal skarns, especially those containing significant amounts of lead, develop in inner arc rather than principal arc environments (see later).

In broad terms, sulfide skarn deposits differ from tungsten skarns in having more oxidized silicate assemblages and developing at shallower crustal levels

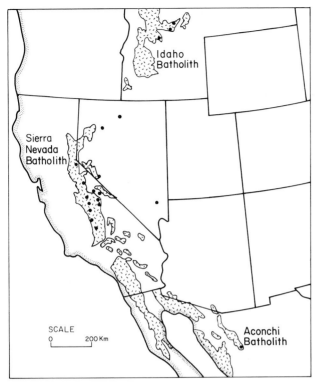

Fig. 1.9. Distribution of tungsten skarn deposits in the western U.S. and northwest Mexico. Note the association of most of these deposits with granitic intrusives of batholithic dimensions (from Meinert et al., 1980)

(Newberry and Einaudi, 1981; Fig. 1.10). A detailed study of the Mason Valley mine deposit in Nevada (Einaudi, 1977a) indicates that the zonal arrangement of skarn minerals from country rock marble toward maximum skarn development is: talc-magnetite-calcite, tremolite-magnetite-calcite, pyroxene-sulfides, garnet-pyroxene-sulfides, and garnet. Compositional changes in silicate minerals are complex in detail and appear to reflect chemical controls and sharp compositional gradients during skarn production.

These, and similar skarns in the region, are distal in type and occur from 1–2 km from mapped contacts of Jurassic granodiorites of the Yerington batholith. Proximal skarns in the region differ in having lower total sulfide (5% or less), much higher chalcopyrite/pyrite ratios (10 or greater), absence of iron oxides, a gangue dominated by andradite, and stronger brecciation. This general sequence of minerals in zoned skarn deposits detailed above (see also Burt, 1974) is repeated in skarn deposits elsewhere in the western U.S. and in British Columbia, Mexico, Japan, and the USSR (Einaudi et al., 1981). However, in skarns developed in dolomitic host rocks, significant amounts of forsterite and

serpentine develop, and in some calcium skarns an outer zone of wollastonite
is present.

Certain sulfide skarns, in particular those rich in copper or magnetite, tend
to contain appreciable quantities of gold (Shimazaki, 1980). At Battle Mountain, Nevada (Blake et al., 1978) skarn gold deposits in a calcareous conglomerate unit, that lies peripheral to a porphyry copper deposit of mid-Tertiary age,
are mined, but whether the environment can be justified as pertaining to a principal arc at the time of mineralization is debatable.

1.3.3 Genesis of Contact Metasomatic Skarn Deposits

Although a number of detailed studies on the mineralogy and zoning of mineralized skarns have been carried out, the fluid inclusion and stable isotope data
base is more limited. However, the available data of this type indicate that
scheelite skarns typically form at temperatures in excess of 500 °C (Newberry
and Einaudi, 1981), whereas base metal skarns from mainly in the temperature
range 500–350 °C (Meinert et al., 1980).

Stable isotope studies (e.g., Taylor and O'Neil, 1977) indicate that prograde
skarn formation and metallization is effected by fluids of magmatic origin, but
that meteoric waters tend to become increasingly important toward the final
stages of hydrothermal activity, and can be responsible for retrograde alteration
and perhaps some redistribution of ore minerals. Understandably, these effects
tend to be more marked in sulfide skarn deposits than in deeper-seated scheelite
skarns.

Detailed studies of the King Island scheelite deposits (Kwak and Tan, 1981)
provide a scenario of mineralizing fluids that progressively decreased in both
temperature (maximum 800 °C) and salinity (max 65 wt% alk. chlorides), both
with respect to distance from the associated Devonian granodiorite and with
time. These changes were accompanied by systematic changes in the chemistry
of garnets, pyroxenes, and amphiboles. Pressure estimates based on fluid inclusion data suggest about 650 bars during mineralization. This relatively shallow
environment plus indicated movement of the North Boundary fault, apparently
allowed mixing of meteoric and magmatic fluids during mineralization, and one
result thereof was the partial dissolution of early Mo-rich scheelite and its redistribution and redeposition as Mo-poor scheelite and molybdenite. Unfortunately, although the King Island deposits exhibit strong similarities to principal
arc scheelite skarns in western North America, it must be stressed that the complex associations of Paleozoic granitoid rocks in Tasmania (Solomon, 1981)
have not as yet yielded to plate tectonic interpretation, so the designation of the
King Island deposits as representative of principal arc metallization is, as stated
earlier, premature.

The Darwin silver-lead-zinc skarn deposit in California (Hall and Mackevett, 1962) has also been the subject of detailed isotopic studies (Rye et al.,
1974). Here, massive replacement sulfide ores occur within contact skarns com-

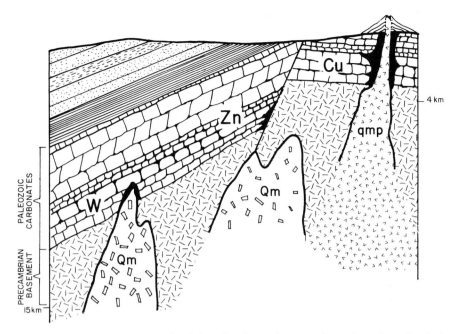

Fig. 1.10. Diagram to illustrate idealized skarn-forming environments in continental margin principal arcs. Note variation of skarn metallogeny as a function of depth of formation. Qm = quartz monzonite, qmp = quartz monzonite porphyry (from Meinert et al., 1980)

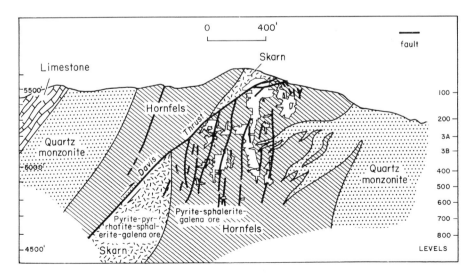

Fig. 1.11. Cross-section of the Darwin skarn ores, California (from Rye et al., 1974)

posed mainly of diopside, garnet, and idocrase adjacent to a quartz monzonite stock of Jurassic age ($\sim$ 180 m.y.) (Fig. 1.11). Prograde skarn formation is separated from sulfide mineralization by a period of fracturing, and isotopic and fluid inclusion studies of this later stage of metallization indicate ore fluids of about 325 °C with salinities up to 25 wt% alkali chlorides. The fluids averaged $\delta^{34}S$ values of $+3\%$, $\delta^{13}C$ of -3.5%, and δD of -66%. Initial pH was estimated at 4.8 and final pH after interaction with skarn and limestones at 6.7. Rye et al. (1974) conclude that metallization was effected by fluids of magmatic origin from the adjacent quartz monzonite, but that the carbon in ore-associated calcite is a mixture of hostrock and magmatic carbon. Recent geologic work in the area, however, has indicated previously unrecognized complexities including the possibility that the deposit is not directly related to the adjacent quartz monzonite (L. Meinert, pers. comm.). Notwithstanding these uncertainties, the Darwin deposit is of interest for it appears to represent an example, albeit small, of lead-zinc mineralization in the Sierra Nevada principal arc setting.

Overall, it appears that most sulfide skarn deposits in principal arcs form in two stages. An initial high temperature zoned stage of lime silicate development and a subsequent lower temperature stage of sulfide metallization; although scheelite may accompany prograde skarn formation, and typically scheelite mineralization precedes sulfide mineralization. Non-magmatic fluids can impinge on skarn ore generating systems, but their role is probably limited to minor redistribution and alteration of previously deposited phases.

1.3.4 Discussion and Suggestions for Exploration

As detailed above, most skarns occur in close proximity to igneous contacts, but some are up to 2 km distant from their related intrusives. In the latter case, a combination of good access structures for the metasomatizing fluids and carbonate-silicate host rock contacts will control the sites of skarn development (Fig. 1.12). Skarn development and associated mineralization tends to be limited in spatial extent compared with porphyry or vein-type mineralization, and thus subsurface exploration for blind skarn orebodies can be particularly difficult. By the same token the potential for the discovery of important blind orebodies of this type always exists in principal arc areas where carbonate units are intruded by intermediate to felsic plutons. Also, many base metal skarns are transitional to porphyry copper deposits. Tungsten skarns, on the other hand, are best sought above plutons or in the roof pendants of batholiths.

Another problem facing the explorationist is the location of optimum metallization within skarn complexes. This requires a knowledge of the zoning characteristics of a particular skarn, both in terms of mineralogy and mineral chemistry. Broad relationships between sulfide concentrations and minerals such as andradite with specific chemistries are now emerging (Einaudi et al., 1981), and with careful work such relationships can probably be used to develop trends from surface and drillcore samples that will aid in the siting of drillholes seeking blind orebodies.

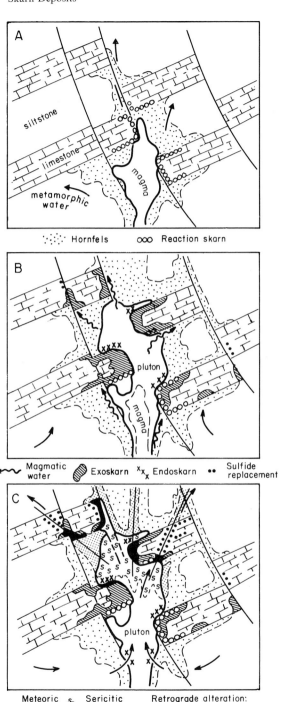

Fig. 1.12. Generalized model for the evolutionary stages of skarn ore formation. (**A**) Initial magma emplacement drives off connate and ground waters and produces a metamorphic aureala and local reaction skarns. (**B**) Magmatic fluids generated from crystallizing magma form exoskarns in limestones along stock and fault contacts and local endoskarns. Some peripheral sulfied replacement bodies in limestone may also form at this time. (**C**) Cooling of the system allows progressive influx of meteoric waters, leading to sericitic alteration of the stock, retrograde alteration of skarn and hornfels, and sulfide-silica-carbonate replacement along major structures and bedding in limestone (from Einaudi et al., 1981)

Geophysical methods of exploration such as magnetics can be used to delineate skarn zones containing magnetite, and igneous contacts in the subsurface. Obviously subsurface skarns containing significant amounts of conductive sulfide minerals will give good conductivity or induced polarization response provided they are not too deep, but the presence of graphite developed from the recrystallization of carbonaceous materials in the host rocks can be problematic in terms of interpretation of these types of geophysical anomaly.

1.4 Vein Deposits

1.4.1 Distribution and Associated Igneous Rocks

Vein deposits are widespread in the upper volcanic portions of principal arcs and within the uppermost portions of stocks and batholiths, and vein ores occur scattered along the arc systems of the circum-Pacific belt where erosion has not cut too deeply. They include copper-gold ± silver veins and epithermal or bonanza gold-silver deposits and, more important in terms of current economics, bulk mineable stockwork or disseminated precious metal deposits.

Examples of this general type of mineralization can be followed from the silver deposits of Chanarcillo and Caracoles, Chile (Ruiz et al., 1965), through gold-quartz and copper veins associated with the Coastal Batholith of Peru (Bellido and de Montreuil, 1972; Agar, 1981), to precious and base metal veins in Ecuador and Colombia (Goossens, 1972, 1976; Baum and Gobel, 1980), and the precious metal vein deposits of Central America (Ferencic, 1971; Kelser, 1978). Further north, the Sierra Madre Occidental of Mexico contains important precious metal vein deposits (e.g., Tayoltita, Smith et al., 1982). The lode gold deposits of California, though not of epithermal type, can be related to the Cretaceous magmatism of the Sierra Nevadan principal arc (Albers, 1981). In western Canada, precious metal vein deposits occur through much of British Columbia and the Yukon (Wolfhard and Ney, 1976).

The principal arc systems of the western Pacific and Indonesia also contain numerous vein deposits. In Japan, a complex series of vein deposits of different ages and different metal content are known (Ishihara, 1978), but the scheelite-gold deposits associated with Cretaceous magnetite-series granitoids, and certain of the precious metal deposits of Neogene age, can be assigned to principal arc settings. Vein gold deposits in the Philippines are widespread (Balce et al., 1981). The large majority lie within a well defined Miocene-Pleistocene belt that runs the length of the Philippine archipelago from eastern Mindanao to northern Luzon. Similar vein deposits occur in Fiji (Colley and Greenbaum, 1980) and along the Indonesian arc system (Djumhani, 1981). Vein deposits are also scattered along the collided arc systems in the southern U.S.S.R., the Caucasus,

(Kovalev and Karyakin, 1980), along the Neogene volcanic chain of the Carpathian arc (Lang, 1979), and through the Balkans.

The epithermal vein deposits, especially those of precious metals, occur predominantly in volcanic rocks, particularly those of andesitic composition. Base metal veins tend to occur within or adjacent to calc-alkaline intermediate to felsic plutonic rocks, as do gold quartz veins of deeper seated aspect (e.g., Au veins associated with the Sierra Nevada Batholith, see Coveney, 1981; Albers, 1981).

1.4.2 Mineralization and Alteration

The vein deposits associated with principal arc development form a somewhat heterogeneous group of deposits, but can be broadly grouped into Au-Ag epithermal (bonanza type) veins, deeper-seated gold-quartz lodes (e.g., Mother Lode), and base metal veins with silver and/or gold.

As noted above, epithermal precious metal veins occur most typically in andesitic hostrocks, and are most commonly manifest as well-defined fissure fillings in which quartz is the dominant gangue mineral. Calcite and/or adularia are also important gangue constituents in some cases. Metallization consists of native gold ($\pm$ gold tellurides) and silver sulfides and sulfosalts; contents of base metals in such veins are notably low, commonly less than a percent or two. Alteration assemblages can vary with depth, but most veins are surrounded by an envelope of chlorite-dominated propylitic alteration. In some instances sericite is developed close to veins, in others alunite and kaolin are present, and disseminations of pyrite are inevitably developed in the hostrocks.

Buchanan (1981), by assembling the data from a large number of epithermal vein deposits in western North America, has attempted to encapsulate the variables of typical epithermal vein systems (Fig. 1.13). He envisages precious metal deposition occurring at shallow depth (~ 200–350 meters) below an intensely altered zone that passes upward into a hot spring system. Below the precious metal horizon, base metals are deposited in the vein system. This generalized model does serve to demonstrate many features found in epithermal vein systems, but it should be emphasized that many exhibit only some of the features it incorporates.

Gold-quartz veins such as those of the Mother Lode and Grassy Hill areas of California (Albers, 1981), and those associated with the batholithic terrains of western South America are clearly formed at greater depths. The vein systems tend to be wider and in many instances more extensive than epithermal fissure veins and contain native gold in a gangue of quartz plus lesser chlorite.

1.4.3 The Baguio, Philippines and Tayoltita, Mexico Vein Systems

Two important precious metal vein systems of which the writer has personal experience are those of Baguio and Tayoltita. Both have sustained mining for

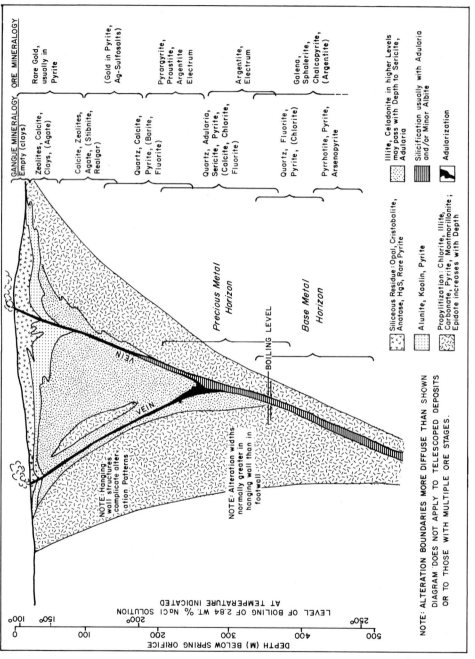

Fig. 1.13. Idealized model for an epithermal precious metal vein system incorporating many of the features found in such systems. In any one

many decades and continue to produce precious metals. Furthermore, both have been the subject of recent research studies (Sawkins et al., 1979; Smith et al., 1982).

In the Baguio district two major sets of fissure veins are the major producers (Fig. 1.14). The steeply dipping veins, which are dominated by quartz gangue, are hosted either in andesitic volcanics or volcaniclastic sediments. In addition, at Acupan, breccia zones in andesite adjacent to a fluidization breccia plug are mineralized where veins impinge upon them (Callow and Worley, 1965), and significant tonnages of ore are present. The gold in both veins and breccias occurs predominantly as native gold in grey, granular quartz containing disseminated pyrite. Later stages of mineralization are represented by white quartz, rhodonite, calcite and anhydrite with minor base metal sulfides and gold tellurides.

A series of discrete ore shoots (up to 75 gm/ton Au) occurs within the vein structures (Fernandez and Damasco, 1979). Some pitch at angles of about 45° or less, whereas most are much steeper, and can be related to vein intersections or splits, or changes in the strike of vein structures. It is noteworthy that the maximum vertical extent of mineralization is 500 meters. Upward, vein structures pass into intensely altered ground and ore shoots do not appear to approach closer than about 300 meters from the elevation of the Baguio erosion surface, a Plio-Pleistocene surface thought to represent the extant surface during the period of mineralization (Sawkins et al., 1979). Wallrock alteration in the Baguio district has produced mainly chlorite and lesser sericite. In vein breccias rock fragments are strongly silicified, and development of disseminated pyrite in these and adjacent wallrocks is ubiquitous. In detail, however, the intensity of alteration adjacent to vein structures is highly variable.

Fluid inclusion studies indicate ore fluids of low salinity (0.6–4.6 eq. wt% NaCl) at temperatures between 205 and 300 °C. No evidence of consistent spatial variations in temperature were observed, but sporadic evidence of boiling of ore fluids was noted. Pressure estimates based on the fluid inclusion data were compatible with the notion that the surface during mineralization was at elevations compatible with that of the Baguio surface. Stable isotope studies indicated that the ore fluids were essentially similar to modern day thermal and ground waters in the area. The considerable lateral extent of the Baguio vein systems, as opposed to their more limited vertical extent, the subhorizontal pitch of certain ore shoots, and the restricted temperature range of vein filling, all suggest that ore deposition was effected by predominantly meteoric fluids with a major horizontal flow direction (Sawkins et al., 1979). The source of the gold is at present equivocal.

The Tayoltita vein system in Durango, Mexico (Smith et al., 1982) (Fig. 1.15) exhibits strong similarities to that of Baguio, although silver-gold ratios are considerably higher (>40 versus 2:1). The Tayoltita vein system is particu-

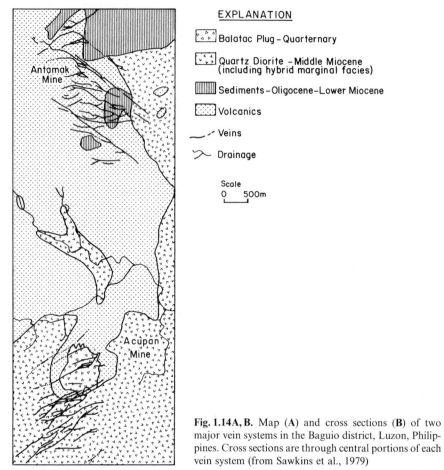

EXPLANATION

Balatac Plug – Quarternary

Quartz Diorite – Middle Miocene
(including hybrid marginal facies)

Sediments – Oligocene – Lower Miocene

Volcanics

Veins

Drainage

Scale
0   500m

Antamok Mine

Acupan Mine

Fig. 1.14A, B. Map (A) and cross sections (B) of two major vein systems in the Baguio district, Luzon, Philippines. Cross sections are through central portions of each vein system (from Sawkins et al., 1979)

Fig. 1.14A

larly instructive, for post-ore tilting combined with steep topography has allowed exposure of the subjacent rock units to depths of almost 1.5 km below the mineralized interval (Fig. 1.16). This favorable zone lies within an alternating sequence of andesites and rhyolites that overlie and are intruded by granodiorite and related plutonic rocks, representative of the uppermost portions of an extensive batholith. Quartz monzonite encountered in the Tayoltita tunnel has been dated at 42.8 m.y.

Veins and vein breccias of the extensive Tayoltita system are dominated by quartz gangue, accompanied by lesser amounts of adularia, johannsenite-rhodonite, and calcite locally. Gold and silver metallization is associated with greyish quartz discolored by occluded materials, and distinctive from earlier and later generations of essentially barren white quartz. Gold occurs mainly as elec-

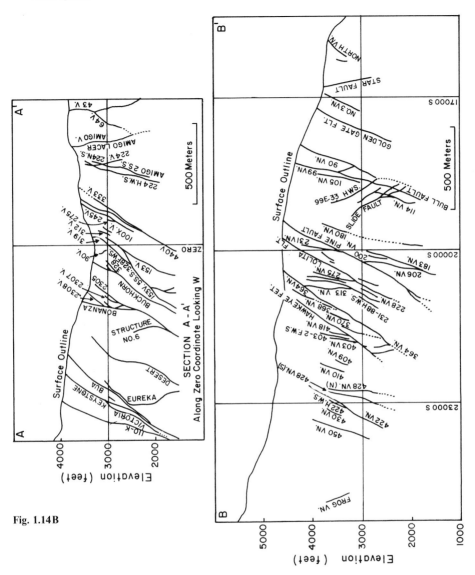

Fig. 1.14B

trum, and silver as argentite and various silver sulfosalts. Base metal sulfides are minor and in most areas represent less than 2% of the ore.

Fluid inclusion studies of mineral-stage quartz indicate deposition largely in the range 250–280 °C (Smith et al., 1982) by fluids of 2–10 eq. wt% NaCl. Considerable evidence for boiling exists, especially toward the top of the ore-bearing interval. Contours of Ag/Au ratios within the veins of the Tayoltita system are predominantly horizontal (pre-tilting) and the flat tongue-like shapes of miner-

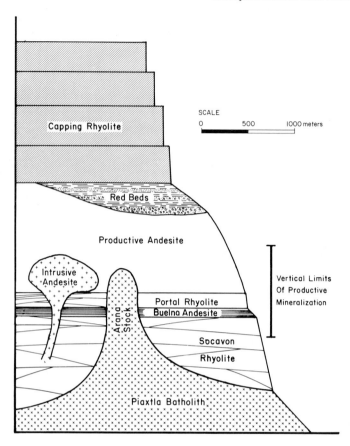

Fig. 1.15A. Diagrammatic section of the stratigraphy and intrusive phases in the area of the Tayoltita Mine, Mexico (courtesy of M. Clarke and Cia. Luismin, Mexico)

alization with lower ratios (higher gold contents) in the central parts of the veins strongly suggest largely horizontal flow of the ore fluids (M. Clarke and T. Albinson, pers. comm.). The fluid inclusion temperature data from ore-stage quartz indicate slightly higher temperatures in the mineralized interval than both above and below it, and this is also suggestive of horizontal flow.

Stable isotope data obtained on vein materials, host rocks, and selvages adjacent to alteration veinlets in the subjacent volcanic and intrusive rocks (Churchill, 1980), define the presence of a large meteoric water-dominated convection system during mineralization. However, high-precision analysis for gold and silver in altered versus fresh volcanic and intrusive rocks from below the mineralized zone failed to support a hostrock leaching origin for the precious metals in the vein ores.

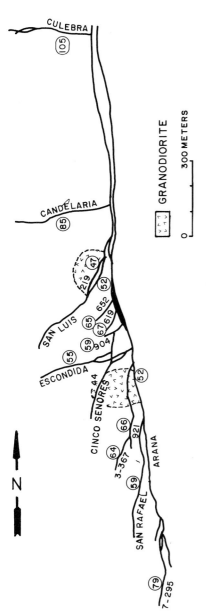

Fig. 1.15B. Plan of Tayoltita vein system showing bulk Ag:Au ratios ④ of the major veins (from Smith et al., 1982)

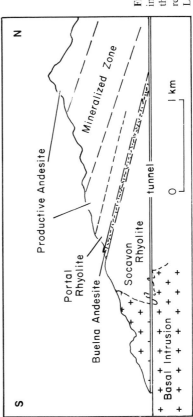

Fig. 1.16. Longitudinal section of the Tayoltita system showing how combination of tilting, erosion, and development of the Tayoltita tunnel allows interpretation of the geologic relationships well below parts of the system (courtesy Cia. Luismin, Mexico)

1.4.4 Discussion and Suggestions for Exploration

Systems of narrow veins have little appeal nowadays to many mining companies because of the high costs and low bulk tonnages inherent in the mining of such deposits. Nevertheless, they deserve attention for some have produced considerable quantities of precious metals, and it is being increasingly realized that large tonnages of disseminated lower grade ore, amenable to bulk extraction, can occur near or adjacent to vein systems. Furthermore, the inherently high-level nature of these deposits involves the possibility that they could represent the distal manifestations of much larger mineralized systems at depth.

The genesis of most precious metal and many base metal vein deposits in principal arcs appears to be closely related to the operation of meteoric water convection cells driven by underlying magmatic heat sources. The fluid inclusion temperature data from such deposits concentrate in the 240–280 °C range, which is precisely that of many modern geothermal systems (Ellis, 1979). What is more problematic is the origin of the metals in these systems.

In many instances the precipitation of the metals appears to be closely linked to the inception of boiling in the ore fluids (Buchanan, 1981). Of more direct concern to the explorationist is the indication that the ore shoots of epithermal vein systems form within a few hundred meters of paleosurfaces, and that the vertical interval over which ore shoots are developed seldom exceeds 500 meters. As opposed to their restricted vertical extent, vein systems of this type are much more extensive laterally and may continue for several kilometers. Also significant is the fact that the zones overlying mineralized horizons commonly lack well-defined vein structures and may be either intensely or weakly altered. Thus, in areas where erosion has not sufficiently incised the terrain, whole vein systems will be essentially blind. In some instances arsenic, antimony, and perhaps mercury dispersion halos exist above these precious metal vein systems and can be sought by geochemical studies. These elements, however, are not enriched in all deposits of this type.

1.5 Precious Metal Deposits of the Western United States

The precious metal deposits of the western U.S. merit separate treatment on a number of counts, for not only are/(were) they of considerable economic importance, but they embrace a spectrum of deposit types and occur in a region of complexly overlapping tectonomagmatic activity. Furthermore, although many of the deposits have been subjected to considerable study, there is still a certain amount of controversy regarding their timing and setting.

1.5.1 Vein Deposits

A large number of vein deposits of precious metals are scattered through the western U.S., particularly within the Basin and Range Province (Guild, 1978;

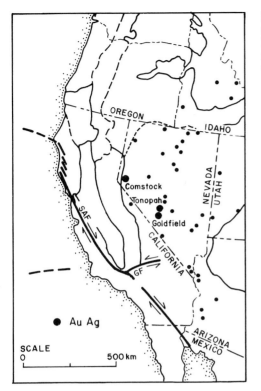

Fig. 1.17. Principal post-Laramide precious metal vein deposits of the Basin and Range, western U.S. Note crude linear array (Walker Lane) of major deposits in western Nevada

Silberman et al., 1976; Silberman, 1978). Although the precise mineralization age of many of the smaller deposits is not known, the vast majority occur within late Cenozoic andesitic volcanics (Silberman et al., 1976), and the major deposits are arrayed along a northwesterly trend in western Nevada called the Walker Lane. This belt is thought to be a transcurrent fault zone, and contains the Tonapah, Goldfield, and Comstock Lode deposits in addition to many smaller deposits and widespread alteration zones (Fig. 1.17). At current prices, the Tonapah and Goldfield deposits have each produced in excess of $1,000,000,000 worth of precious metals and the Comstock Lode well over $2,000,000,000. These and numerous other deposits are essentially similar to epithermal precious metal deposits in principal arcs (Nolan, 1933).

The quartz veins in the Tonapah district contained ore grade mineralization within a well-defined favorable zone (Fig. 1.18). The chief ore minerals are argentite, polybasite, and pyrargyrite. Silver-gold ratios are about 100:1 and the gold was present chiefly as electrum (Nolan, 1933). Detailed observations of the hydrothermal alteration patterns at Tonapah are reported by Bonham and Garside (1979) who recognized a zonal arrangement of alteration facies. The innermost zone, adjacent to the quartz veins, consists of quartz, sericite and adularia,

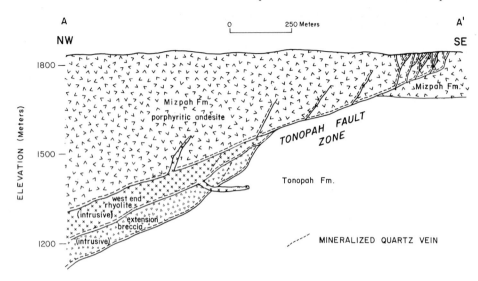

Fig. 1.18. Generalized cross section through the main part of the Tonapah district, looking northeast. Note restriction of the mineralization to a limited part of the volcanic stratigraphic section (from Fahley, 1981)

plus disseminated pyrite. This potassium silicate zone grades outward to an intermediate argillic zone that can be divided into an inner subzone of kaolinite-halloysite, plus some quartz and sericite, and an outer subzone characterized by montmorillonite, plus lesser kaolinite and sericite. Disseminated pyrite occurs in this intermediate zone, and both it and the inner zone are bleached. The combined widths of these two zones away from veins can reach 40 meters.

The inner and intermediate zones of hydrothermal alteration are set within a broad zone of propylitic alteration that decreases in intensity outward from the center of the district. Chlorite, calcite, albite, and hydrothermal potassium feldspar are the main minerals developed, and the innermost portions of this propylitic zone contain disseminated pyrite. The altered rock is a greenish gray color. Mineralized quartz veins toward the margins of the district pass upward into quartz and calcite stringer zones: pyrite is essentially the sole sulfide present in these vein tops and propylitic alteration extends upwards from them for up to 200 meters. Little silver or gold is present.

Isotopic studies (Taylor, 1973) indicate that large volumes of the volcanic hostrocks at Tonapah are equilibrated with ^{18}O and deuterium-depleted meteoric waters. Both the isotopic data and increasing silver/gold ratios indicate a temperature zonation from about 300 °C to lower values, outward from the center of the district. Thus, a convecting, meteoric water-dominated hydrothermal system powered by an underlying intrusive body seems to be clearly indicated for the formation of the Tonapah ores.

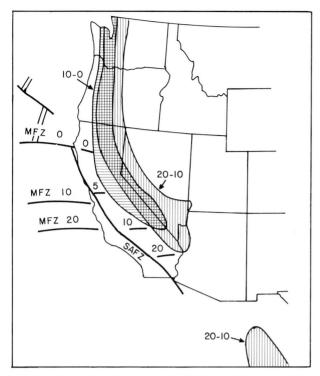

Fig. 1.19. Illustration of the westward withdrawal of the zone of calc-alkaline volcanism during the late Cenozoic to its present position in the Cascades. MFZ = Mendicino Fracture Zone; SAFZ = San Andreas Fracture Zone. Numbers refer to age ranges (m.y.) of calc-alkaline volcanics (from Burchfield, 1979)

The major epithermal precious metal deposits of western Nevada are Miocene in age (Silberman et al., 1976) and, as noted above, occur predominantly within andesitic volcanics. By Miocene time, extensional tectonic activity and related rhyolite and basalt volcanism was already well established further east in the Basin and Range Province, but it appears that principal arc magmatism was withdrawing westwards at that time toward its present position along the Cascades (Snyder et al., 1976) (Fig. 1.19). Presumably this westward movement of principal arc magmatism was due to steepening of the underlying subducting slab, as has been suggested by geochronologic and petrologic studies in Arizona and northern Mexico (Keith, 1978; Clark et al., 1982).

1.5.2 Carbonate-Replacement Gold Deposits

Carbonate-replacement deposits in which the gold occurs in disseminated, and thus bulk-mineable, form are presently known mainly from central and eastern

Nevada (Radtke, 1983). These deposits typically exhibit high Au/Ag ratios (>20:1), range in grade from 4–8 gm/ton, and vary in size from 5 to 80 million tons (A. Radtke, pers. comm.). They have been called Carlin-type deposits because this type of gold occurrence was first recognized in the area that eventually became the Carlin mine. Other important examples in Nevada include the Gold Quarry, Cortez, and Jerritt Canyon deposits.

The combination of subjacent magmatism, high angle faulting, and reactive carbonate host rocks appears to provide the critical environments in which such Carlin-type deposits can form. In a sense these ores can be considered distal, low temperature equivalents of gold-bearing skarns, and the formation of replacement bodies of jasperoid above and adjacent to orebodies is a feature of some. The orebodies themselves exhibit a variety of geometries, such as tabular zones parallel to bedding, and pipes and vein-like forms cutting across bedding. High angle faults of limited offset were important controls of ore-fluid plumbing, and orebody sites and shapes tend to be controlled by the intersection of such faults, either with favorable beds or other faults.

The ores are characterized by a well-defined suite of trace elements. Of these, arsenic is the most prominent and commonly occurs in concentrations of between 100 and 1 000 ppm. Similarly, antimony (10–50 ppm), mercury (1–30 ppm) and thallium are distinctive associated elements.

Detailed studies of the Carlin deposit (Radtke et al., 1980; Radtke, 1983) have provided a clearer understanding of the genesis of this type of deposit. The Carlin ores occur primarily as tabular replacements of Paleozoic thin-bedded argillaceous arenaceous beds rich in carbonate, that are exposed in a window through the upper plate of the Roberts Mountain thrust (Fig. 1.20). Subsequent normal faulting has been extensive in the area and resulted in intense shattering of the lower plate carbonate-rich sediments. Larger Basin and Range faults have caused rotation of the sedimentary units, but are almost certainly post-mineralization in age.

Most of the orebodies occur within the upper 250 m of sediments of the Roberts Mountain Formation. This formation is overlain by the Popovich Formation, which in turn is overlain and truncated by the Roberts Mountain thrust. Three ore zones, west, main and east, have been delineated (see Fig. 1.20) and consist primarily of stratigraphically controlled, tabular zones adjacent to faults. The primary unoxidized ores are of various types, the major type consisting of rocks closely resembling unaltered host rocks, but where calcite has been removed and fine-grained pyrite and silica, together with gold, arsenic, tallium, antimony, and mercury have been introduced. Siliceous ore, on the other hand, contains large amounts of introduced fine-grained silica and grades into jasperiod. Other types that represent variants of mineralization style are pyritic, carbonaceous, and arsenical ores.

In detail, the tenor of gold and its associated trace metals is highly variable. The gold occurs primarily in association with arsenic, antimony and mercury as fracture fillings and coatings on pyrite grains and to a lesser extent with or-

Fig. 1.20. Generalized geologic map of the Carlin gold deposit. Note the substantial development of normal faulting and its control of most of the ore bodies (from Radtke et al., 1980)

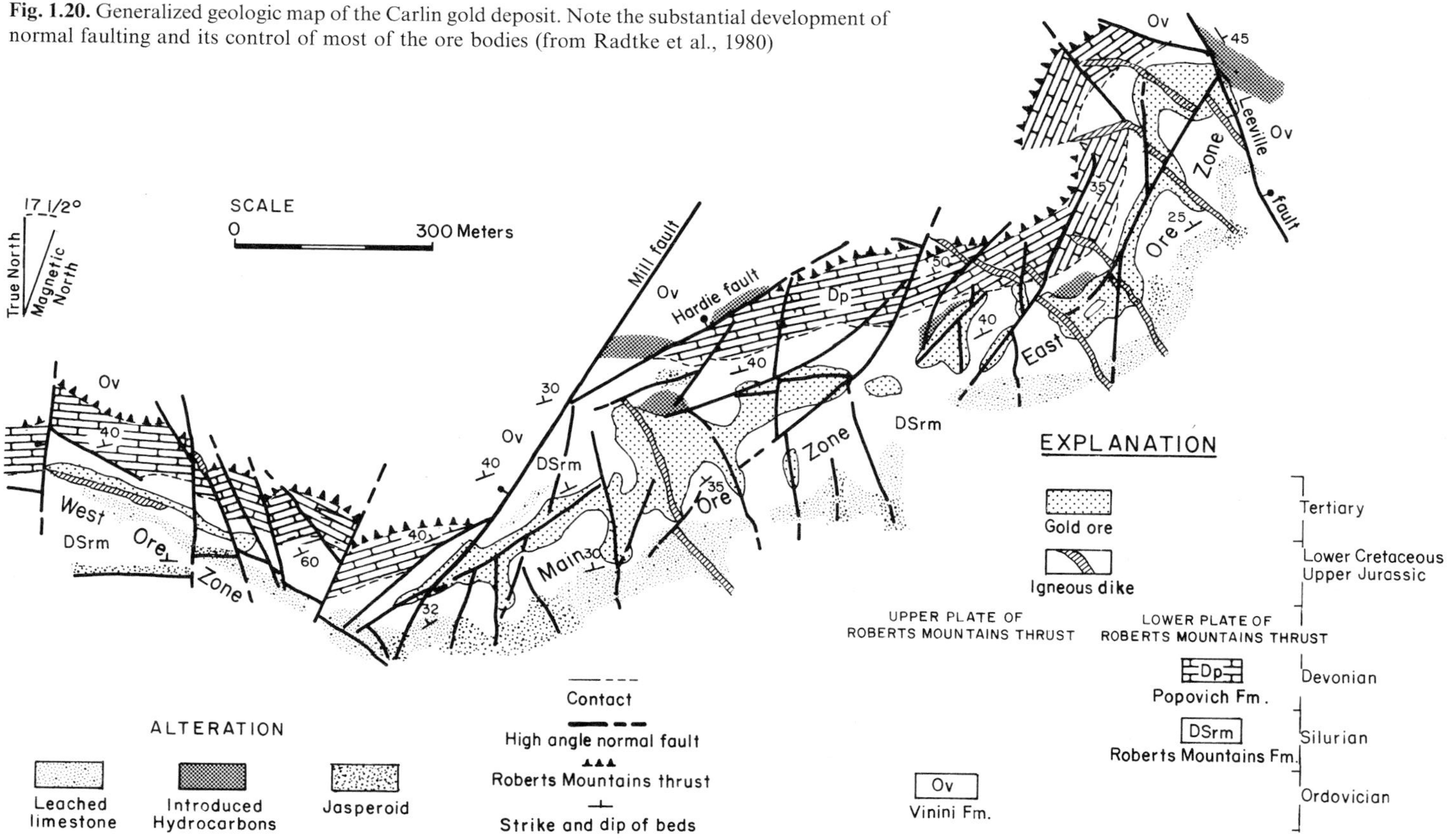

EXPLANATION

Gold ore

Igneous dike

UPPER PLATE OF
ROBERTS MOUNTAINS THRUST

Ov   Vinini Fm.

LOWER PLATE OF
ROBERTS MOUNTAINS THRUST

Dp   Popovich Fm.

DSrm   Roberts Mountains Fm.

Tertiary
Lower Cretaceous
Upper Jurassic
Devonian
Silurian
Ordovician

———— Contact

▲▲▲ High angle normal fault
     Roberts Mountains thrust

⊢ Strike and dip of beds

ALTERATION

Leached limestone

Introduced Hydrocarbons

Jasperoid

SCALE

0   300 Meters

17 1/2°
True North Magnetic North

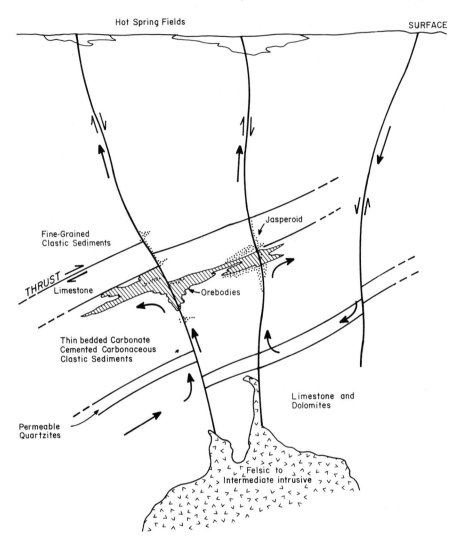

Fig. 1.21. Schematic cross section of a disseminated replacement (Carlin-type) gold deposit (from Giles and Nelson, in press).

ganic carbon. The uppermost portions of many orebodies have been subjected to varying intensities of acid leaching and are strongly altered and oxidized. The rocks in this zone consist mainly of fine-grained quartz and illite, with lesser kaolinite, sericite, and minor montmorillonite and iron oxides. Gold in this material occurs as tiny particles (up to 10 microns), contained either in quartz or associated with iron oxides or clay minerals.

Fluid inclusion and stable isotope studies of the Carlin ores (Radtke et al., 1980) indicate that main stage mineralization was effected at 175–200 °C by fluids of low salinity (1–4 eq. wt.% NaCl), but that during later stage acid leaching temperatures increased to about 275 °C. At this point boiling was widespread and salinities increased to approximately 17 eq. wt.% NaCl. Stable isotope data for hydrogen and oxygen indicate that the fluids involved in ore deposition were of meteoric origin (δD − 140 to − 160‰), but that they were highly exchanged with heavier ^{18}O from the country rocks. In addition $\delta^{18}O$ values increased substantially (from 3 to 10‰) during the episode of late boiling indicated by the fluid inclusion data.

The range of $\delta^{34}S$ values from hydrothermal pyrites (4–16‰) is comparable with that obtained from diagenetic pyrite in the hostrocks, suggesting a sedimentary origin for the sulfur in the deposit. Overall, the data available for the Carlin deposit suggest an ore-generating system consisting of a meteoric water convective cell that utilized the fault and fracture systems that characterize the area (Fig. 1.21). The driving mechanism was presumably an underlying Tertiary felsic magma body. Radtke et al. (1980), and Radtke (1983) suggest that the components of the ores were derived by leaching from the sedimentary country rocks within the deeper portions of the convection system.

Rhyodacite and rhyolite flows of Miocene age occur a few kilometers to the west of the deposit, but gold-bearing equigranular stocks of probable early Tertiary age are present within three kilometers of the deposit (Sillitoe, pers. comm.). The age of the Carlin and related carbonate-hosted gold deposits is thus critical to the interpretation of their tectonic setting. If the deposits are all late Tertiary in age, as suggested by Radtke et al. (1980), then they must be assigned to rear-arc rifting events (see Chapter 3). However, if their age is early to mid-Tertiary as indicated by the geochronologic studies of Silberman et al. (1976) on the Cortez deposit and on other intrusives in this general area, they can be assigned to a principal arc setting. This latter alternative, although as yet speculative, is more in keeping with the tendency of gold deposits to form in relation to principal arc magmatism.

1.5.3 Hot Spring-Type Gold Deposits

Another type of disseminated gold deposit, involving ore deposition close to the paleosurface, has been recognized in recent years and termed hot spring-type gold ore. Known examples of such deposits in western North America include the Round Mountain deposit, Nevada (Berger and Eimon, 1982) and the Cinola deposit in British Columbia (Kimbach et al., 1981). Another important example is the Pueblo Viejo deposit in the Dominican Republic (Russell et al., 1981). The available data from these deposits are still scanty, but suggest near surface deposition of disseminated gold either within or just below the lower portions of hot spring systems (Fig. 1.22). A mushroom-shaped cap of weak sericite alteration and silicification forms that typically contains a sulfide core and sur-

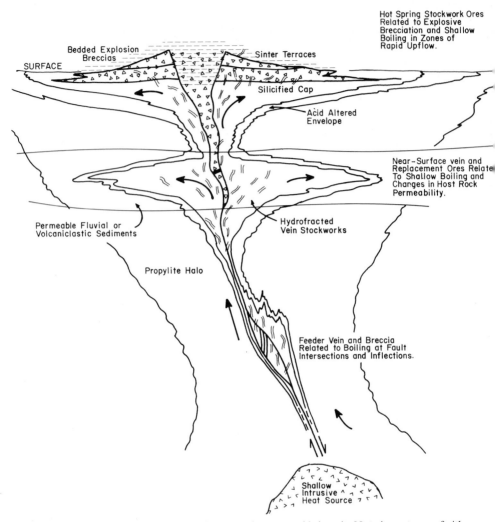

Fig. 1.22. Schematic cross section of a hot-spring-type gold deposit. Note importance of either hydrofracture or explosive brecciation in creation of near-surface bulk tonnage gold ores (from Giles and Nelson, in press)

rounding zones of minor alunite, kaolinite and finally montimorillonite alteration. Ore material typically contains native gold and electrum as tiny blebs, generally as small as a few microns each. The accompanying opaque minerals are characteristically pyrite and/or marcasite and various silver sulfosalts.

The tectonomagmatic setting of hot spring-type gold deposits appears to be largely that of principal arcs, but arc-related rift environments and even leaky transform fault settings may turn out to host such deposits.

1.5.4 Discussion

This somewhat extended treatment of the precious metal deposits of the western United States is considered justified, because it is a complex area within which new types of gold mineralization have been identified. Such deposits, containing just a few ppm gold, are neither easy to find or recognize unless exploration programs are specifically targeted toward them. However, as we learn more about their character and setting it seems probable that additional examples will be found, perhaps mainly in the young island arc systems of the western Pacific.

Firm exploration guides for such deposits have yet to emerge, but the presence of considerable fine-grained silica, argillic alteration and hydrothermal breccias are certainly positive indications. If such areas are also characterized by anomalous amounts of arsenic, antimony, or mercury, further careful work, and perhaps shallow drilling are justified.

1.6 Additional Deposits of Principal Arcs

1.6.1 Massive Magnetite Deposits

There are a number of massive magnetite deposits around the Pacific margin that represent important local sources of iron ore (Park, 1972). The majority of these occur as contact metasomatic replacements adjacent to diorite or granodiorite stocks intruded into volcanics or sediments, and in some cases the distinction between these and magnetite skarn deposits is difficult to make. In reality there is probably a complete spectrum between end-member types. A well defined north-south zone of these deposits 600 km long occurs in central Chile (Ruiz et al., 1965) (Fig. 1.23 A), and several other deposits are known in Peru (Park, 1972). Essentially similar magnetite deposits occur at Las Truchas, Michoacan, Mexico (Salas, 1975), and Texada, British Columbia (Sangster, 1925).

Recent detailed studies of the El Romeral magnetite ores, central Chile are reported by Bookstrom (1977). Here, a series of steeply dipping, lenticular magnetite-rich masses occur in a north-south array adjacent to the El Romeral fault, which cuts the El Romeral diorite along the ore trend (Fig. 1.23 B). Field evidence indicates both pre- and post-ore intrusive and faulting events. The ores consist of fine-grained assemblages of magnetite-actinolite replacing either andesite porphyry (e.g., main orebody) or Paleozoic schists (e.g., north orebody). The orebodies exhibit gradational boundaries, and altered rocks within and around them contain magnetite, actinolite, plagioclase (An_{22-32}), diopside, clinozoisite, sphere, chloroapatite, scapolite, tourmaline, chlorite, pyrite, calcite, micas, and clays. Minor element contents of the magnetite ore are low, especially with respect to base metals. Based on experimental data of equilibrium phase relationships for similar mineral assemblages, a temperature range of 475–550 °C and pressures of approximately 2 kb are suggested.

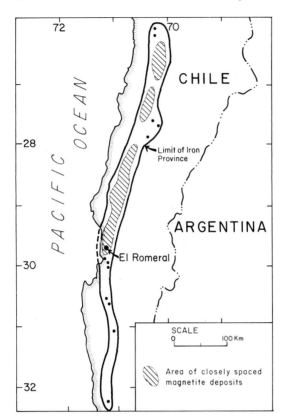

Fig. 1.23 A. Belt of magnetite deposits in north-central Chile
(adapted from Ruiz, 1975).

Whether the ores of El Romeral and similar deposits of massive magnetite in principal arcs are truly hydrothermal in origin, or represent intrusive equivalents of the massive magnetite flows at El Laco, Chile (Park, 1961) and Cerro Mercado, Durango, Mexico, is not clear at present. These magnetite flow deposits are associated with felsic volcanics and appear to represent apatite-rich immiscible fractions separated from felsic magmas, but how such magnetite-rich melts achieved the bouyancy to permit their extrusion is problematic. Whether some of the circum-Pacific iron deposits are intermediate between contact-metasomatic and flow types is simply not clear at the present time. The iron orebody at Acari, Peru occurs as a long plunging rod in undeformed granodiorite and may be of magmatic segregation origin.

1.6.2 Manto-Type Copper Deposits

Manto-type copper deposits are essentially limited to Chile in their occurrence, although possibly similar examples are found in Peru and British Columbia (Sil-

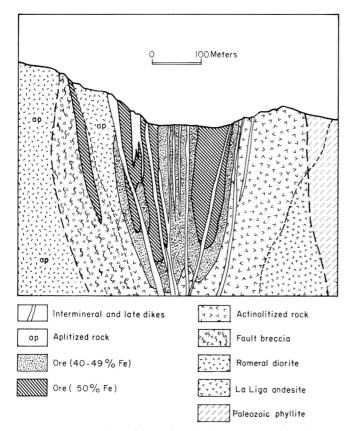

Fig. 1.23B. Cross section of the Main orebody at El Romeral iron deposit, Chile (after Bookstrom 1977)

litoe, 1981a). Despite their rarity elsewhere, manto-type copper deposits are an important facet of Chilean metallogeny, and at Buena Esperanza, Antofagasta Province 25,000,000 tons of 3% copper ore were mined. There, and elsewhere in Chile, manto-type deposits consist of broadly stratiform bodies in volcanic rocks, volcaniclastic sediments, and in minor instances in limestones. Maximum thicknesses of mineralized intervals are about 30 meters, but the deposits may extend for kilometers along strike (Sillitoe, 1977). The ore minerals consist of hypogene chalcocite, bornite and chalcopyrite emplaced as disseminations, vesicle fillings and veinlets, commonly in the upper parts of permeable volcanic units. Development of gangue minerals and alteration assemblages is subtle, and orebodies tend to exhibit well-defined tops but gradational lower contacts.

At Buena Esperanza (Ruiz et al., 1971) 28 mineralized horizons occur within a 270 m thick sequence of Jurassic andesites. Individual ore horizons range in thickness from 2 to 28 m and occur within vesicular flow tops and intercalated clastic sediments. Chalcocite and bornite represent the ore minerals and occur in a 4:1 ratio. Further south, between latitudes 30° and 34° south disseminated bornite mineralization occurs in the tops of lower Cretaceous andesite flows. Irregular disseminations of copper sulfides in volcanics also occur elsewhere in Chile and are probably of similar origin; for example, at Lo Aguirre in Santiago Province, ores of this type containing 20–30 million tons of 2% copper are known (Ruiz et al., 1965).

The formation of this type of copper deposit presumably relates to the circulation of heated meteoric fluids through cooling volcanic piles, with leaching of copper and its subsequent deposition in flow tops, interflow sediments or lagoonal limestones (Sillitoe, 1977).

1.7 Discussion

Principal arcs are linear, typically continuous, belts of batholiths, stocks and coeval volcanics generated above actively subducting lithospheric slabs. In arcs where the dip angle of subduction remains constant for significant periods of time (tens of millions of years) principal arcs tend to be narrow, but if the dip angle changes with time the principal arc axis will shift and the resultant arc will

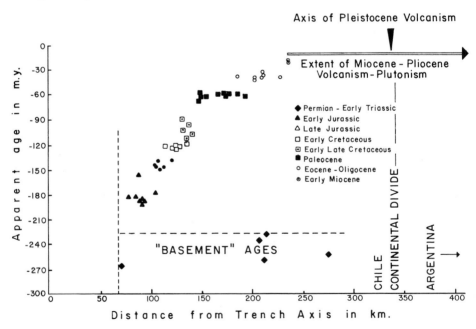

Fig. 1.24. Diagrammatic plot to illustrate progressive shift of calc-alkaline magmatism with time in northern Chile (from Clarke et al., 1976)

Table 1.1. Relative importance of ore-deposit types in principal arcs

Volcano-plutonic arc	Age	Base-ment	Porph Cu	Massive Magnetite	Skarn Fe-Cu-Au	Skarn W-Mo	Manto Cu	Pluton-Related Veins	Epi-thermal Au-Ag	Reference
W. Andes, N. Chile-S. Chile	Jurassic-Pliocene	C	P	I	I	-	I	I	I	Sillitoe (1976b)
West and Central Cordillera, Colombia	Triassic-Pliocene	O (W) C (E)	I	-	m	-	-	I	I	Barrero (1976)
West Mexico	Cretaceous-Eocene	O (W) C (E)	P	I	m	m	-	m	P	Salas (1975)
Costa Rica-Panama	Miocene-Pliocene	O	P	-	-	-	-	-	I	Kesler (1978)
Philippines	Paleocene-Pliocene	O	P	-	I	m	-	m	P	Gervasio (1971)
Papua New Guinea	Miocene-Pleistocene	O (NE)	P	-	m	-	-	m	P	Grainger and Grainger (1974)
Solomon Islands	Pliocene-Pleistocene	O	m	-	-	-	-	-	m	Taylor (1976)
Fiji	Miocene-Pliocene	O	I	-	m	-	-	m	P	Colley and Greenbaum (1980)
E. Lachlan belt, NSW, Australia	Silurian-Devonian	?O	I	-	P	-	m	I	-	Gilligan (1978)
W. British Columbia, Canada	Triassic-Eocene	O+C	P	?m	P	I	m	I	-	Sutherland Brown et al. (1971)
N. Honshu, Japan	Cretaceous	?C	m	-	I	I	-	I	-	Isihara (1978)
Balkans, Bulgaria	U. Cretaceous-Paleocene	C	P	?-	I	-	-	-	-	Bogdanov et al. (1974)
Chagai belt, Pakistan	?Late Cretaceous-Miocene	?C	I	m	m	-	m	m	-	Sillitoe (1978)

O = oceanic; C = continental; P = principal and economically viable ore-deposit type; I = important ore-deposit type; m = minor ore-deposit type; - = essentially absent (from Sillitoe 1981a)

be broader and more diffuse. In the principal arcs of the Andes, Mexico and the southwestern U.S.A. there has been a tendency for the angle of subduction to decrease with time and as a result a well-defined inward younging of magmatic events (Fig. 1.24) is discernible (e.g., Clark et al., 1976). In such instances it becomes difficult to separate magmatic events that pertain to bona fide principal arcs versus those more appropriately assigned to inner-arc environments. Perhaps inner-arc magmatism merely represents igneous activity related to low angle subduction.

From the previous sections it is clear that the metallogeny of principal arcs is dominated by copper, iron, and precious metal deposits together with lesser tungsten and molybdenum mineralization locally. Arrays of deposits in almost all instances parallel the trench axis, but their distribution tends to be controlled in part by across-arc tectonic segmentation (Sillitoe, 1974a). The intrusive rocks associated with these deposits are mainly tonalites, granodiorites, and lesser adamellites, but more mafic types (diorite, quartz diorite) and more alkaline types (monzodiorite, monzonite, and syenite) are important locally.

Sillitoe (1981a) has detailed the relative importance of ore deposit types within specific principal arcs (Table 1.1). The fact that the same spectrum of ore deposit types characterizes these arcs, despite their variations in maturity, crustal setting and age, indicates that magma generation and subsequent ore deposition must not be influenced in any significant way by these variations.

It has been noted that porphyry copper deposits in island arc settings tend to be gold-rich and molybdenum-poor and that the converse is true for porphyries in Cordilleran (continental margin) arcs (Kelser, 1973). Exceptions to this rule do occur, however, and include the gold-rich Bajo de La Alumbrera porphyry deposit in Argentina, and the molybdenum-rich Sipalay porphyry copper, Philippines (Sillitoe, 1979, 1980). The metal chemistry of porphyry deposits, and, for that matter, of the majority of deposits found in principal arcs is apparently more closely related to magmatic evolution and crustal thickness, than regional variations in the lithochemistry of the country and basement rocks in different areas. Thus, both the restriction of tungsten deposits to Cordilleran principal arcs and larger average size of porphyry copper deposits within such arcs, may be influenced by the greater crustal thickness inherent in Cordilleran arcs vis a vis oceanic arcs (Sillitoe, 1981a).

Chapter 2   Metal Deposits on the Inner Sides
of Principal Arcs

In mature island arc systems (e.g., Japan) and Cordilleran belts a spectrum of
metal deposits form that are sufficiently distinctive from those of principal arcs
to merit separate consideration. They tend to exhibit a close spatial association
with isolated stocks that intrude the zone on the inner side of principal arcs. The
precise demarcation of this zone is not easy and is particularly tenuous in

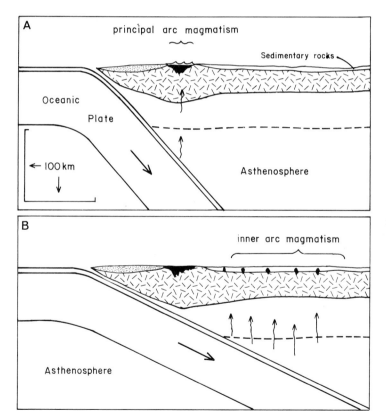

Fig. 2.1A, B. Schematic illustration of (**A**) a narrow belt of magmatic activity (principal arc) above
a steeply dipping lithospheric slab and (**B**) a broad diffuse zone of magmatic activity (inner arc)
above a shallow dipping lithospheric slab

situations where the principal arc itself has migrated back and forth relative to the trench axis. As suggested in the previous chapter, inner arc magmatism and related metallogenesis is probably a function of subduction attaining some critical low angle (Fig. 2.1). Nevertheless, inner arc metal deposits are sufficiently distinctive to warrant separate treatment vis a vis principal arc deposits.

2.1 Contact Metasomatic Deposits

Contact-metasomatic deposits, characterized by major amounts of zinc, lead, and silver, occur on the east side of the coastal batholith of central Peru (Petersen, 1965), east of the Sierra Madre Occidental in Mexico (Salas, 1975) and on the eastern side of magmatic arcs related to subduction in the western United States during Cretaceous to mid-Tertiary time (Sillitoe, 1981a). Similar occurrences possibly include the skarn deposits of the Sanin belt, Honshu, Japan (Shimazaki, 1980), and related deposits in southern Korea. The isolated stocks that are typically adjacent to such deposits range in composition from diorite to granite, but are most commonly granodiorite or quartz monzonite. The carbonate hostrocks of the deposits typically represent earlier miogeoclinal or stable platform environments.

2.1.1 Mineralization

The development of these contact-metasomatic deposits results from replacement of the carbonate units adjacent to stocks, and a wide spectrum of orebody geometries can result (Fig. 2.2). At Naica, Chihuahua, Mexico, for example, flat-lying mantos controlled by bedding are interspersed with pipe or chimney-like deposits (Stone, 1959), whereas in other instances (e.g., Morochocha and Yauricocha, Peru; Petersen, 1965) ore occurs mainly in steeply dipping chimneys. Most of the deposits in this category are associated with strong development of skarns, but others contain relatively minor amounts of skarn. The orebodies either crosscut their hostrocks at high angles or merely follow shallow or steeply dipping carbonate units.

Zinc, lead, and silver are the most characteristic metals of these inner-arc deposits, but most contain a certain amount of copper, and in some instances it may represent the major metal of economic significance. In the latter case, deposits generally exhibit a well-defined zonal pattern with the lead-zinc ores lying peripheral to those of copper (Petersen, 1965). For the most part the intrusive stocks spatially associated with the deposits are unmineralized, but some important exceptions to this rule are known. At Bingham, Utah, for example, a major porphyry copper deposit lies at the center of the district (see Econ Geol., v. 73, no. 7). Adjacent to the stock that hosts the Bingham porphyry deposit, are important bedding-controlled copper skarn deposits (Atkinson and Einaudi,

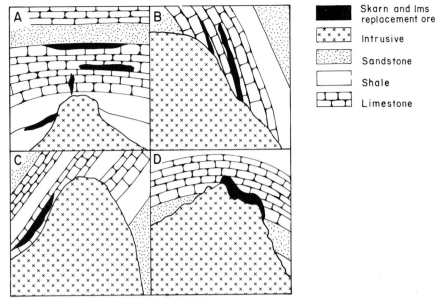

Fig. 2.2. Typical geometries of skarn and limestone replacement deposits found in inner-arc regions of the western U.S. and Mexico

1978), and fringing these are lead-zinc-silver replacement deposits (Fig. 2.3). The ores of these deposits tend to be massive in character, especially where skarn development is restricted. Iron sulfides in many instances represent a significant fraction of the massive ore and occur as pyrite, in some instances accompanied by lesser pyrrhotite.

The Cerro de Pasco replacement deposit in central Peru (Einaudi, 1977b) is of particular interest, both in terms of its size and its unusual setting within a volcanic vent. It is estimated that the deposit contained 100 million tons of pyrite, 4 million tons zinc, 2 million tons lead, over 1 million tons copper, 10 thousand tons of silver, and lesser quantities of gold and bismuth. This quantity of contained metals clearly marks it as a world class deposit. Adjacent to the volcanic vent, hydrothermal solutions formed a steep funnel-shaped massive quartz-pyrite body by replacement of Paleozoic shales and Mesozoic limestone (Fig. 2.4). This large iron sulfide body was itself replaced locally by pyrrhotite pipes and lead-zinc orebodies. The latter also extend out into carbonate host-rocks locally. Most of the copper ores occur as steep veins cutting the volcanic vent, and consist primarily of pyrite-enargite, with minor associated quartz, barite, and epidote. Alteration of quartz monzonite dikes and volcanic breccia produced sericite-pyrite-quartz assemblages, but advanced argillic alteration envelopes are present around some of the copper-bearing veins. Einaudi (1977b) has demonstrated that the considerable complexity of the ores probably relates

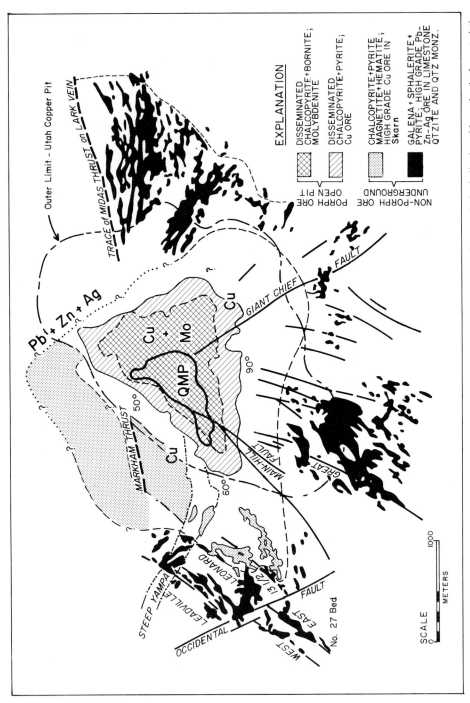

Fig. 2.3 Zonal distribution of porphyry-, skarn-, and limestone replacement ores centered on the Bingham stock. Such district-wide zoning is characteristic of strongly mineralized areas in inner-arc regions (from Atkinson and Einaudi, 1978).

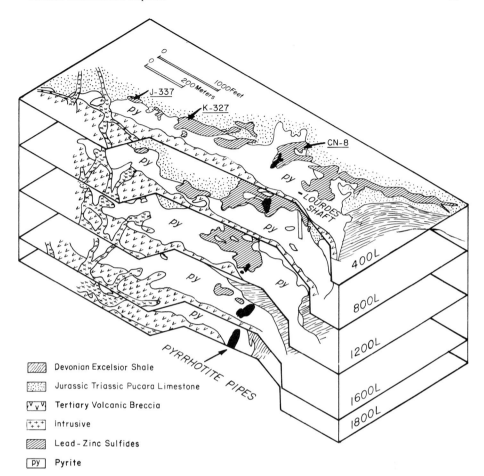

Fig. 2.4A. Isometric diagram of the Cerro de Pasco ore deposit showing relationships between lithologic units, pyrite body, pyrrhotite pipes, and lead-zinc ores. Slight vertical exaggeration of scale

to rapid sulfide deposition from an ore fluid that fluctuated widely in sulfidation-oxidation state. Although the Cerro de Pasco ores are in many respects unique, partial similarities to other inner-arc contact metasomatic deposits (e.g., Magma and Bisbee, Arizona) and porphyry copper-related vein deposits (e.g., Butte, Montana) can be recognized.

The ore-associated calc-silicate assemblages of inner-arc contact metasomatic deposits are complex, but resemble those described in more detail for principal arc sulfide skarns. However, in many instances (e.g., Naica: Stone, 1959) garnets tend to be grossularitic rather than andraditic in composition. Pathways of ore fluids are inevitably controlled by structural breaks in the host rocks, and the carbonate units just above older basement tend to be important

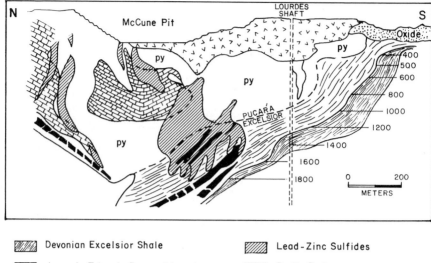

Devonian Excelsior Shale   Lead-Zinc Sulfides

Jurassic Triassic Pucara Limestone   py   Pyrite Body

V V Tertiary Volcanic Breccia   Pyrrhotite Pipe

Fig. 2.4 B. Vertical, north-south cross sections, looking east through the central portions of the Cerro de Pasco ore deposit (from Einaudi, 1977)

hosts for mineralization. However, the precise reason why certain carbonate units are mineralized preferentially to others is in many instances unclear. In addition, the structures involved in channelling the ore fluids are in many cases subtle and difficult to map.

2.1.2 The Providencia Ag-Pb-Zn-Cu Deposit, Zacatecas, Mexico

The massive sulfide chimneys at Providencia have produced over seven million tons of high-grade base metal ore rich in silver, and represent a well-studied example of inner-arc, contact metasomatic ore deposition (Sawkins, 1964; Rye, 1966). Elongate pipe-like bodies of lead-zinc sulfide ore occur in steeply dipping Upper Jurassic and Cretaceous limestones adjacent to and near the southern margin of the Providencia stock (Fig. 2.5). This granodiorite intrusive is continuous in the subsurface with the Concepcion del Oro granodiorite to the southeast where important copper skarn deposits occur (Buseck, 1966), and where substantial additional tonnages of copper-tungsten skarn ore have recently been discovered. K-Ar and Rb-Sr age determinations of minerals from the granodiorite and from the ores indicate an age of close to 40 million years for both intrusives and mineralization. Initial strontium ratios are 0.705 (Ohmoto et al., 1966).

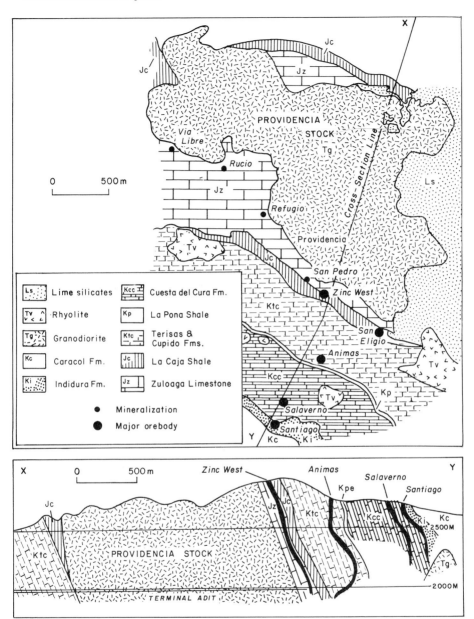

Fig. 2.5. Map and cross section of the Providencia Mine area, Mexico. In detail the Pb-Zn-Ag sulfide replacement pipes exhibit considerable irregularities in their shapes (from Sawkins, 1964)

The Providencia massive sulfide pipes exhibit a combination of fracture and bedding control and contain predominantly pyrite, sphalerite and galena. Silver occurs largely in tetrahedrite and much lesser bournonite and geocronite. Small amounts of chalcopyrite occur in the ores and appear to increase somewhat with depth. The principal gangue mineral is pink manganiferous calcite, but minor amounts of dolomite occur locally, and kutnahorite and rhodochrosite are present in one of the pipes (Salaverna). Lime silicates, mainly grossular garnet, are admixed with sulfide minerals in the deepest levels of the larger pipes (e.g., Zinc West, Animas), whereas quartz is rare or absent at depth, but increases steadily in amount upwards within the pipes. Unreplaced shale bands altered to muscovite could be observed locally in the Animas and Salaverna pipes, and this material was used in part in the age determination studies cited above.

Fluid inclusion studies, utilizing mainly zoned sphalerite crystals, indicate that the final 30 percent of ore deposition at Providencia took place mainly from 370–300 °C, with very minor amounts of sulfide deposition continuing to 200 °C (Sawkins, 1964). Although temperature decreased steadily, no evidence of a drop in temperature relative to elevation was found over the 400 meter interval sampled. The salinity of the ore fluids varied erratically between 5 and 40 wt% alkali chlorides during mineralization, with evidence that episodes of high salinity were accompanied by boiling. A pressure of approximately 500 bars during mineralization is indicated from the fluid inclusion data.

Stable isotope studies of the Providencia ores (Rye, 1966; Rye, 1974; Rye and O'Neil, 1968) support a magmatic origin for the sulfur, carbon and ore fluids involved in ore deposition at Providenica. $\delta^{34}S$ values from sulfides fall within the restricted range of -3 to $+6‰$, whereas $\delta^{13}C$ values for carbonates are close to $-7‰$, except at the end of ore deposition where they tend towards marine limestone ($\delta^{13}C = 0‰$). The $\delta^{18}O$ values, both from minerals and fluid inclusions, indicate the ore fluids ranged in composition from 8.8–7.9‰. These isotopic results, taken in conjunction with the -68 to -83 δD values obtained from fluid inclusions, all reinforce the conclusion that ore deposition at Providencia was effected by fluids of magmatic origin, that underwent little modification between their source and the sites of ore deposition. Chemical analysis of these fluids preserved in fluid inclusions (Rye and Haffty, 1969) indicate chloride was the major anion and sodium, potassium, and calcium the major cations. Maximum base metal concentrations of inclusion waters in quartz, a late stage mineral, were found to be 890 ppm zinc and 530 ppm copper.

2.1.3 Discussion and Suggestions for Exploration

The contact metasomatic deposits that form in the vicinity of isolated intermediate to felsic stocks intruded on the landward side of principal arcs are important sources of base metals and silver. In the Andes and northern Mexico the combination of such stocks and carbonate country rocks almost invariably produces some indications of mineralization. The position of ore bodies relative to an intrusive stock can vary however. In the case of the Santa Eulalia and Naica deposits in Mexico the orebodies are above the roofs of stocks, whereas at San Martin, Mexico (Burton, 1975), Providencia, and Bingham the orebodies occur mainly along the steeply dipping flanks of intrusives.

Inasmuch as contacts between ore and hostrocks are typically sharp and geometries of individual pipes or mantos can be complex, the search for blind orebodies is inevitably difficult. If ores are zinc-poor, EM geophysical techniques may be effective, but in the final analysis drilling is the only way to truly test unexplored ground. Careful attention to the subtle effects of limestone recrystallization and to the distribution of limesilicates, especially in impure carbonate units, can, however, isolate areas of higher potential. Recognition of structural and lithologic features that may have influenced the pathways of ore fluids is also important.

The massive or semi-massive nature of lead-zinc contact metasomatic deposits tends to generate strong electromagnetic and induced polarization anomalies. Furthermore, magnetic geophysical techniques can be used to help define intrusive contacts in the subsurface. Application of all these techniques is warranted in areas where prior geologic work indicates the possible presence of subsurface mineralization near granodioritic stocks intrusive into carbonate terrains.

2.2 Polymetallic Vein Systems

Polymetallic vein systems containing silver-lead-zinc ($\pm$ copper) also characterize the inner side of principal arc systems and exhibit a similar areal distribution to the contact metasomatic deposits discussed in the preceeding section. The major difference is that these vein systems develop primarily in non-carbonate hostrocks. In many of the more important inner-arc mineral districts, such vein deposits occur intermixed with contact metasomatic ores (e.g., Morococha, Peru: Petersen, 1965). Where zoning is well developed in such districts, the distal veins contain primarily silver and merge in character with typical epithermal vein deposits. Gold contents, however, tend to be much subordinate to those of silver.

Major polymetallic vein deposits in the central Andes include San Cristobal, Casapalca, Huaron, and Morococha (see Petersen, 1965; Bellido and de Montreuil, 1972), and there are a host of smaller vein systems mined primarily for their silver content (e.g., Finlandia (Kamilli and Ohmoto, 1977); Julcani (Petersen et al., 1977); Caudalosa (Sawkins and Rye, 1976)). It is noteworthy that most of these vein systems exhibit fracture controls that intersect the regional northwest trending structural grain of the Andes at high angles.

In these vein deposits the major base metals occur as sphalerite, galena, and chalcopyrite, although in some instances enargite or tetrahedrite-tennantite are the major copper-bearing phases. Silver is present mainly in a variety of sulfosalt minerals, and quartz and calcite are the predominant gangue minerals in the veins.

In most instances the hostrocks for such vein systems are Tertiary volcanics, and locally redbeds or even schists (e.g., San Cristobal) enclose the vein systems, but it is rare to find significant such systems developed in intrusive rocks. Wall-rock alteration is generally represented by some combination of sericitization, silicification, and chloritization.

Essentially similar vein-type mineralization occurs in Mexico at places such as Taxco, Pachuca, Fresnillo, San Luis Potosi, and Parral (Salas, 1975), and a number of polymetallic and precious metal vein deposits occur in the western United States (Guild, 1978). Vein deposits are especially widespread in the Colorado Mineral Belt (Tweto and Sims, 1963), but they are largely of post 30 m.y. age, and are more properly discussed later under arc-related rift environments.

2.2.1 The Casapalca Ag-Pb-Zn-Cu Deposit, Peru

This important vein system in central Peru has been the subject of detailed fluid inclusion, stable isotope, and mineralogic studies (Rye and Sawkins, 1974; Wu and Petersen, 1977). Here, an extensive system of northeast trending veins has been emplaced in a series of folded early Tertiary volcanics and redbeds (Fig. 2.6).

Veins are mostly narrow (~ 1 meter) and the wallrocks adjacent to them ex-hibit pyritization, silicification, and sericitization. In the central part of the vein system this alteration affects a substantial volume of country rock, but toward the extremities of the system alteration envelopes narrow down to widths com-parable to those of the vein itself. Although the veins are well defined, some mineralization occurs in small parallel fractures adjacent to them, and this is im-portant from an economic viewpoint, because it partially negates the dilution problem involved in mining the narrow veins.

Most veins are relatively tightly filled, but some splits that dip vertically are extremely vuggy locally. Paragenesis studies on such material indicated a se-quence in which sphalerite, galena, and chalcopyrite accompanied by pyrite and quartz (main stage) are succeeded by lesser amounts of pale sphalerite, galena, tetrahedrite and other sulfosalts, again with pyrite and quartz (late stage). The final stage of vein filling is represented by calcite in various crystallographic forms, essentially barren of metallic minerals (postsulfide stage). Fluid inclusion studies indicate that temperatures dropped steadily from 370 °C to 280 °C dur-ing the main and late stages of ore deposition, whereas the calcites were de-posited at still lower temperatures (Rye and Sawkins, 1974). During main stage deposition salinities of the ore fluids varied from 5–40 wt% alkali chlorides and sporadic boiling occurred.

Stable isotope analysis on both inclusion fluids and vein quartz representa-tive of main and late stage materials generated a tight data set indicative of

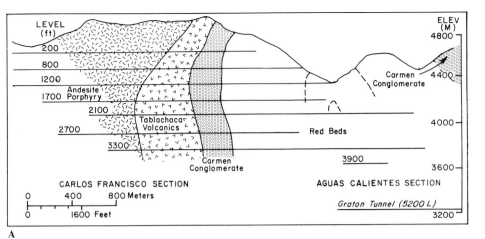

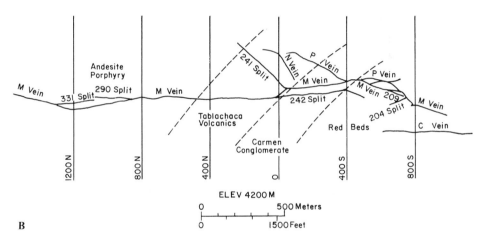

Fig. 2.6. (A) Longitudinal cross section and (B) 1 700 level plan of the Casapalca vein system, central Andes, Peru (from Rye and Sawkins, 1973)

fluids of magmatic origin (Fig. 2.7). However, δD and $\delta^{18}O$ values from fluids in calcites exhibit a sharp trend toward waters strongly depleted in deuterium and oxygen 18, similar to present day meteoric waters in the region. Overall, the data provide a clear picture of incursion of local meteoric waters into the vein system, but only after metallization had essentially ceased. The $\delta^{34}S$ values obtained from sulfides indicate a narrow isotopic range for sulfur and an average value of sulfur in the ore fluids of close to $+1‰$ $\delta^{34}S$. $\delta^{13}C$ values suggest an increasing marine carbonate component in the later calcite stages.

Despite their profound differences in terms of geometry and hostrock character, the Casapalca and Providencia (see previous section) deposits exhibit an

CASAPALCA VEIN SYSTEM

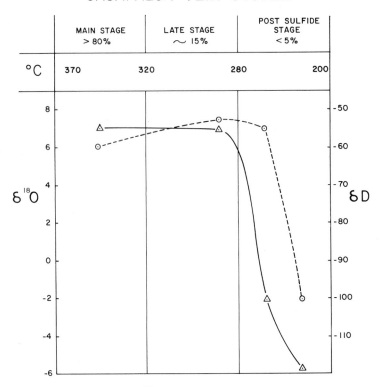

Fig. 2.7. Generalized plot of $\delta^{18}O$ (circles) and δD (triangles) values of Casapalca ore and post-ore fluids versus paragenetic stage. Note sharp change in isotopic values from late stage to postsulfide (carbonate) stage of vein filling (modified from Rye and Sawkins, 1973)

almost uncanny similarity in terms of paragenesis, depositional temperatures, ore fluid salinities, and isotopic systematics. The important inference that can be drawn from this observation is that the fundamental control of such deposits lies primarily in the evolution of ore fluids from magmatic source regions, rather than the lithologies of immediate hostrocks.

2.2.2 Discussion and Suggestions for Exploration

Although many vein systems in inner-arc regions can be properly designated as polymetallic, many others contain relatively minor amounts of base metals and are perhaps more correctly designated as epithermal precious metal deposits. In fact, recognition of a spectrum from polymetallic to true precious metal epithermal deposits is more realistic. Of particular interest in this regard is the Caudalosa vein deposit in central Peru (Sawkins and Rye, 1976). Here, fluid in-

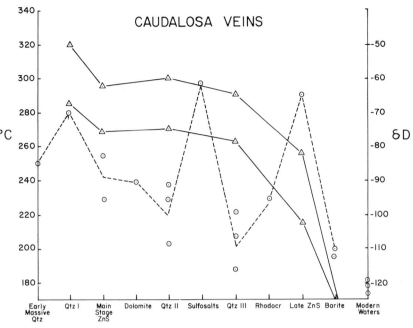

Fig. 2.8. Plot of temperature and δD variations versus paragenetic stage for the Caudalosa ore fluids. Triangles show maximum and minimum temperatures for each stage. The sharp variations of the δD values (circles) suggest differing involvement of magmatic (less depleted) and meteoric (more depleted) waters in each stage of the paragenesis (modified from Sawkins and Rye, 1976)

clusion studies indicated temperatures ranging from 320–200 °C, and low to intermediate ore fluid salinities. δD values of inclusion fluids indicate the mixing of two fluids in the vein system with ore minerals deposited mainly by fluids of more magmatic character and gangue minerals by fluids characterized by more isotopically depleted meteoric signatures (Fig. 2.8). Isotopic studies of the Finlandia polymetallic vein, central Peru, by Kamilli and Ohmoto (1977) gave two sets of δD values for the ore fluids in the range -48 to $-75\permil$ and approximately $-100\permil$, and $\delta^{18}O$ values of -10 to $+2\permil$, which led the authors to suggest a mixing of waters of connate origin and meteoric origin during ore deposition.

Vein systems, because of their extent and associated alteration, are generally easy to discover in the rugged terrains that characterize Cordilleran regions. However, once in production they represent a challenge in terms of location of splits and other mineralized structures parallel to major veins that may be blind upward. There is also the ever present problem of maintaining ore reserves in such operations. Careful attention to all aspects of the local geology, especially structure, is important. Furthermore, studies of metal ratio zoning patterns in known veins (see Goodell and Petersen, 1974) can provide an important tool in terms of understanding the anatomy of any particular vein system.

2.3 Tin Tungsten Deposits

On the extreme inner side of some Cordilleran arc systems, belts of intermediate to felsic igneous rocks occur that have tin and/or tungsten deposits associated with them. The prime example is the Bolivian tin belt in the Andes (Fig. 2.9), but essentially similar situations occur in northwestern Canada (Fig. 2.10), and locally in Korea and New South Wales, Australia (Sillitoe, 1981a). In Mexico there are also one or two minor tin occurrences within the inner-arc lead-zinc-silver province.

The igneous rocks associated with this group of deposits are primarily quartz monzonites and granites, and appear to represent both I and S types. In Bolivia tin-tungsten veins are associated with Triassic granodiorite intrusives in the Cordillera Real (see Fig. 2.9). Further south, the tin-silver deposits of Miocene age largely occur with subvolcanic complexes of felsic calc-alkaline composition and presumed I type (Grant et al., 1977, 1980). Sillitoe (1981a), however, cites several observations that suggest that both the older Cordillera Real igneous suite and the Miocene suite may have S-type affiliations.

The important tungsten province of mid- to late-Cretaceous age in the Northwest Territories and Yukon provinces of Canada (Archibald et al., 1978) (see Fig. 2.10) is associated with quartz monzonite and granodiorite plutons

Fig. 2.9. Major igneous provinces of the Eastern Cordillera of Bolivia and associated tin deposits (modified from Grant et al., 1979)

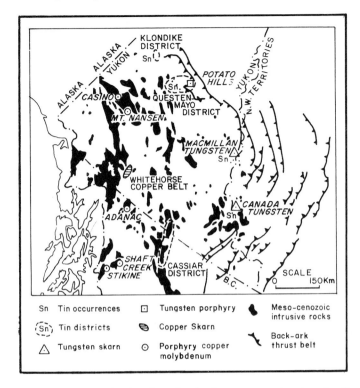

Fig. 2.10. Map showing location of major inner-arc tungsten deposits of northwestern Canada. Note that both here and in Bolivia there is a strong flexure in the trend of the arc system (from Sillitoe, 1981a)

(Gabrielse and Ressor, 1974). Recent work (e.g., Kuran et al., 1982) indicates that these intrusives are of S-type. There are also a number of skarn tin prospects in the vicinity of the tourmaline-bearing leucocratic Seagull Batholith (Dick, 1979), but the position of these, about 200 km southwest of the main tungsten belt is puzzling, however.

A belt of tin and tungsten-bearing granites, which extends for about 1400 km from southwestern Burma to Phuket in southern Thailand (Mitchell and Garson, 1981) forms the so-called Western Tin Belt of southeast Asia (Fig. 2.11). Isotopic age studies (Beckinsale et al., 1979) indicate that the plutons along this belt range in age from early Cretaceous to early Tertiary. In Burma, cassiterite and wolfram mineralization occurs in quartz veins and greisen zones marginal to biotite adamellites and two-mica granites. In peninsular Thailand, the tin mineralization is restricted to biotite and two-mica granites of predominantly S-type, and occurs in quartz veins, stockworks in hornfels, and pegmatites (Ishihara et al., 1980).

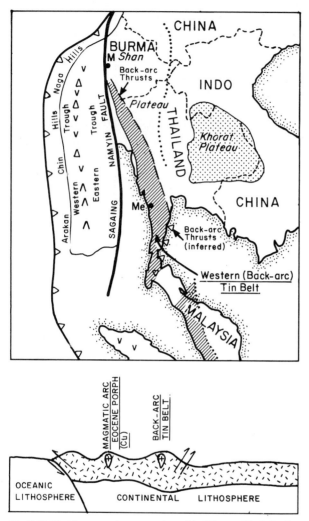

Fig. 2.11. Sketch map and cross section of the Western Tin belt of Southeast Asia during the Eocene. Western Burma is restored to its inferred position prior to late-Cenozoic opening of the Andaman Sea (from Mitchell and Garson, 1981)

The tectonic setting of these deposits is complicated by later tectonic events such as late Tertiary movement along the Sagaing Fault, that has resulted in several hundred kilometers of northward movement of a principal arc terrain originally lying west of the tin belt (Curray et al., 1980). The belt was thus developed between an arc system to the west and a zone of back arc thrusts to the east (Mitchell and Garson, 1981), and as such, it is comparable with the back-arc tin belt of Bolivia. There is also a belt of peraluminous muscovite granites that overlaps the Cordilleran thrust belt of the western United States (Miller and Bradfish, 1980). Minor tin and tungsten deposits are known to be associated with certain of these granites, some of which have been shown to be of probable anatectic origin, due to their high initial strontium ratios.

The important belt of Mesozoic granites in southeastern China, that contains a significant portion of the world's tungsten resources, consists almost entirely of S-type intrusives (Tu et al., 1980). Bor-Ming Jahn et al. (1976) have suggested that this granitic magmatism could have been triggered by northwestward subduction of oceanic lithosphere. The most productive intrusives are in the western part of this belt, and thus appear to have the same inner-arc setting as the tin and tungsten provinces described above.

The tin deposits of eastern Australia occur largely on the inner side of north-south arrays of granitic intrusives that are I-type in the east and S-type further west. In the Lachlan orogen of New South Wales the ages of these igneous rocks are lower to mid-Paleozoic, whereas farther north upper Paleozoic intrusives predominate (Richards, 1980; see also Sillitoe, 1981a, Fig. 9). Considerable uncertainty exists as to whether these belts are subduction related, but, if they are, the tin deposits certainly fit an inner-arc designation in terms of their geographic position.

2.3.1 Mineralization

This group of tin and/or tungsten deposits is a somewhat heterogeneous one in terms of deposit type and associated metals. In Bolivia, the older deposits in the Cordillera Red are tin-tungsten deposits (Turneaure and Walker, 1947), whereas the Miocene tin-silver deposits farther south include veins, breccia pipes and, most important, tin porphyries (Sillitoe et al., 1975; Grant et al., 1980). Such porphyry deposits are known at Llallagua, Oruro and Potosi, and are characterized by large tonnages of low grade cassiterite ore within stockwork-veinlets or breccias, within or adjacent to subvolcanic quartz latite porphyries. Alteration associated with mineralization has sericitized and tourmalinized the hostrocks.

In northwestern Canada the bulk of the tungsten deposits are of skarn type and contain scheelite and, commonly, lesser chalcopyrite. The skarns themselves are characterized by early anhydrous assemblages of garnet (grossular-andradite) and hedenbergitic pyroxene, but exhibit retrograde effects with development of amphiboles and biotite during tungsten mineralization (Dick, 1979; Dick and Hodgson, 1982). Pilcher and McDougall (1976) suggest that the scheelite stockworks at the Potato Hills locality represent a porphyry-type tungsten deposit. Here the hostrocks are adamellite and diorite stocks. Perhaps an even better example of porphyry tungsten mineralization in this area is the Logtung Deposit at Logjam Creek (Templeman-Kluit, 1981; Sillitoe, 1982a).

Sillitoe (1981a) suggests that the Sangdong tungsten-molybdenum-bismuth skarn of Cretaceous age in southern Korea, and the important cassiterite limestone replacement deposits of Paleozoic age in Tasmania may also have formed in back-arc tectonic settings. In eastern Australia tin and tungsten deposits occur mainly as vein or pipe deposits associated with greisens. At Ardlethan, New South Wales, pipe-like breccias mineralized with quartz, cassiterite, pyrrhotite and lesser lead-zinc sulfides occur within highly differentiated S type granites cut by quartz porphyry dikes (Paterson, 1976). Tourmaline, sericite, and chlorite are developed as alteration phases.

No single genetic model is likely to be appropriate for this diverse group of deposits, but their invariable time-space association with felsic magmatism indicates that magmatic hydrothermal processes must have been a common denominator in the genesis of most. This conclusion is supported by the relatively few indepth studies available. Kelly and Turneaure (1970), for example, reported high temperatures (up to 500 °C) and high salinities (up to 46 wt% NaCl) for fluid inclusions in minerals from northern Bolivian vein tin-tungsten deposits. Similar results have been generated from studies of the Chorolque subvolcanic tin deposits in southern Bolivia (Grant et al., 1980). Little in the way of quantitative data has been published on the conditions of formation of the scheelite deposits in the Canadian northwest, but Zaw (1976) reports fluid inclusion temperatures in the range of 520–550 °C from minerals in the Cantung E-zone orebody in the Northwest Territories, and Dick and Hodgson (1982) have carried out mineralogic and chemical studies on the MacTung deposit.

2.3.2 The Llallagua Tin Porphyry Deposit, Bolivia

The Llallagua deposit occurs approximately in the center of the 800 km Bolivian tin belt (see Fig. 2.9), and with a production in excess of half a million tons of metallic tin is probably the largest hard-rock tin deposit in the world.

The tin mineralization is closely associated with the Salvadora stock, a small quartz latite body (Fig. 2.12), intruded into an overturned anticline of Silurian-Devonian greywackes, sandstones, and shales (Turneaure, 1935, 1971). Any comagmatic extrusive rocks that may have been present have been removed by erosion. Hydrothermal breccias, containing both igneous and sedimentary fragments in a matrix of rock flour, are widely developed, both within the stock and at its margins. The breccias have the form of irregular pipes and dikes that exhibit widths from tens of meters down to a few centimeters (Grant et al., 1977, 1980). The intrusive porphyry and some of the adjacent sedimentary rocks show pervasive sericitic alteration, whereas the breccias are mainly altered to quartz and tourmaline (Sillitoe et al., 1975). Beyond the main zone of sericitic alteration, chlorite occurs as a replacement of mafic minerals in porphyry dikes.

Bulk mineralization at Llallagua consists predominantly of cassiterite and pyrite in a stockwork of veinlets, and as disseminations in altered rocks. Mineralized fragments in breccias and mineralized veinlets that cut breccia indicate that brecciation was both preceded and followed by mineralization events. Tin

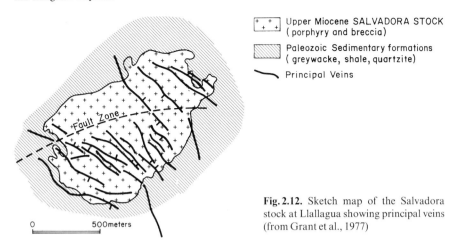

Upper Miocene SALVADORA STOCK
(porphyry and breccia)

Paleozoic Sedimentary formations
(greywacke, shale, quartzite)

Principal Veins

Fig. 2.12. Sketch map of the Salvadora stock at Llallagua showing principal veins (from Grant et al., 1977)

values appear to be higher in the breccias, especially as replacements along fragment rims, but Sillitoe et al. (1975) report that the stock and breccias average 0.3% Sn. There is local evidence that pyrite is more concentrated around the margins of the deposit in a manner reminiscent of the pyritic halos around porphyry copper deposits.

In addition to this porphyry-type tin mineralization, the Salvadora stock is also cut by a series of northeast-trending veins (see Fig. 2.12) that post-date both sericitic alteration, brecciation, and bulk mineralization. These quartz veins exhibit an early stage of bismuthinite-cassiterite deposition followed by pyrrhotite and frankeite, and finally stannite, sphalerite, and chalcopyrite. A late stage alteration of the pyrrhotite to pyrite-marcasite-siderite similar to that reported by Kelly and Turneaure (1970) is also evident, and there is a group of late veinlets that contain sphalerite, siderite, fluorite and hydrous phosphates.

Fluid inclusion studies of the Llallagua hydrothermal system (Grant et al., 1977) indicate temperatures of approximately 400 °C and salinities of less than 26 wt% NaCl. Both temperature and salinity of the fluids tended to decrease as the system evolved (Fig. 2.13), but maximum temperatures and salinities are lower than those reported by Grant et al. (1980) for the Chorolque system. The observations of Sillitoe et al. (1975) and the more detailed studies of Grant et al. (1980) on porphyry tin mineralization in Bolivia have led to the formation of a comprehensive genetic model for these deposits (Fig. 2.14). Based on their detailed geologic, alteration, fluid inclusion, and stable isotopic studies, Grant et al. envisage four stages in the evolution of such systems. The intrusive and hydrothermal events they detail are remarkably similar to those postulated for porphyry copper systems; in particular the brecciation and fracturing events, the evolution of high salinity and high temperature magmatic fluids, and the later involvement of a meteoric water convection system. One difference of note

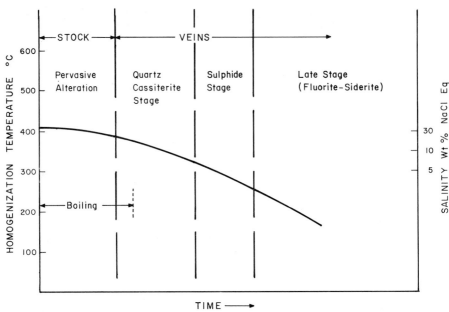

Fig. 2.13. Summary diagram of fluid inclusion data for the Llallagua hydrothermal system (from Grant et al., 1977)

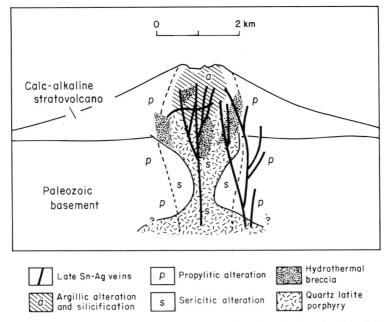

Fig. 2.14. Generalized model for the development of porphyry tin deposits. Note the broad similarity to that suggested for porphyry copper deposits (from Sillitoe et al., 1975)

is that the tin porphyry ores are cut by later quartz-cassiterite vein ores that were the primary focus of mining activity prior to recognition of the disseminated mineralization (see Fig. 2.14).

2.3.3 Discussion and Suggestions for Exploration

As emphasized above, the tin and/or tungsten deposits that form in inner-arc environments embrace a variety of deposit types from porphyries to pipes, skarns, and veins. In view of this, and the possible association of some deposits with low Mg I-type granitic intrusives and others with more prevalent S-types, it is not possible to view them as a cohesive group, other than that most deposits occur on the innermost side of the inner-arc environment (see Mulligan, 1971).

From an economic standpoint large skarn and porphyry type deposits amenable to bulk mining techniques are clearly the most important. In terms of future discoveries, it seems likely that more potential lies with skarn deposits, for they form in somewhat deeper environments, and have less vertical extent and less obvious peripheral alteration than porphyry deposits. The existence of blind skarn orebodies is thus more likely. Porphyry tin deposits on the other hand are emplaced at very shallow subvolcanic levels, and are thus susceptible to removal by erosion. The mid to late Tertiary age of all the known examples of porphyry tin mineralization (Evernden et al., 1977) is in accord with this observation. However, additional examples of such deposits may lie buried beneath the two substantial areas of Neogene ignimbrites present in the central parts of the Bolivian tin belt (see Fig. 2.9), but exploration for these would be difficult.

Exploration for blind tungsten skarn deposits would also be extremely challenging, unless there are sufficient associated sulfides to generate conductivity anomalies that could be sought using appropriate geophysical techniques. The margins of small and intermediate size stocks intruded into carbonate terrains along the innermost zones of inner-arc regions should be optimum areas on which to concentrate such exploration efforts.

Chapter 3   Metal Deposits of Arc-Related Rifts

As discussed briefly in an introductory chapter, the development of extensional tectonic regimes behind or within convergent plate boundary arcs is not an uncommon phenomenon (Vine and Smith, 1981). Such regimes develop more readily perhaps in or behind island arc systems constructed in oceanic sites, or adjacent to, rather than within, continental margins. However, the extensional tectonics that characterize the western United States and northern Mexico after about 30 m.y. ago are considered to be an example of this same phenomenon developed within the continental portion of the North American plate (Keith, 1978; Lipman, 1980; Eaton, 1979). Lorenz and Nicholls (1976) have suggested that an environment similar to that of the Basin and Range pertained during Permian time in central and western Europe, although it was clearly less potent in metallogenic terms. In the case of the Andes in South America, extensional regimes are only clearly documented in the extreme south, where the Rocas Verdes terrain is representative of a Cretaceous arc-related rifting event (Dalziel, 1981).

Magmatic suites related to extension behind subduction zones can be complex, however. In the western United States, for example, the onset of extensional tectonics and bimodal basalt-rhyolite volcanism in post-Laramide time (Leeman, 1982) did not invoke the total cessation of calc-alkaline magmatism which retreated gradually westward from about 40–10 m.y. ago (see Chapter 1). The relationships of tectonics to this series of igneous events have been discussed by Snyder et al. (1976), but numerous models have been proposed to explain tectono-magmatic events in this area. Some authors (e.g., Dickinson and Snyder, 1979) suggest a relationship to the progressive overriding of the East Pacific Rise and related development of the San Andreas transform. Other proposals include changes in Benioff zone inclination (Zoback and Thompson, 1978), a reduction in the absolute western motion of North America (Cross and Pilger, 1978), and development of a broad zone of dextral shear (Livaccari, 1979). Most recently, Ingersoll (1982) has attempted to explain the extension and related phenomena in terms of northwestward and clockwise movement of coastal blocks relative to the continental interior, caused primarily by northward migration of the unstable Mendocino triple junction. Analogous examples of back-arc extension in continental environments in Europe are perhaps the Pannonian Basin behind the late Tertiary Carpathian volcanic arc (Royden and

Sclater, 1981), and the early Permian Rotliegende setting of western Europe (Lorenz and Nicholls, 1976).

Several important types of metal deposits are generated within such regimes; some are limited to late Cenozoic time, others appear to be represented in terrains of many ages.

3.1 Climax-Type Porphyry Molybdenum Deposits

The bulk of world molybdenum production comes from a series of large molybdenum deposits that are spatially associated with the Rio Grande Rift System and/or the Colorado Mineral Belt (Fig. 3.1). The northeast trending Colorado Mineral Belt (Tweto and Sims, 1963; Warner, 1978) is recognized as a major crustal flaw of considerable antiquity, and fault activity along it dates back to at least 1.7 b.y. Bookstrom (1981) notes that both Precambrian and Tertiary igneous and metamorphic rocks along the Colorado Mineral Belt exhibit significant enrichments in molybdenum, and suggests the existence of a Colorado molybdenum province.

The major molybdenum deposits are associated with a series of high silica, alkali-rich rhyolite porphyries, emplaced between 33 and 17 m.y. ago as composite diapiric stocks. Compositionally, these intrusives are quite distinctive from the calc-alkaline intrusives associated with molybdenum-dominated variants of porphyry copper deposits in principal arc systems (Sillitoe, 1980a). In addition, Climax-type molybdenum porphyries tend to contain substantially higher grades than arc-type molybdenum porphyries.

The generation of the alkali-rich rhyolitic igneous rocks with which Climax-type molybdenum deposits are associated in time and space (see Fig. 3.1) is apparently related in some manner to a transition stage between decreased convergence and the onset of true back-arc rifting in an area which is now a thousand kilometers or more inboard from the western continental margin (Fig. 3.2). White et al. (1981) envisage that this transition occurred in the Rocky Mountain region about 30 m.y. ago, and involved steepening of the underlying slab and concommitant uprise of mafic asthenospheric material in the back-arc region. Heat from these mafic magmas caused low-volume fractional melting in previously undepleted portions of the lower crust to produce rhyolitic magmas enriched in lithophile elements. White et al. (1981) further postulate that repeated diapiric uprise of these magmas from the lower crust gave rise to the mineralized igneous complexes of Climax-type.

The important porphyry molybdenum deposit of Questa, New Mexico formed 22 m.y. ago at the intersection of the Rio Grande Rift and the northeast trending Jemez lineament, locus of an earlier belt of calc-alkaline igneous activity (see Bookstrom, 1981). The youngest major molybdenum porphyry system, Mt. Emmons (17 m.y.), formed within the Colorado Mineral Belt after the inception of rift-related basaltic volcanism.

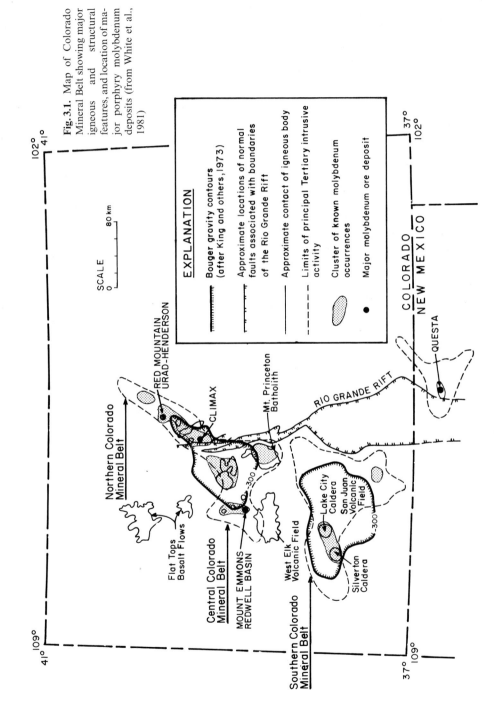

Fig.3.1. Map of Colorado Mineral Belt showing major igneous and structural features, and location of major porphyry molybdenum deposits (from White et al., 1981)

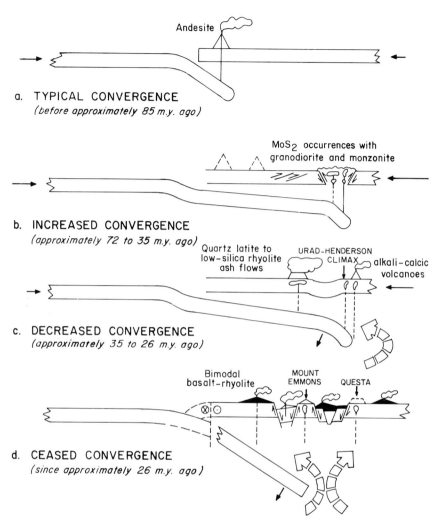

Fig. 3.2. Hypothetical plate tectonic cross sections showing inferred changes in subduction, tectonism, and magmatism in the Colorado Rocky Mountain region in relation to the generation of porphyry molybdenum deposits (from Bookstrom, 1981)

3.1.1 Mineralization and Alteration Patterns

Climax-type molybdenum deposits are lithophile element enriched deposits (tungsten, tin, uranium, niobium, tantalum) that contain essentially no copper. The orebodies consist of zones, typically in the form of inverted bowls, of intersecting stockwork veinlets of quartz and molybdenite. Mineralization is concentrated just above or within the uppermost portions of specific porphyry in-

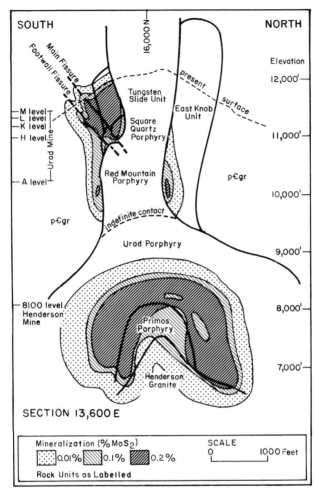

Fig. 3.3. Diagrammatic section showing the geologic relationships of the various intrusive units and their associated mineralization in the Urad-Henderson porphyry molybdenum district, Colorado (from Wallace et al., 1978)

trusives, and at both Climax and Urad-Henderson successive mineralization events are related to successive porphyry intrusive events (Fig. 3.3).

In general, the molybdenite contained in the stockwork quartz veinlets is very fine grained and intimately intergrown with quartz and lesser amounts of sericite, pyrite, and fluorite. In the deeper seated mineralization of the Henderson orebody (see Fig. 3.3), the major proportion of molybdenum is in veinlet form, but within the Henderson granite molybdenite occurs as clots and rosettes along veinlet walls and disseminated within greisen-type pods and segregations (Wallace et al., 1978).

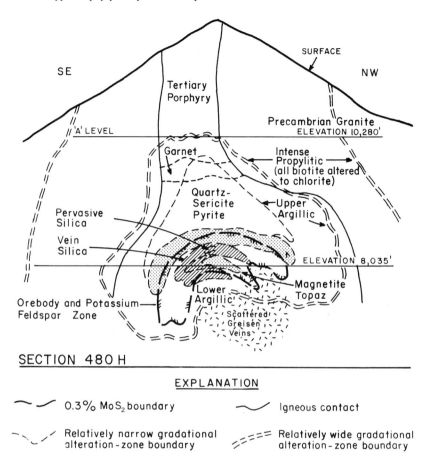

SECTION 480 H

EXPLANATION

⌒‿ 0.3% MoS₂ boundary   ‿⁄ Igneous contact

⁀‿⁄ Relatively narrow gradational   ⁓≡≡ Relatively wide gradational
     alteration-zone boundary   alteration-zone boundary

Fig. 3.4. Section through the Henderson deposit illustrating the spatial relationships of the alteration zones associated with development of the molybdenum porphyry orebody (from White et al., 1981)

Pyrite is the most common sulfide mineral in these deposits. It occurs predominantly above and peripheral to ore zones and may reach concentrations of 10 percent locally. Where pyrite and molybdenite occur together, pyrite veinlets commonly cut molybdenite-bearing veinlets. Wallace et al. (1978) conclude that, during the formation of the Henderson orebody, the molybdenite and pyrite were deposited simultaneously in their respective zones and the apparent age difference was caused by the innermost pyrite zone impinging on the outermost molybdenite zone during inward collapse of both zones. Other minor minerals associated with this group of deposits are mainly huebnerite, magnetite, hematite, sphalerite, galena, and chalcopyrite, but in all cases except at Climax, molybdenite is the only mineral recovered. At Climax, however, there was re-·

covery of huebnerite, and lesser amounts of cassiterite and monazite, in addition to molybdenite and secondary molybdenum oxide minerals (Wallace et al., 1968).

Zonal patterns of hydrothermal alteration types are less pronounced in Climax-type molybdenum deposits, presumably because the multiple intrusion-mineralization events that characterize these deposits tend to obscure simple alteration zoning patterns. Alteration phases include quartz, potassium feldspar, sericite, and fluorite, accompanied locally by lesser amounts of clay minerals, rhodochrosite, biotite, chlorite, and epidote.

In the Henderson orebody, complexities due to multiple intrusion-mineralization events and shallow meteoric water circulation events are minimal, and here, MacKenzie (1970) was able to decipher the principal zones of alteration (Fig. 3.4). The major alteration event produced a central zone of potassium feldspar alteration, including a biotite subzone and a silicified zone, succeeded progressively outward by a quartz-topaz zone, a sericite-quartz-pyrite zone, an argillic zone, and a broad zone of propylitic alteration. This series of alteration events was followed by a much weaker alteration consisting of a greisen zone overlain by an argillic zone. This later event is thought to be related to the Henderson granite. The major alteration zoning at Henderson is thus closely analogous to that characterizing porphyry copper deposits.

Fluid inclusion studies of the Henderson deposit (Kamilli, 1978; White et al., 1981) indicate a temperature range of 500–650 °C during the quartz-molybdenite stage of mineralization down to 250 °C in the final stage. Three types of inclusions were found: liquid rich inclusions containing 30–65 eq. wt.% NaCl and numerous additional daughter minerals; vapor rich inclusions containing 5–20 eq. wt.% NaCl; and very low salinity (<2 eq. wt.% NaCl) liquid-rich inclusions. Investigators have concluded that much of the intense fracturing was caused by the high vapor pressures of the evolving hydrothermal fluids, and that the average temperature of quartz-molybdenite mineralization was at least 500 °C.

3.1.2 Discussion and Suggestions for Exploration

Although Climax-type molybdenum deposits occur predominantly within a relatively limited area of the western United States and were emplaced during a time interval of approximately 20 million years, their economic importance justifies their designation as a distinctive metal deposit type. Furthermore, their association with an intrusive suite of alkali-rich, high silica rhyolites, that can be related to the initiation and development of arc-related rifting is reasonably clear-cut. Whether similar deposits have been generated at other places and times during continental evolution is not clear, but some of the molybdenum porphyry deposits in the U.S.S.R. seem to be representative of this type (Laznicka, 1976).

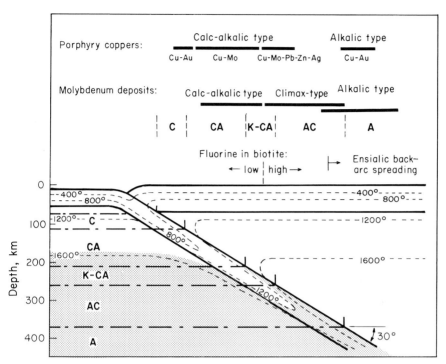

Fig. 3.5. Diagrammatic illustration of the relationships of porphyry copper and porphyry molybdenum deposits to subduction regime and associated magma chemistry (from Westra and Keith, 1981)

Westra and Keith (1981) have reviewed the relationship between magma chemistry and porphyry molybdenum deposits, and demonstrated that a convincing interdependence between magma chemistry, degree of lithophile metal enrichment, and tectonic setting is exhibited by the three main sub-types of porphyry molybdenum deposits (Fig. 3.5). They conclude that the differences between Climax-type deposits and their calc-alkaline and alkalic counterparts result from initial magma chemistry and the subsequent evolution of the magmatic hydrothermal system. They also posit a subcrustal source for the major constituents in such systems, based on isotopic considerations. This important contribution by Westra and Keith not only adds substantially to the understanding of porphyry molybdenum deposits, but convincingly demonstrates that when the empirical data base is sufficiently broad, as for western North America, the relationships between certain deposit types and coeval plate tectonic activity emerge with enhanced clarity.

The importance of the systematics detailed above to the exploration geologist are self-evident, and it is probably true to say that the impressive increase in molybdenum ore reserves in North America during the past decade has in

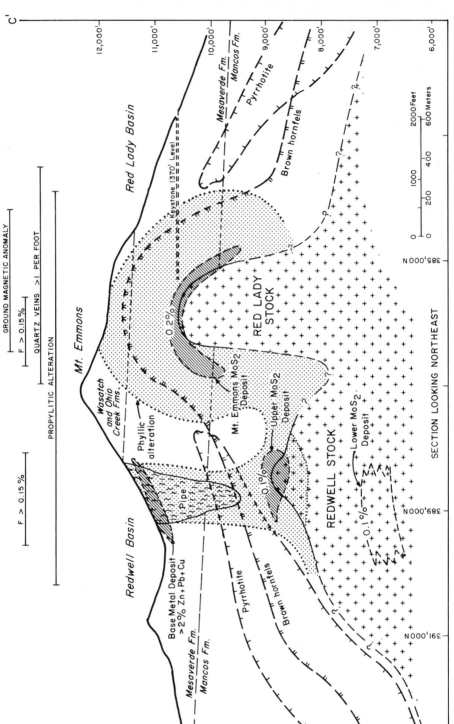

Fig. 3.6. Diagrammatic section showing the geologic relationships of the three porphyry molybdenite deposits of Mt. Emmons. Note that in the case of the Mt. Emmons orebody the present surface only intersects the uppermost edge of the phyllic alteration envelope. This emphasizes the importance of a full understanding of possible alteration zonal patterns in the search for blind porphyry deposits (from Thomas and Galey, 1982).

large measure resulted from the utilization of these systematics. On a more specific level, the recognition that many Climax-type molybdenum deposits contain a series of vertically stacked ore zones is critical in planning drilling programs on prospects, especially where there is evidence of multiple intrusive events. The search for blind molybdenum porphyries is more difficult, but attention to the occurrence of high level alkali rich rhyolite intrusives or near vent volcanics of similar composition, and careful evaluation of distal alteration zones is required. The recent discovery of the three separate ore zones at Mt. Emmons (Fig. 3.6) provides an elegant example of the successful application of these principles (Thomas and Galey, 1982). The strong relationship between potassium and molybdenum enrichment emphasized by Westra and Keith (1981) is also of significance in the search for and evaluation of such deposits.

3.2 Additional Lithophile Suite Deposits in Arc-Related Rifts

Sillitoe (1981a) details a series of lithophile suite deposits of somewhat lesser importance that can be associated with arc-related rifting. These include the series of fluorite deposits in northeastern Mexico (Kesler, 1977) and along the Rio Grande Rift in the United States (Van Alstine, 1976) that, in general, exhibit a relationship of fluorine-rich rhyolite intrusives.

A varied group of lithophile element deposits are also associated with rhyolitic volcanics in arc-related rift settings. These include the numerous small tin deposits associated with the mid- to late-Tertiary rhyolitic ignimbrite province of west central Mexico (Lee-Moreno, 1980; Ypma and Simons, 1970). Mineralization occurs as either cassiterite or wood tin in narrow fissure veins and volcanic breccias, or as disseminations in tuffs and a spatial relationship to volcanic centers is indicated.

An example of uranium and separate mercury mineralization in a caldera setting is provided by the Miocene age McDermitt district on the Nevada-Oregon border (Rytuba, 1981) (Fig. 3.7), where both the uranium and the mercury deposits occur in tuffaceous caldera-lake sediments. Vein deposits of uranium accompanied by fluorite and molybdenum also occur at Marysvale, Utah, and a series of mid- to late-Tertiary beryllium deposits are known in the western United States, although the only one of consequence is that at Spor Mountain, Utah. Here, bertrandite occurs in a large stratabound lens in tuff and breccia associated with topaz rhyolite (Lindsey, 1977).

The igneous rocks associated with this diverse group of deposits are almost invariably alkali-rich, high silica intrusives or extrusives, and it seems clear that the metals and fluorine involved originated from them, although in at least some instances, circulating meteoric waters were probably involved in the ore forma-

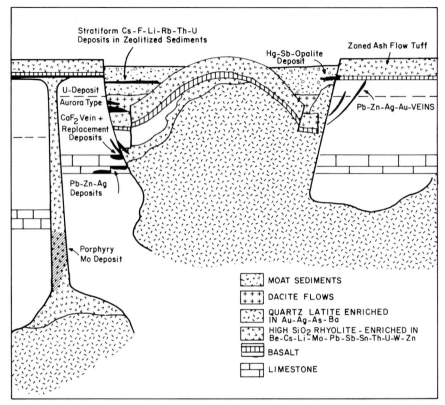

Fig. 3.7. Diagrammatic illustration of the possible ore deposits that can occur in caldera environments related to high silica, rhyolitic volcanism. Based mainly on the McDermit area, Nevada (from Rytuba, 1981)

tion process. As in the case of Climax-type deposits, all the examples of this lithophile suite are from North America. Whether this area is unique in tectonic and/or lithogeochemical terms, or whether similar provinces elsewhere in the world have yet to be recognized is unclear at this point in time.

3.3 Kuroko-Type Massive Sulfide Deposits

Polymetallic conformable lenses of massive sulfide ore, hosted by felsic volcanics, represent an important and widespread type of metal deposit. The type examples occur within the so-called Miocene Green Tuff region of Honshu and Hokkaido in Japan (Fig. 3.8), but production has been dominated by the cluster of deposits within the confines of the Hokuroko Basin. Essentially similar de-

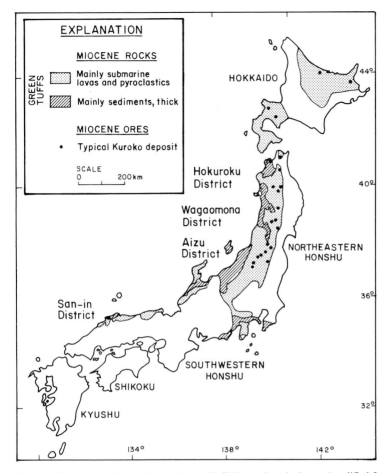

Fig. 3.8. Distribution from Miocene Green Tuff Formations in Japan (modified from Sato, 1974)

posits occur in many Phanerozoic terrains characterized by the presence of submarine felsic volcanics (Table 3.1).

All deposits exhibit a close time-space relationship to fragmental submarine volcanics of dacitic to rhyolitic composition. In Japan, all the Kuroko deposits and related vein deposits were formed during a relatively restricted period that marked the end stages of a major pulse of volcanic activity initiated in late Oligocene time (Sato, 1974) (Fig. 3.9). This coincides with the time at which the Pacific Plate experienced a change of direction, as recorded by the age of bending of the Hawaiian-Emperor seamount chain (~25 m.y. Jackson et al., 1972). A plate tectonic control of this volcanic pulse is thus indicated. In the Hokuroko district, where most detailed studies have been concentrated, there is strong evidence of a period of rapid subsidence and accompanying dacitic volcanism

Table 3.1. Kuroko-Type Massive Sulfide Deposits

Deposit or District	Age	Metal Comp.[a]	Ore-Associated Volcanics	Petrologic Affiliation	References
Undu Peninsula, Fiji	Late Miocene–early Pliocene	Zn, Cu	Dacite	Island-arc tholeiite and andesite	Colley and Greenbaum (1980)
Kuroko districts, Japan	Mid-Miocene	Zn, Cu, Pb	Dacite, rhyolite	Calc-alkaline andesite	Sato (1974)
Pontid Belt, Turkey	Late Cretaceous	Cu, Zn	Dacite	Island arc tholeiite and andesite	Leitch (1981) Egin et al. (1979)
Sierra Madre del Sur, Mexico	Early Cretaceous	Zn, Pb, Cu	Rhyolite, dacite	Calc-alkaline	Loriaczi and Miranda (1978)
East Shasta, Calif.	Triassic	Cu, Zn	Rhyolite	Island-arc tholeiite? andesite	Albers and Robertson (1961)
West Shasta, Calif.	Mid-Devonian	Zn, Cu	Rhyolite	Island-arc tholeiite andesite	Kinkel et al. (1956) Barker et al. (1979)
Buchans Newfoundland, Canada	Silurian	Zn, Pb, Cu	Dacite	Calc-alkaline basalt, dacite	Thurlow and Swanson (1981)
Avoca, southeast Ireland	Late Ordovician	Cu, Zn, Pb	Rhyolite	Calc-alkaline	Platt (1977) Stillman and Williams (1978)
Precambrian Examples[b]					
Jabal Sayid, Saudi Arabia	Late Proterozoic	Cu, Zn, Pb	Rhyolite	Calc-alkaline	Sabir (1979) Brown (1980)
Prescott, Jerome and Bagdad, Ariz.	Middle-Proterozoic	Cu, Zn	Rhyolite	Calc-alkaline	Anderson and Guilbert (1979) Donnelly and Hahn (1981)
Noranda, Quebec, Canada	Archean	Zn, Cu	Rhyolite	Island-arc tholeiite	Spence and De Rozen-Spence (1975)

[a] Metals are listed in order of decreasing abundance. All deposits also contain recoverable gold and silver values

[b] See Chap. 4

Acknowledgement: Modified somewhat from Sillitoe (1982b)

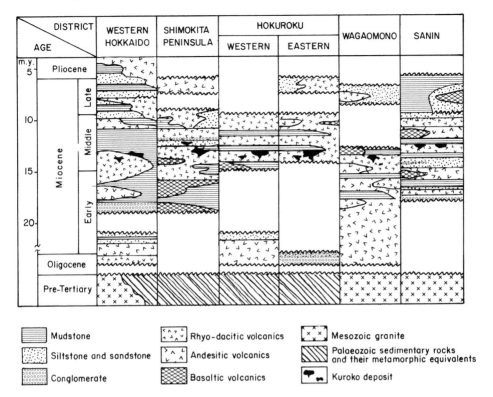

Fig. 3.9. Generalized comparative stratigraphic sections of Green Tuff areas that contain Kuroko-type metal deposits. Note restriction of the deposits to a narrow time interval during the middle Miocene (from Lambert and Sato, 1974)

(Nishikurosawa Stage) at the beginning of the Middle Miocene (Sato et al., 1974; Fujii, 1974). The important massive sulfide deposits of this district were formed during the waning stages of this pulse of volcanism.

This subsidence has been interpreted as being due to caldera formation by some workers (e.g., Ohmoto, 1978; Sillitoe, 1980b). Whether the entire Hokuroko Basin is a single large collapse-caldera structure is uncertain, but isopach mapping indicates a series of northeast trending normal faults that were active during this middle Miocene period. As detailed by Sillitoe (1980b), Uyeda and Nishiwaki (1980), and Dewey (1980), certain island arcs can undergo periods of tension, typically associated with the opening of back-arc basins (Vine and Smith, 1981). In the case of the Japanese arc system, opening of the Japan Sea occurred earlier, but renewed development of a tensional regime is closely associated with the particular period of volcanic activity that spawned the Kuroko suite of deposits (Sillitoe, 1982b).

In other areas where Kuroko-type deposits occur, the operation of intra-arc or back-arc rifting is not always as easy to document, but can be inferred for the massive sulfide deposits on the Undu Peninsula, Vanua Levi, Fiji, and those of the Pontid belt of Turkey (Sillitoe, 1982b). However, the strong similarities of many massive sulfide ores and their host rocks to the Japanese situation is such that essentially similar volcano-tectonic environments can be postulated (Table 3.1). Sillitoe (1982b) also notes that the appearance of minor basaltic rocks in many massive sulfide districts indicates the development of bimodal mafic-felsic suites at the time of mineralization. As noted previously, such bimo-dalism is a signature of extensional tectonic regimes (see Martin and Piwinskii, 1972). As we shall see later, felsic volcanic-hosted massive sulfide deposits can also form in tensional environments unrelated to subduction terrains.

3.3.1 Mineralization and Alteration Patterns

Although individual Kuroko-type deposits can exhibit considerable variability in terms of geometry and metal contents, a valid general model for such deposits has evolved (Fig. 3.10). Three basic ore types are recognized: a low-grade under-lying stockwork (Keiko) ore, consisting of quartz veinlets containing pyrite and chalcopyrite; yellow (Oko) ore, consisting mainly of massive pyrite plus chalco-pyrite; and black (Kuroko) ore, consisting of massive galena, sphalerite, and barite with variable amounts of chalcopyrite and pyrite. Overlying these lenses of massive sulfide, locally are barite layers containing some sulfides, and in some instances a ferruginous chert layer is present on top of the sequence, al-though this is by no means a universal feature.

Whereas mineral banding in these deposits is typically restricted to the up-permost or peripheral portions of the black ore, they are nonetheless broadly layered in nature. In general, grain size decreases upward through a deposit, and in much of the black ore the larger grains of major minerals do not exceed 200–300 microns in diameter (Shimazaki, 1974). Minor minerals are usually an order of magnitude smaller. Within the lower portions of black ore lenses the mineral assemblage is typically just sphalerite-galena-chalcopyrite-pyrite-barite, but up-ward there is an increasing concentration of minor elements such as arsenic, gold, silver, and nickel, and this is reflected mainly in the presence of sulfosalt minerals, especially tetrahedrite-tennantite.

Most ores are compact and massive, but bedded, brecciated, or colloform textures dominate locally, and graded bedding in black ore has even been ob-served in several localities. The average tenor of the ores mined in the Hokuroko district is approximately 2% Cu, 5% Zn, 1.5% Pb, 21% Fe, 12% Ba, 1.5 gm/ton Au and 95 gm/ton Ag (Lambert and Sato, 1974). Each of the major mines in this area is centered on a cluster of separate ore lenses (Fig. 3.11) that range in size from less than 0.1 million tons to about 10 million tons, and total ore ton-nage of the district is estimated to be 90 million tons (Sangster, 1980). The stratabound lenses are typically elongate, with sharp upper boundaries and

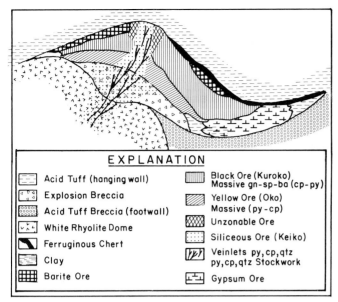

EXPLANATION

Acid Tuff (hanging wall)		Black Ore (Kuroko) Massive gn-sp-ba (cp-py)	
Explosion Breccia		Yellow Ore (Oko) Massive (py-cp)	
Acid Tuff Breccia (footwall)		Unzonable Ore	
White Rhyolite Dome		Siliceous Ore (Keiko)	
Ferruginous Chert		Veinlets py,cp,qtz py,cp,qtz Stockwork	
Clay		Gypsum Ore	
Barite Ore			

Fig. 3.10. Idealized section of a typical Kuroko deposit to show relationships between various ore types and associated geologic units (from Franklin et al., 1981)

more diffuse lower boundaries, that grade downward through lower grade stockworks into unmineralized footwall volcanics and tuffs (see Fig. 3.10).

The alteration patterns associated with Kuroko-type ore lenses (Fig. 3.12) have been superimposed on a regional zeolite facies alteration that characterizes the Green Tuff formations in Japan. In general, the stockwork zone and the immediate environs of the ore lenses exhibit strong Mg-chlorite plus sericite alteration and local silicification. Surrounding this, and commonly extending well up into the overlying rocks (up to 200 m) is a zone of less intense alteration containing sericite, interstratified sericite-montmorillonite, and Fe/Mg chlorite, with development of albite and potassium feldspar (Iijima, 1974). The most distal alteration, which grades into the regional zeolite facies alteration, contains montmorillonite as the main clay mineral accompanied by lesser amounts of cristobalite and zeolites. The extension of alteration assemblages well up into the hanging wall rocks indicates continued, or at least intermittent, hydrothermal activity for periods of up to one or two million years after cessation of ore deposition (Iijima, 1974) (see Fig. 3.12). In chemical terms, alteration represents strong Mg metasomatism in all zones, and K metasomatism in the footwall alteration zones. Calcium and especially sodium are removed during the alteration process except in the distal alteration above ore lenses. The 'white rhyolite' domes closely associated with many of the Kuroko-type deposits (Date and Tanimura, 1974) appear to have originally been dacite, now intensely altered to quartz-sericite assemblages.

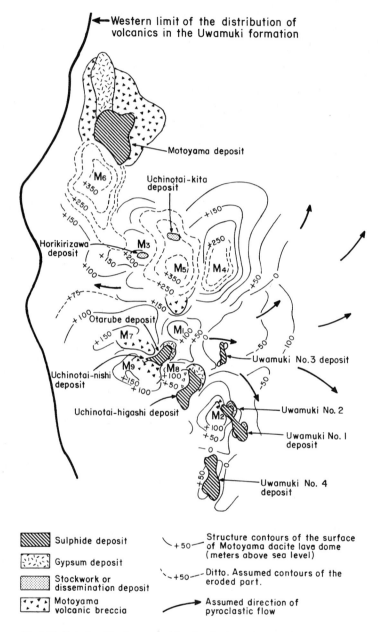

Fig. 3.11. Relationships between white rhyolite lava domes, massive sulfide lenses and mineralized stockworks, Kosaka Mine, Hokuroko district, northeast Honshu. Note tendency of massive sulfide lenses to occur in clusters (from Urabe and Sato, 1978)

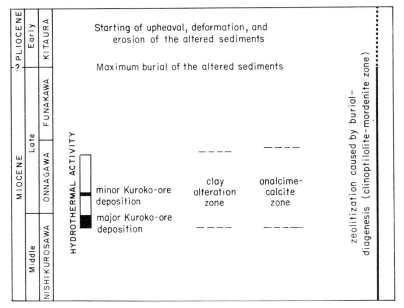

Fig. 3.12. Diagrammatic illustration of alteration of the volcanic section that hosts Kuroko deposits. Note that alteration can reach upward a considerable distance about the ore lenses, indicating that hydrothermal activity must have continued for considerable time periods after the syngenetic formation of the ore deposits (from Iijima, 1974)

The preceding generalized comments on the mineralization and alteration patterns manifest in the massive sulfide deposits of the Hokuroko Basin can be applied, in greater or lesser extent, not only to other Kuroko-type ores in Japan, but to the great majority of Phanerozoic massive sulfide deposits generated in similar lithologic-tectonic settings. It should be borne in mind, however, that variations on the theme are not uncommon in individual cases, especially in terms of metal ratios and the presence or absence of associated sulfate bodies.

3.3.2 Fluid Inclusion and Stable Isotope Data

A number of fluid inclusion studies have been carried out on quartz, sphalerite, and barite from Kuroko-type deposits (e.g., Tokunaga and Houma, 1974; Farr and Scott, 1981). These indicate that ore deposition occurred in the range 320–200 °C. The highest temperatures are found in stockwork quartz and temperatures progressively decrease upward into black ore zones (Fig. 3.13). Fluid inclusion salinities fall mainly in the range of 2.4 to 8.4 eq. wt.% NaCl, but some higher salinities have been reported. As in the case of temperatures the salinities of fluid inclusions are higher (5–8 eq. wt.% NaCl) in stockwork ore than in bedded ore.

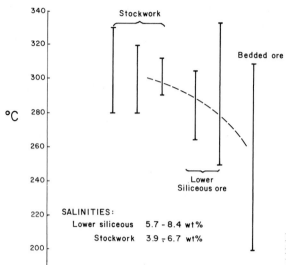

Fig. 3.13. Compilation of representative fluid inclusion data available for Kuroko deposits

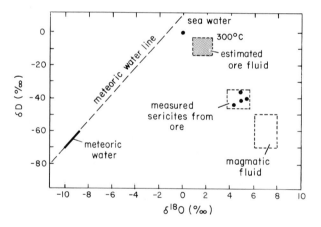

Fig. 3.14. Plot of ^{18}O vs D data pertinent to Kuroko ore fluids. These data, although not unequivocal, provide strong support for a genetic model involving a certain contribution of magmatic water to Kuroko ore fluids (from Hattori and Muehlenbachs, 1980)

Stable isotope studies of minerals and inclusion fluids in Kuroko-type deposits (Ohmoto and Rye, 1974; Ishihara and Sasaki, 1978; Hattori and Sakai, 1979; Hattori and Muehlenbachs, 1980) indicate a major component of seawater in Kuroko ore fluids, but consistent negative δD values indicate the involvement of another fluid in the ore formation process. Several workers (e.g., Urabe and Sato, 1978; Hattori and Muehlenbachs, 1980; Farr and Scott, 1981; Sawkins, 1982b) have suggested that the isotopic and salinity data are most logically explained in terms of the admixture of small amounts of magmatic water to evolved seawater in Kuroko-type ore generating systems. The data of Hattori and Muehlenbachs (1980) in particular strongly support this concept (Fig. 3.14).

3.3.3 Buchans Polymetallic Sulfide Deposit, Newfoundland

The important Buchans camp has produced almost 18 million tons of ore from a number of orebodies with an average grade of 14.6% Zn, 7.6% Pb, 1.34% Cu, 105 gm/ton Ag, and 1.2 gm/ton gold (Thurlow and Swanson, 1981). On the basis of contained metal tonnage the Buchans deposit is comparable with the Noranda and Hokuroko districts, that contain numerous ore bodies spread over much larger areas (Sangster, 1980).

The complex assemblage of volcanic and sedimentary rocks known as the Buchans Group has been dated at 446 ± 13 m.y. (Bell and Blenkinsop, 1981). The ore-associated felsic volcanic rocks are in part comagmatic with the intrusive Feeder Granodiorite (Fig. 3.15). Due to structural complexities the thickness of the Buchans Group is imprecisely known, but estimates indicate a probable thickness of from 5–9 km (Thurlow and Swanson, 1981). A thick flysch sequence underlies the Buchans Group, whereas red sandstones and conglomerates of Carboniferous age unconformably overlie it.

Within the Buchans Group, the volcanic rocks range in composition from basalt to rhyolite, and despite a relative paucity of andesite, the volcanics exhibit typical calc-alkaline chemical trends (Thurlow et al., 1975). The lower portion of the sequence is composed predominantly of pillowed amygdaloidal basalts, whereas the upper portion contains a high proportion of felsic pyroclastics. Clastic sediments occur mainly in what must have been local basins within the felsic pyroclastic sequence. The major orebodies at Buchans occur near the top of the Lower Buchans Group within the Lucky Strike Ore Horizon Sequence (Fig. 3.16), which, prior to thrust faulting, was probably time equivalent to the

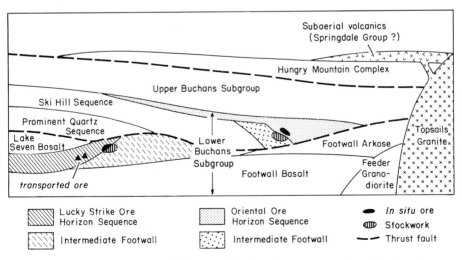

Fig. 3.15. Schematic cross section to illustrate relationships between the various volcanic, sedimentary, and intrusive units in the Buchans area, Newfoundland (from Thurlow and Swanson, 1981)

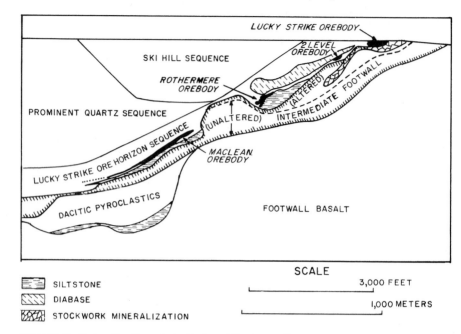

Fig. 3.16. Vertical section through the Buchans Mine area to illustrate the relationships between the in situ Lucky Strike orebody, the transported orebodies, and enclosing rock units (from Thurlow and Swanson, 1981)

Oriental Ore Horizon Sequence (see Fig. 3.15). Both these units and the intermediate footwall rocks represent a marked change toward very local litho-units of volcanics and sediments, as compared with the broad extent of the underlying footwall basalt and the footwall arkose to the east. Based on amygdule contents of basalts and the strongly pyroclastic nature of the felsic volcanism, Thurlow and Swanson (1981) suggest that water depths were relatively shallow during accumulation of the Buchans Group, and at the time of ore deposition, during initial accumulation of the Ore Horizon pyroclastics, a rugged subaqueous paleotopography is indicated.

The metallization events at Buchans produced three types of ore: stockwork ore; in situ ore; and transported ore (Fig. 3.17), the two latter types accounting for approximately 98% of production. Stockwork ore emplaced in intermediate footwall rocks occurs below and adjacent to the Lucky Strike massive, in situ orebodies, and consists of a network of sulfide veins and veinlets cutting pervasively altered hostrocks. The central portions of stockwork orebodies are characterized by silicification and/or chloritization, whereas the peripheral portions exhibit clay alteration (mainly illite, Henley and Thornley, 1981). Pyrite, as veinlets and disseminations, occurs marginal to central zones in which the veins contain base metals and barite. Overall, the Buchans stockwork mineralization

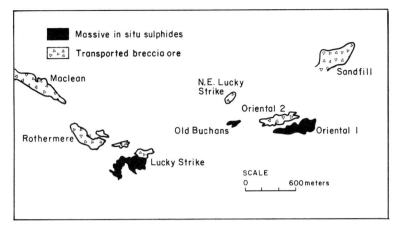

Fig. 3.17. Simplified plan to illustrate the spatial relationships between in situ and transported ores (ore breccias) in the Buchans district (from Walker and Barbour, 1981)

and alteration forms a blanket-like zone that does not exceed 100 m in thickness.

The Lucky Strike orebody is a thick lens of massive base metal sulfides that lacks well developed banding and contains less than 10% pyrite. The fine-grained ore is crudely zoned with chalcopyrite-rich yellow ore lying mainly below predominant lead-zinc rich black ore. Typical ore consists of a fine-grained aggregate of sphalerite, galena and barite, with lesser chalcopyrite, and minor tetrahedrite, bornite, and silver minerals such as argentite.

The Rothermere, Maclean, and other transported orebodies occur in a roughly linear array along a paleochannel trending northwest from the Lucky Strike orebody, and a similar line of transported orebodies trends northeastward from the Oriental 1 in situ orebody (Fig. 3.17). These transported orebodies consist of mechanical mixtures of sulfides and lithic fragments (including puzzling rounded granodiorite clasts). Sharp contacts with the enclosing pyritic siltstones and dacitic tuffs are common, and locally, weak imbrication of tabular fragments is visible, indicating transport away from the Lucky Strike area (Walker and Barbour, 1981). Detailed observations indicate that individual orebodies are in some instances the result of multiple downslope slumping events of massive sulfide ores. It is of some interest that isolated base metal clasts have been observed in drillholes up to 6 km away from the nearest known in situ massive sulfide orebodies (Thurlow and Swanson, 1981), and that some of these occur at stratigraphic levels for which no massive sulfide mineralization is known.

Paragenetic and stable isotopic studies, concentrated mainly on stockwork mineralization (Kowalik et al., 1981) indicate that initial pervasive chloritization and pyritization of the rocks subjacent to the Lucky Strike orebody were followed by silicification and associated pyrite and chalcopyrite deposition.

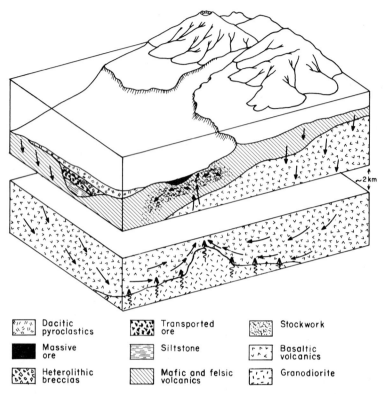

Dacitic pyroclastics

Massive ore

Heterolithic breccias

Transported ore

Siltstone

Mafic and felsic volcanics

Stockwork

Basaltic volcanics

Granodiorite

Fig. 3.18. Idealized reconstruction of the environment of ore formation at Buchans. Seawater was the dominant fluid in the convecting hydrothermal system (solid arrows), but a component of magmatic fluid is added from the crystallizing felsic magmatic system (wavy arrows) that provides the heat for seawater convection. Both the basalts and the magmatic system can be envisaged as sources for the metals in the Buchans ores, but the majority of lead is probably of magmatic derivation (from Sawkins and Kowalik, 1981)

Subsequently, deposition of sphalerite and galena occurred, and the gangue mineralogy changed from quartz to barite and calcite. Stable isotope data for quartz-chlorite pairs indicate depositional temperatures in the range 243–371 °C and a range of 140–322 °C for galena-sphalerite pairs, and also indicate that temperatures decreased away from the major plumbing system. $\delta^{34}S$ data suggest that the sulfur in the deposits was predominantly of seawater origin, and, as such, similar to that in Japanese Kuroko deposits. $\delta^{18}O$ and δD data also indicate the hydrothermal fluids were mainly of seawater origin, but are permissive of a magmatic component of up to 15%.

The possibility of a significant magmatic contribution of lead and other base metals to the Buchans ore-generating system is supported by an analysis of lead budgets at Buchans, where transportation of at least 2.7×10^{12} gm of lead was effected (Sawkins and Kowalik, 1981). Extraction of this lead from the basalts that underly the Buchans ores would involve a hydrothermal convection cell of unrealistic size (600 km^3), whereas a magmatic-hydrothermal source for the bulk of the lead and other metals requires a magma body of only about 50 km^3. Such a model does not violate any aspect of the empirical data base available for Buchans and most other Kuroko-type deposits (Fig. 3.18).

The similarities of the Buchans ores to those of the Japanese Kuroko province are strong, for close equivalence in stockwork ores, yellow ores, black ores, and bedded barites, as well as isotopic characteristics, can be demonstrated. Minor disparities exist, however. The 'white rhyolite' bodies present at Buchans do not exhibit the close spatial relationship to ore manifest in many Kuroko districts. Furthermore, gypsum is absent at Buchans, and the ores are both notably higher grade and less pyritic than average Kuroko ores. Finally, the mechanical redistribution of ores by slumping is far more pronounced at Buchans.

3.3.4 Discussion and Suggestions for Exploration

Although a great deal of research has been carried out on Kuroko-type deposits, some outstanding problems remain. In particular, the restriction of the Kuroko-type deposits in the Green Tuff region of Japan to a narrow mid-Miocene time interval is puzzling. This narrow time-stratigraphic interval, and broad area over which Japanese Kuroko-type deposits formed, suggests some fundamental arc-wide tectonic or tectonomagmatic control of their formation.

The source of the metals in Kuroko-type deposits is also problematic, although many workers (e.g., Large, 1977; MacGeehan and Maclean, 1980) favor a model involving leaching of subjacent volcanics as a source of the metals in such deposits. However, within the Green Tuff region the stratigraphic interval between the massive sulfide deposits and pre-Tertiary basement rocks is less than 500 m in many areas, and thus in these instances the volumes of subjacent Miocene volcanics and volcaniclastics available for leaching by seawater convective systems are limited. The compositions and narrow range of lead isotopes throughout the Kuroko ore province (Sato and Sasaki, 1973; Sato, 1975) preclude the various pre-Tertiary basement rocks in the region as significant sources of lead. To circumvent this problem, proponents of a leaching model have suggested leaching of metals from the underlying intrusive systems that provided both the Miocene volcanics and the requisite heat to drive the seawater convection systems (Ohmoto, 1978). In view of the consistent evidence noted earlier for negative δD values in the Kuroko ore fluids, and the occurrence of salinities significantly greater than those of seawater, a direct magmatic contribution of metals from underlying magmatic systems, perhaps with a minor addition of leached metals appears to represent a more viable genetic model (Sawkins, 1982b). The main significance of seawater convection systems in this model relates to their role in focussing the discharge of the strongly diluted magmatic metalliferous fluids at specific points (Fig. 3.19). The rapid cooling of these dis-

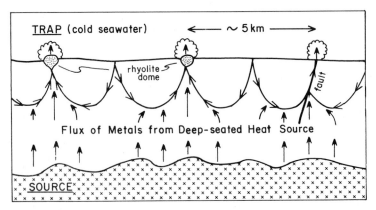

Fig. 3.19. Generalized genetic model for Kuroko-type deposits favored by the writer. Convecting seawater systems are seen as important factors in the focussing of the discharge of metalliferous fluids of deeper (probably magmatic) origin

charging fluids by ambient seawater causes the precipitation of the metal sulfides.

Kuroko-type orebodies present challenging targets to the exploration geologist due to their relatively small size and stratabound character. Their tendency to occur within restricted time-stratigraphic intervals in volcanic sequences is clearly important, as are their spacing characteristics, which are controlled by the typical dimensions of thermal convection cells in rocks (~ 5 km, see Sawkins, 1980). The strong tendency toward magnesium enrichment and sodium depletion in footwall rocks near Kuroko-type ore bodies has been carefully documented in Japan and is used as an aid to exploration. Geophysical methods involving electrical potential, electromagnetics, and induced potential have all been used with success in locating massive sulfide orebodies, especially those of high iron sulfide content, and those that have been rotated into attitudes of steep dip.

Sangster (1980) has noted the tendency of Kuroko-type massive sulfides to occur in clusters within well-defined districts. Each district is presumably related to a specific volcanic center, and typically contains one major deposit and a number of smaller ones. Realization of the full ore potential of such districts requires not only detailed compilation of all available geologic and lithogeochemical data, and considerable application of geophysical techniques, but a willingness to use the diamond drill as an additional exploration tool.

3.4 Base and Precious Metal Vein Deposits

Examples of vein deposits that are emplaced in arc-related extensional settings include those of the Colorado Mineral Belt (Steven and Ratte, 1960; Steven et

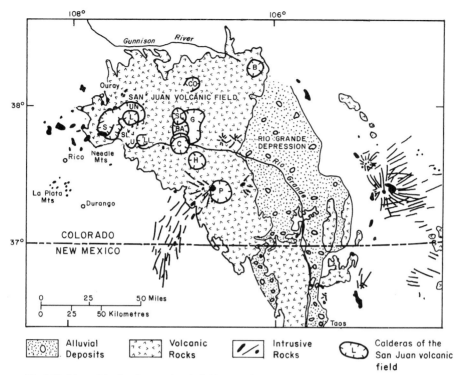

Fig. 3.20. Map of the San Juan volcanic field at southwest end of Colorado Mineral Belt. Note that only some of the caldera systems are known to have mineralization associated with them. B = Bonanza, Ba = Bachelor, C = Creede, CO = Cochetopa, G = La Garita, H = Mt. Hope, L = San Luis, U = Ute Creek, UN = Uncompahgre (modified from Lipman et al., 1976)

al., 1974; Casadevall and Ohmoto, 1977; Slack, 1980), veins in the Kuroko districts of Japan (Lambert and Sato, 1974), and possible gold veins in Devonian rift settings in New South Wales, Australia (McIlveen, 1974).

The most important of these regions in terms of metal production is that of San Juan Mountains at the southwest end of the Colorado Mineral Belt. Here, the Belt is at its widest and the Tertiary geology is dominated by a series of large caldera complexes (Fig. 3.20). It is noteworthy that less than half of these calderas are known to be mineralized, although each can be shown to have evolved through a complex series of magmatic events. Typically, during the early stages of caldera development voluminous calc-alkaline volcanics were erupted, mostly as andesites and quartz latites that give K-Ar ranges from 31.1–34.7 m.y. (Lipman et al., 1970). Next, ash-flow sheets of more felsic composition than the earlier volcanics, were erupted between 26.7 and 29.8 m.y. Finally, after about 25 m.y. ago, volcanism produced widespread basaltic lavas and local rhyolitic flows and tuffs.

In general terms the ore deposits are related to the youngest, most differenti-ated intrusives in the caldera cycles. Lipman et al. (1976) have demonstrated that the earlier intrusives of more intermediate composition did generate hy-drothermal convection systems, but that they produced only alteration and bar-ren quartz-pyrite veins. Thus, the richest ores in the region, those associated with structures related to the Silverton Caldera, formed 5–15 m.y. after caldera collapse, and exhibit a time-space relationship to minor intrusions of quartz-bearing silicic porphyry. One exception to this is the base and precious metal mineralization associated with the relatively young Lake City caldera (Slack, 1980), where the radiometric data indicate the mineralization was closely associ-ated in time with caldera formation 22.5 m.y. ago.

The transition from compressional to tensional environments in this portion of North America Cenozoic arc system was clearly a complex matter, but the very transition from early central-type volcanism to caldera formation is indic-ative of a relaxation of regional compression. Furthermore, the emplacement of the great bulk of the ores in the Colorado Mineral Belt subsequent to the ini-tiation of basalt-rhyolite bimodal volcanism justifies their inclusion within the category of deposits related to arc-rifting environments.

Chapter 4   Additional Aspects
of Arc-Related Metallogeny

In the foregoing chapters we have examined the most important types of deposits found in largely post-Paleozoic arc-related tectonic settings. These younger arc terrains are clearly more tractable to tectonic analysis than their older counterparts, where a combination of deeper erosion levels and later orogenic events render plate reconstructions more tenuous. There are, however, many important metal deposits in older orogenic belts that must, I feel, be included in any meaningful synthesis of the relationships of metal deposits to plate tectonics. Furthermore, there are a number of metal deposits in post-Paleozoic arc systems that do not fall into the tectonic subdivisions of arcs dealt with in chapters 1, 2, and 3. We shall deal with this latter group prior to a discussion of the metallogeny of older arc-related metal deposits.

4.1 Metal Deposits Related to Fore-Arc Felsic Magmatism

In modern convergent plate boundary environments the arc-trench gap is an important area of sediment accumulation. Thick sequences of poorly fossiliferous turbidites accumulate in this zone and igneous rocks are typically restricted to slices of ophiolite that become tectonically incorporated in the sedimentary piles during subduction-related imbricate thrusting along the inner trench wall. The deeper levels of these sequences in older arc systems are characterized by low temperature-high pressure metamorphism (blue schists).

The fore-arc terrains of southern Alaska, southwest Japan and western Sumatra contain granitic intrusives emplaced between the magmatic arc and trench. The origin of such granitic magmas in areas generally characterized by low heatflow is puzzling, but Marshak and Karig (1977) and Delong and Schwarz (1979) have suggested that the subduction of spreading ridges associated with triple junction plate configurations would cause sufficient local heating of the base of the fore-arc sedimentary pile to induce melting. Hudson et al. (1979) report petrologic and strontium isotope data from granodioritic plutons in the Chugach Mountains of Alaska that strongly indicate an anatectic origin for the biotite tonalite, biotite granodiorite, and granite intrusions there. In contradistinction to the petrogenetic model above, however, they suggest that cessation of accretionary offscraping of cold materials to the base of the sedimentary pile would allow temperatures to rise sufficiently to permit partial melting.

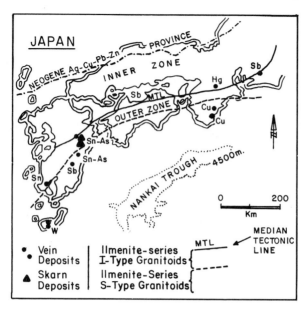

Fig. 4.1. Distribution of mid-Miocene vein and skarn deposits in Outer Zone of Japan. Note that granitoids are all ilmenite-series, but include S-types (nearest trench) and I-types in discrete belts, and the roughly coeval magnetite-series Ag-Cu-Pb-Zn belt to north of Inner Zone (from Sillitoe, 1981a)

No mineralization of consequence has been reported from these fore-arc intrusives in Alaska or from those in Sumatra, but the ilmenite-series Cenozoic plutons within the thick flysch type sediments of the Shimanto Belt of southwest Japan have minor tin, tungsten, copper and antimony deposits associated with them (Fig. 4.1) (Oba and Miyahisa M., 1977). In addition, Mitchell and Garson (1981, p. 172–173) suggest that the early Devonian granites of the southern Uplands of Scotland, emplaced within flysch-type sediments of late Ordivician to Silurian age, could represent Paleozoic examples of fore-arc magmatism. Minor uranium and copper mineralization is associated with this igneous suite.

Although this mineralization is of limited significance when compared with other facets of arc metallogeny, the recognition of fore-arc igneous suites and possible associated mineralization is important to a full understanding of arc systems. The only other metal deposits found in fore-arc terrains are those associated with slices of ophiolite that can become incorporated in the imbricate zones that characterize fore-arc outer belts. Because their presence results purely from tectonic processes, they are more appropriately related to the metallogeny of spreading ridge systems (see following chapter).

4.2 Paleozoic and Older Porphyry Copper Deposits

In discussions of the epigenetic metal deposits of principal-arc and inner-arc regions in previous chapters, it was emphasized that such deposits are emplaced

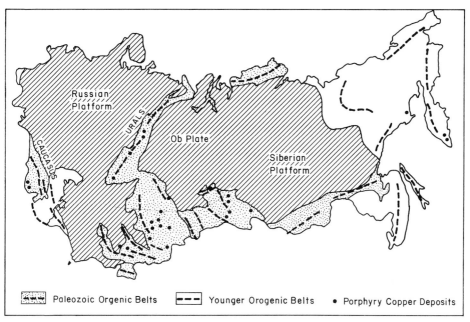

Fig. 4.2. Phanerozoic orogenic belts in the U.S.S.R., showing location of porphyry copper deposits (modified from Laznicka, 1976)

within a few kilometers of the earth's surface and are thus particularly prone to erosion, especially in continental margin arc systems that tend to stand high with respect to sea level. It follows that deposits of this type should be increasingly less common in progressively older arc systems. This is, in fact, the case. Porphyry copper deposits, for example, are predominantly of post-Paleozic age and Cenozoic deposits are considerably more common than Mesozoic deposits. Notable examples of Mesozoic porphyry copper deposits include Bisbee (180 m.y.), Ely (115 m.y.), and Yerington (approx. 140 m.y.) in the western U.S. (Titley and Beane, 1981), and a number of major porphyry copper deposits of western Canada that fall within the 140–200 m.y. age range (Ney and Hollister, 1976).

   In Russia the major belts of porphyry copper deposits are Paleozoic in age (Fig. 4.2), but despite this Laznicka (1976) has demonstrated that most of these deposits can be related to either island arc or Andean margin type geotectonic settings. Just why these deposits did not suffer uplift and erosion subsequent to their formation is not clear at present. A number of examples of porphyry-type copper-molybdenum mineralization ranging in age from Silurian to early Cretaceous, occur in eastern Queensland, Australia. Horton (1978) has demonstrated that four periods of mineralization, Siluro-Devonian, Permo-Carboniferous, Permo-Triassic, and early Cretaceous can be recognized within this portion of the Tasman Orogenic Zone. The deposits occur mainly within discrete northwest trending narrow belts up to 400 km long. Unfortunately, the grades of these deposits are mostly low and none currently support mining.

Hollister et al. (1974) report on porphyry copper and molybdenum occurrences of the Appalachian orogen of eastern North America that stretch from Maine to Newfoundland. Within this belt a general shift with age from porphyry copper mineralization (Cambrian-Ordivician) to porphyry molybdenum mineralization rich in lithophile elements (Devonian) is apparent. Hollister et al. (1974) conclude that these porphyry systems are typical of their Tertiary counterparts, but believe they demonstrate features indicative of emplacement at somewhat deeper crustal levels. These are manifest in relatively high Mo/Cu ratios, and a predominance of equigranular rather than porphyritic textures in associated, typically quartz monozonitic, intrusives.

Porphyry copper-type mineralization in Precambrian terrains is rare, but examples have been reported from the Canadian Shield (Poulsen and Franklin, 1981; Franklin and Thorpe, 1982; Kirkham, 1972) and from Africa (Wakefield, 1978). In addition, at Haib, Namibia porphyry-type mineralization occurs within a Proterozoic, calc-alkaline terrain of typical volcano-plutonic, principal arc character (Reid, 1977). The Don Rouyn Mine near Noranda, Quebec, contains copper-molybdenum mineralization as disseminations and fracture fillings in trondhjemitic intrusions, and is operated as a source of cupriferous siliceous flux for the Noranda smelter (Goldie et al., 1979). Later metamorphism has overprinted any original hydrothermal alteration patterns, but the deposit is considered by Goldie et al. to be an example of deeper-seated porphyry copper mineralization.

Although these older examples of porphyry-type mineralization do not match the tonnage and grade characteristics of top rank Tertiary deposits, occurrences such as Kounrad, U.S.S.R. (Paleozoic) indicate that major porphyry copper metallogenesis was not confined to the latter portions of Phanerzoic time. As stated earlier, the marked decrease in porphyry copper deposits in older arcs is best explained in terms of erosion of the upper portions of these arcs. The same considerations apply equally to the other major type of epigenetic arc-related deposits such as skarns, limestone replacement deposits and, in particular, epithermal vein deposits.

4.3 Massive Sulfide Deposits of the Caledonides, Scandinavia

A discontinuous belt of massive sulfide deposits extends for approximately 1500 km along the western edge of Scandinavia (Vokes, 1976). It occurs within a series of strongly deformed allochthonous sheets composed primarily of Ordovician metavolcanics and metasediments. Major clusters of deposits occur in the Trondheim, Grong and Sulitjelma areas, but a number of other districts can be delineated (Fig. 4.3). Individual massive sulfide deposits vary in size from less

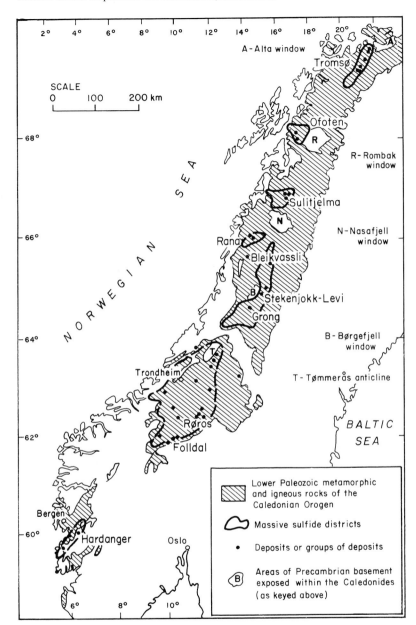

Fig. 4.3. Generalized map of Norwegian Caledonides showing location of major massive sulfide districts

than 1 million tons to 25 million tons, and, with the exception of the Bleikvassli and Mofjell deposits in the Rana district, virtually all deposits fall along the Cu-Zn tieline on a Cu-Zn-Pb compositional plot.

The deformed and metamorphosed nature of the hostrocks and ores of most of these deposits makes reconstruction of the precise environments in which they formed difficult, and for many years a number of Scandinavian geologists considered the ores to be epigenetic in origin (see Vokes, 1976). In very broad terms, stratigraphic reconstructions of the Caledonide rocks indicate deposition of an Eocambrian and Cambrian clastics sequence of passive continental margin character, followed during the Ordovician by predominantly mafic volcanics, and then more complex sequences that include felsic pyroclastics and sediments.

These rocks are overlain by Silurian sedimentary rocks lacking volcanic components. Trace element studies of the mafic volcanics (Gale and Roberts, 1974; Gale and Pearce, 1982) suggest development of an ensimatic arc during early Ordovician time, accompanied by rear-arc marginal basin development. This basin, floored by oceanic crust, received sediments and volcanics of a heteorogeneous nature until mid-Silurian time when it was obducted onto the older continental crust lying to the east.

The Caledonian massive sulfide deposits, despite their apparent arc and rear arc tectonic setting, differ markedly from Kuroko-type deposits in several important respects. As noted above, they are primarily copper-zinc deposits, but, more significantly, the majority are associated with basaltic rocks, and most of the remainder with bimodal volcanic assemblages in which the felsic component is relatively minor (Nilsen, 1978). The deposits in the southern extremity of the belt occur predominantly within an ophiolite terrain (Franklin et al., 1981, p. 515).

The largest known massive sulfide deposit in the Scandinavian Caledonides is that at Lokken, southwest of Trondheim. Here, approximately 25 million tons of massive sulfide ore grading 2.1% Cu, 1.9% Zn, 19 gm/ton Ag, and 0.29 gm/ton Au occur within a sequence consisting primarily of little-metamorphosed basaltic pillow lavas. The deposit has a lensoid shape and is stratigraphically underlain by hydrothermally altered quartz-albite rock containing stringer sulfides. Above the massive sulfide lens (Fig. 4.4) is a layer of sulfidic black chert and the overlying thin bedded volcanics contain several horizons of quartz-magnetite-stilpnomelane rock interbedded with fine-grained pyritic layers (Grammelvedt, 1979). Apart from its size, the Lokken deposit is typical of many Caledonian massive sulfide deposits, although some have undergone considerably higher rank metamorphism (Vokes, 1968).

The two massive sulfide deposits in the Caledonian province that contain significant amounts of lead, Bleikvassli and Mofjell in the Rana district are atypical. They occur within high grade gneisses and schists of probable sedimentary origin and have been reported to be of Proterozoic age (Frietsch et al., 1979, p. 995).

S   N

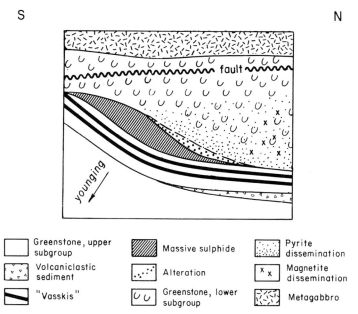

	Greenstone, upper subgroup		Massive sulphide		Pyrite dissemination
	Volcaniclastic sediment		Alteration		Magnetite dissemination
	"Vasskis"		Greenstone, lower subgroup		Metagabbro

Fig. 4.4. Generalized cross section of the Lokken orebody ("Vasskis" = pyritic chert). It is now believed by many that the basaltic rocks that host this deposit are part of a disrupted ophiolite complex. If this is correct then Lokken must be considered as a Cyprus-type deposit (see following chapter) (from Franklin et al., 1981)

The early Paleozoic metallogenesis of the province is thus clearly one of copper-zinc mineralization primarily associated with basaltic volcanism although some of the ores (e.g., Stekenjokk deposit; Zachrisson, 1982) are definitely associated with felsic volcanics. As noted earlier, Gale and Roberts (1974) and Gale and Pearce (1982) have studied the trace element geochemistry of these volcanics and concluded that they were probably generated in marginal basin and early arc settings. Grenne et al. (1980), however, have demonstrated that the massive sulfide ores of the important west Trondheim district exhibit many similarities, in terms of form, composition, and associated basaltic rocks and chemical sediments, to Cyprus-type deposits (see following chapter). Furthermore, the conspicuous presence of metagabbros in the west Tronheim region, and the recent discovery of basaltic dike swarms there have led Grenne et al. to suggest that all the mafic rocks present may represent a deformed and somewhat dismembered ophiolite complex.

4.3.1 Similar Massive Sulfide Deposits Elsewhere

Despite the foregoing, it seems unlikely that all the massive sulfide deposits associated with basaltic rocks that are found in older orogenic belts can be at-

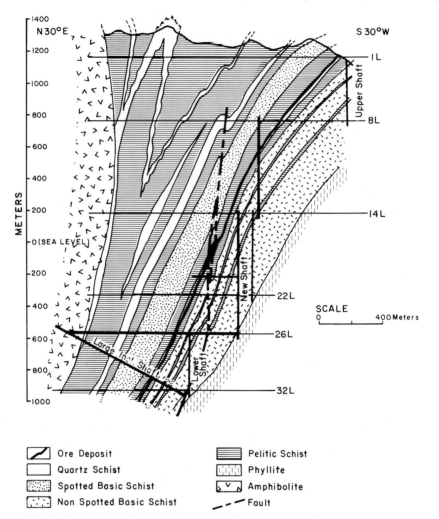

Fig. 4.5. Cross section of the Besshi massive sulfide deposit, Japan. Note extreme elongation of the sulfide zone (from Franklin et al., 1981)

tributed to tectonic incorporation of slices of original oceanic crust. In northern Newfoundland, for example, copper-zinc massive sulfide deposits (e.g., Point Leamington) occur in what appears to represent a mafic early arc sequence overlying oceanic crust of Cambrian age (Swinden and Strong, 1976).

The Besshi-type deposits of Japan occur within a thick, late Paleozoic sequence of flysch type sediments and basaltic rocks of the Sambagawa metamorphic terrain. The highly deformed and altered aspect of the mafic rocks renders tectonic interpretation difficult, but petrochemical studies (Kanehira and Tat-

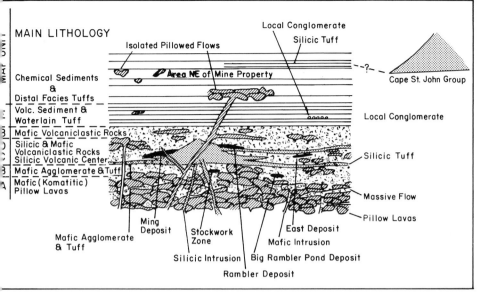

Fig. 4.6. Diagrammatic interpretation of the distribution of sulfide deposits in the Rambler area. All deposits are either associated with the silicic volcanic center or occur within mafic volcanics at the same stratigraphic level (from Tuach and Kennedy, 1978)

sumi, 1970) indicate that they were originally low K tholeiites, and thus an early arc setting seems possible. The Besshi deposit itself (Fig. 4.5) is extremely thin but stratigraphically extensive, a feature that could be due to tectonic flattening. Shanks (1977), however, has suggested it may represent an ancient analogue of contemporary mineralization in the Red Sea (see Chap. 8).

Sawkins (1976c) included the Elizabeth Mine, Vermont (Howard, 1959), the Matahambre deposit, Cuba (Benes and Hanus, 1967), and occurrences of Cu-Zn massive sulfide mineralization associated with pillowed basalts Prince Willian Sound, Alaska (Wilse and McGlasson, 1973) in this general category of deposits. Although the precise tectonic setting(s) of this group of deposits remains elusive, the recognition that major massive sulfide deposits can occur within mafic volcanic sequences, in addition to felsic volcanic environments, is an important exploration concept. In particular, it appears that early arc basaltic terrains deserve attention in the search for copper-zinc massive sulfide deposits.

The group of massive sulfide deposits in the Rambler area, northeastern Newfoundland consist of iron sulfide rich lenses containing copper and zinc sulfides and, in the case of the Ming deposit, significant precious metal values (Tuach and Kennedy, 1978). Although the tonnage of known massive sulfide ore in the area aggregates to less than 5 million tons, their lithologic setting is of some interest. The ore lenses exhibit a spatial relationship to a small center of felsic pyroclastic volcanism that overlies a pile of mafic and komatiitic pillow lavas, thought to be of early Ordovician age (Fig. 4.6). This lithoenvironment is similar to Archean massive sulfide deposits (see later) and the tectonic setting is probably that of behind-arc spreading, adjacent to an immature arc system.

Other important groups of massive sulfide deposits in volcanic settings of Paleozoic age occur in southern Iberia, New South Wales and Tasmania, Australia, and New Brunswick, Canada (Franklin et al., 1981). However, although the orebodies exhibit broad similarities to both Kuroko deposits and those in greenstone belts, and are associated with felsic volcanics, their geotectonic setting is uncertain. It can be demonstrated that they formed in extensional settings, but, the possibility that this extensional environment was related to simultaneous, subduction-related arc formation nearby, seems unlikely. In view of this, these groups of massive sulfide deposits will be discussed in a later chapter dealing with rift environments.

4.4 Massive Sulfide Deposits in Greenstone Belts

In contradistinction to epigenetic arc-related deposits, massive sulfide deposits associated with arc and rear-arc volcanism are distributed throughout geologic time. This is especially true if one accepts the proposition that greenstone belts

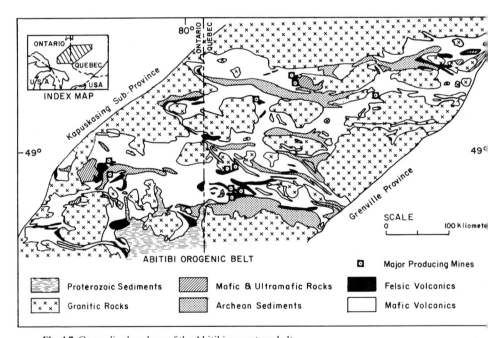

Fig. 4.7. Generalized geology of the Abitibi greenstone belt

represent Precambrian analogues of rear-arc or intra-arc basins. Many workers (e.g., Tarney et al., 1976; Tarney and Windley, 1981) see evidence for rifting in the environment on which Archean greenstone belts formed, but it should be emphasized that the rear-arc model for greenstone belt development involves just that, and allows for the possibility that such volcanic and sedimentary sequences can form either over older continental type crust or over oceanic crust. Perhaps this problem will never be finally settled, but the model favored here does allow for the necessary dissipation of the larger amounts of mantle heat during the Archean by relatively rapid accretion and destruction of numerous small plates. Recently, Sleep and Windley (1982) have made the interesting suggestion that Archean oceanic crust may have been much thicker ($>20\,km$) during Archean time and that intra-arc spreading produced greenstone belts.

Uncertainties notwithstanding, copper-zinc massive sulfide deposits are an important facet of greenstone belt metallogeny (see Table 3.1). The Abitibi greenstone belt has an areal extent of about 94,000 km^2 (Fig. 4.7) and contains within it eleven discrete eruptive centers, and although felsic volcanic rocks account for only 3.6% of the area (Goodwin and Ridler, 1970), the large majority of known massive sulfide deposits are spatially associated with these felsic rocks. This statement pertains equally to other Archean and younger greenstone belts known to contain massive sulfide deposits, in various shield areas around the world (e.g., May and Schmidt, 1982).

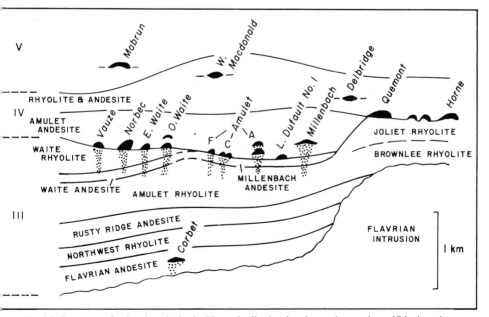

Fig. 4.8. Sequence of volcanic units in the Noranda district showing main massive sulfide deposits. Note tendency of deposits to concentrate strongly at specific stratigraphic intervals (from Franklin et al., 1981)

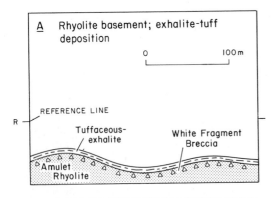

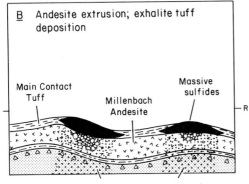

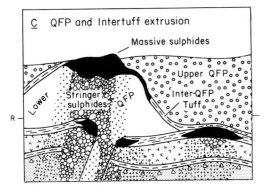

Fig. 4.9. Cross-sections showing sequence of events related to formation of a massive sulfide lens in the Millenbach Mine, Noranda district (from Riverin and Hodgson, 1980)

The volume of literature that has been generated on the massive sulfide deposits of the Canadian Shield is awesome (see Franklin et al., 1981; Franklin and Thorpe, 1982), but the deposits of the Noranda camp have been particularly well studied and serve as useful examples of massive sulfide metallogenesis in greenstone belts. As in the case of the Kuroko province of Japan there is a strong tendency for deposits to be concentrated at a particular volcanostratigraphic horizon marked by felsic volcanism (Fig. 4.8). This tendency is, however, not as marked as that in Japan. Underlying and intrusive into the andesite to rhyolite, multicyclic volcanic sequence containing the massive sulfide deposits is the Flavrian tonalite-trondhjemite intrusion (Goldie, 1979), whose age (2,710 m.y., Krogh and Davis, 1971) and composition suggest that it is comagmatic with the felsic volcanic rocks.

Well-developed alteration pipes containing stringer copper zones, in some instances of ore grade, underlie most of the deposits, and in many cases these have been controlled by synvolcanic fractures (Scott, 1980). Although some orebodies occur within mafic volcanic rocks, most are close to small domes of massive rhyolite (Franklin et al., 1981), and this situation is particularly well displayed by the Millenbach deposit (Fig. 4.9). Another noteworthy aspect of the majority of deposits in the Noranda camp, and for that matter in greenstone belt massive sulfides in general, is that orebodies tend to occur at horizons where the presence of tuff and chert layers indicate a break in volcanic activity. This is similar to the situation in the Hokuroko Basin in northern Honshu, where thin mudstones accumulated at the level of massive sulfide emplacement.

4.4.1 The Kidd Creek Massive Sulfide Deposit, Ontario

The Kidd Creek mine, which probably contains over 100 million tons of ore, is one of the largest volcanic-hosted massive sulfide deposits known. Since its discovery in 1963, up to 1975 it produced 25 million tons of ore grading 9.75% zinc, 1.5% copper, 0.40% lead, and 121 gm/ton silver.

The Kidd Creek deposit lies north of Timmins in the western portion of the Abitibi greenstone belt, within a sequence of steeply dipping, overturned mafic and felsic volcanic rocks (Fig. 4.10), that in the mine area have been precisely dated at 2,717 m.y. (Nunes and Pyke, 1980). The Kidd Creek orebodies occur within the uppermost portion of a group of felsic rocks consisting of rhyolitic tuffs and agglomerates and massive rhyolite, some of which appears to be intrusive (Walker et al., 1975). A series of carbonaceous rocks that include argillites, cherts and heterogeneous volcaniclastics, occurs at the level of sulfide mineralization, whereas stratigraphically above are a series of basaltic and andesitic flows and some large masses of metadiabase. Below the rhyolitic rocks are altered ultramafic rocks.

The pervasive lower and middle greenschist metamorphism present in the area makes recognition of alteration associated with mineralization difficult, but the alteration or meta-alteration minerals include sericite, chlorite, quartz, carbonate, biotite, talc, tourmaline, albite, and fluorite (Walker et al., 1975). Structurally the area is complex with folding at all scales, and shearing controlled in part by stratigraphy. The felsic carbonaceous rocks are also characterized by strong schistosity of variable orientation.

The Kidd Creek ores are more or less typical of the massive sulfide deposits in the Abitibi greenstone belt. Below the massive ores are copper-rich (av 2.5

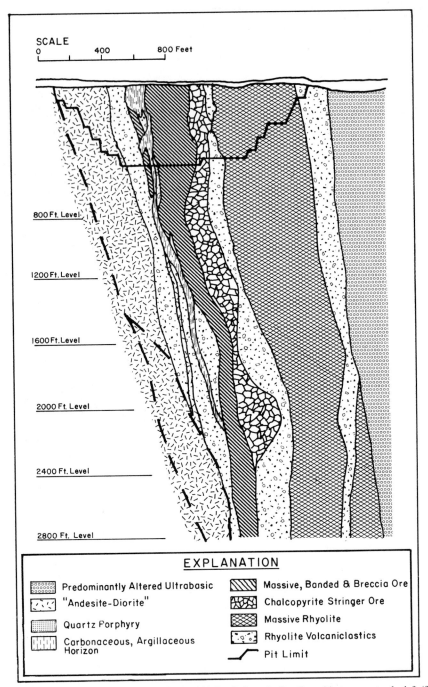

Fig. 4.10. Geologic cross-section of the Kidd Creek deposit. Stratigraphic tops are to the left (from Walker et al., 1975)

percent Cu) stringer ores which ramify through silicified rhyolitic pyroclastics. The massive ores consist of both homogeneous massive sulfides and complex sulfide mixtures, whereas the banded varieties contain pyrite-sphalerite, sphalerite-chalcopyrite, or pyrite-sphalerite-chalcopyrite. Bedded ores are present within the carbonaceous horizon, as laminated or thinly bedded sulfidic sediments containing numerous primary sedimentation features. Finally, breccia ore is present and consists of fragments of pyrite and sphalerite mixed with fragments of volcanic and sedimentary rocks. Walker et al. (1975) report sulfide fragments up to 10 meters across in these breccia ores. The pyrite content of Kidd Creek ores is somewhat variable, but in the ore mined has averaged about 40 percent of that mineral.

Overall, the geologic relationships at Kidd Creek suggest that ores formed near a felsic volcanic center by submarine fumarolic activity during a lull in explosive volcanism. Beaty and Taylor (1983) have obtained $\delta^{18}O$ data from altered rocks below the Kidd Creek orebodies, and calculate the $\delta^{18}O$ value of the fluids involved to have ranged from 6–9%. These values are distinctive from those for ore fluids indicated for the much smaller Amulet massive sulfide deposit in the Abitibi greenstone belt (Beaty and Taylor, 1982) and for Kuroko ore fluids (see Chap. 3). These heavy oxygen isotopic values could be indicative of a major magmatic component in the ore fluids responsible for this giant massive sulfide deposit.

4.4.2 Discussion and Suggestions for Exploration

The essential similarities between Phanerozoic volcanic-hosted massive sulfide deposits and those present in greenstone belts are now clearly recognized, despite the inevitable metamorphic overprinting of the latter. Thus Hodgson and Lydon (1977) have attempted to apply the insights garnered from the Kuroko ores and modern geothermal systems to the formulation of conceptual models for these Precambrian deposits. As a result, they emphasize the importance of resurgent caldera structures, contemporaneous faulting, and the sealing of hydrothermal convective systems prior to exhalative events.

The main uncertainty regarding the genesis of Precambrian hosted volcanic-massive sulfide ores, as with their younger analogues, relates to the origin of the ore metals, a point discussed in some detail by Franklin et al. (1981). Fox (1979) has noted that, although most volcanic-hosted massive sulfides occur in association with rhyolitic volcanics, petrochemical data indicate that these and their associated more mafic rocks can be categorized as either belonging to tholeiitic (high iron) or calc-alkaline (low-iron) suites. The massive sulfide ores in tholeiitic sequences tend to be Zn-Cu types with abundant associated iron sulfides, whereas those in calc-alkaline sequences tend to be Pb-Zn-Cu types that include relatively iron-poor sphalerite-rich ores. This is important because electrical geophysical techniques are the major method used for locating massive sulfide deposits in Precambrian terrains (Hohmann and Ward, 1981) and considerable difference in geophysical response can be expected between the two types of ore.

Interpretation of anomalies generated by airborne electromagnetic surveys is an important facet of massive sulfide exploration in Precambrian terrains, for most of the anomalies found are generated by units such as graphitic schists and barren sulfide iron formation. Nevertheless, the large majority of the over 100 significant volcanic-hosted orebodies found in the Canadian Shield in the last 65 years were first located by geophysics (Boldy, 1981). The effective depth of penetration of most geophysical techniques used in massive sulfide exploration is less than 300 m, and because diamond drilling can reach considerably deeper, there is considerable scope for the application of geochemical techniques and geologic inference in the search for deeper orebodies, especially in established massive sulfide districts.

Mercury leakage haloes can in some cases be identified up to 700 m above orebodies (Boldy, 1981), but considerable attention has been focussed on the petrochemistry of the volcanics themselves and their altered equivalents, in attempts to follow favorable stratigraphic intervals that could host ore (e.g., Marcotte and David, 1981). The great majority of known massive sulfide deposits in greenstone belts of the Superior Province are clearly proximal and contain stringer zones (in some cases of ore grade) stratigraphically below them. However, MacGeehan et al. (1981) have demonstrated that the ore lenses of the Norita Mine in the Matagami district, Quebec are of distal type and their location was controlled by submarine paleotopography. Such ores may be more common in greenstone belts than currently indicated, but their location will require careful attention to the geometry of rock units at favorable horizons prior to deformation.

4.5 Additional Aspects of Greenstone Belt Metallogeny

It is noteworthy that massive sulfide deposits are rare in pre-3 b.y.-old greenstone belts. However, a series of baritic lenses containing zinc, lead and minor copper have been reported from a greenstone belt in the Pilbara craton of western Australia (Sangster and Brook, 1977). Their composition and spatial association to rhyolite domes indicate a very strong similarity to Kuroko-type deposits. Model lead data suggest an age of 3.5 b.y. for these small, but intriguing deposits. The Murchison Range greenstone belt in southern Africa (Muff, 1978) contains a line of sub-economic copper-zinc occurrences in massive pyrite-pyrrhotite lenses reminiscent of Noranda-type deposits (Fig. 4.11), but is more renowned as a major world source of antimony. The antimony deposits occur along a zone of cherty carbonate, quartzite, and schist rocks within the upper sedimentary portion of the greenstone belt. The ores are considered by Muff (1978) to be of exhalative origin.

In 1966 the Kambalda nickel deposits were discovered in Western Australia. This led to an intense exploration effort for nickel sulfide deposits in the

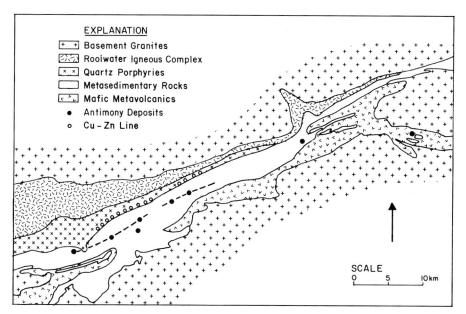

Fig. 4.11. Map of central portion of the Murchison greenstone belt, South Africa showing linear array of antimony deposits and line of copper-zinc massive sulfide occurrences (modified from Muff, 1978)

Archean greenstone belts of the Yilgarn block, and by 1979 over fifty nickel sulfide deposits had been discovered in this area, making it the third largest producing region of sulfide nickel in the world (Ross and Travis, 1981). Recently (see Economic Geology, vol. 76, no. 6), a great deal of information on the geology and geochemistry of these Australian nickel ores and their host-rock has become available.

An excellent review of these nickel sulfide ores has been presented by Marston et al. (1981) and the following details are summarized from their contribution. The nickel deposits are strongly concentrated in the eastern part of the Archean Yilgarn block, and occur almost entirely within greenstone belts. Two principal types of nickel deposits are found, those associated with intrusive dunites cluster mainly in the north, and those associated with volcanic peridotites are encountered mainly in the south (Fig. 4.12).

The nickel deposits associated with dunitic intrusives tend to be larger but lower grade than those within ultramafic volcanics (e.g., Mt. Keith 290 million tons 0.6% Ni). Their dunitic hostrocks occur mainly as lenses of magnesium-rich peridotite that were emplaced as sills or dike-like bodies. The 'magmas' are thought to have consisted of olivine-sulfide mush and probably represent the residue after eruption of komatiitic lavas at the surface. The nickel sulfides typically occur near the center or at the margins of the thickest part of the intrusive

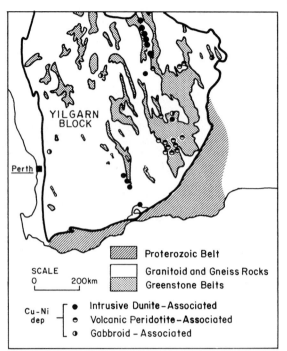

Fig. 4.12. Map of the Archean Yilgarn Block showing locations of major western Australian nickel deposits

lens (Fig. 4.13), and within the mineralized zones low grade iron and nickel sulfides are abundant and enclose small higher grade areas of more massive ore. Ni/Cu ratios in these ores range from 19 to 70 and Ni/Co ratios from 30 to 70.

The smaller, higher grade volcanic-associated ores (< 5 million tons, 2–4% Ni) occur at or near the base of volcanic flows of ultramafic komatiite, which are locally present within metabasalt sequences low in the greenstone stratigraphic sequences. The nickel deposits of this type are strongly concentrated in the Kambalda-Norseman zone of the Wiluna greenstone belt, which contains 87 percent of the volcanic-associated deposits. The mineralization occurs in the lowermost zones of thicker flows, at or near the base of the periodotite lava sequences, and tends to occupy original depressions in the surface over which the host flows are erupted (see Fig. 4.13). The ores consist of thin, discontinuous massive sulfides overlain by thicker continuous and more extensive zones of matrix and disseminated sulfides. The sulfide fraction of these volcanic ores contains 5 to 23 percent Ni and exhibits Ni/Cu ratios of 10 to 16 and Ni/Co ratios of 40 to 65. The sulfides are thought to have segregated from the host magmas by a combination of gravitational settling and flow differentiation, and to have suffered a certain amount of physical modification during later metamorphism. In certain cases, however, assimilation of sulfide-rich iron formation appears to have provided some of the sulfur in the ores (e.g., Windarra deposits; Groves

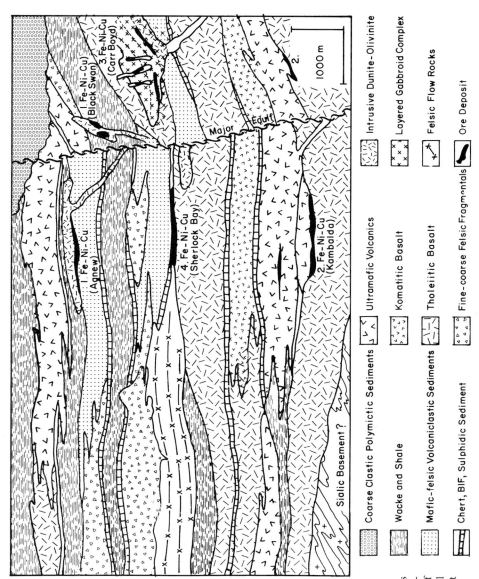

Fig. 4.13. Schematic cross section showing stratigraphic relationships of western Australian nickel deposits (from Marston et al., 1981)

Sialic Basement?

1. Fe-Ni-Cu (Agnew)
2. Fe-Ni-Cu (Kambalda)
3. Fe-Ni-Cu (Carr Boyd)
4. Fe-Ni-Cu (Sherlock Bay)
1. Fe-Ni-Cu (Black Swan)

Major Fault

1000 m

Coarse Clastic Polymictic Sediments

Wacke and Shale

Mafic-felsic Volcaniclastic Sediments

Chert, BIF, Sulphidic Sediment

Ultramafic Volcanics

Komatitic Basalt

Tholeiitic Basalt

Fine-coarse Felsic Fragmentals

Intrusive Dunite-Olivinite

Layered Gabbroid Complex

Felsic Flow Rocks

Ore Deposit

et al., 1979). Some minor nickel deposits associated with gabbroid intrusives have also been discovered in the Yilgarn block, and rare examples of sediment-hosted conformable and vein type deposits rich in arsenic are also known.

The volcanic peridotite nickel deposits of Western Australia have analogues in greenstone belts in Canada (Green and Naldrett, 1981). In both areas the deposits occur within 2.7 b.y. old greenstone belts, but the older (>3 b.y.) greenstone belts of southern Africa do not appear to contain such deposits, despite considerable exploration activity. The tectonic situations that generate these high-magnesium magmas are not known, but a high degree of partial melting of the mantle must have been involved to produce them. It seems likely that the tectonic conditions during the early stages of greenstone belt formation (subduction?) caused perturbations in the asthenosphere and generation of these melts, but this still does not explain the restriction of nickel sulfide deposits to late-Archean greenstone belts, and their strong concentration within a single greenstone belt in the Yilgarn block of Western Australia.

4.6 Gold Deposits in Greenstone Belts

Proceeding, as before, with the assumption that greenstone belts are related to Precambrian plate convergence, the gold metallogeny of such belts merits inclusion at this point. Two basic types of deposit are encountered: vein-type deposits that exhibit clear crosscutting relationships to the volcanosedimentary stratigraphy, and bedded deposits closely associated with reduced facies iron formation. Although some of the vein-type deposits may be pretectonic, many appear to have formed during the deformation and low-grade metamorphism that inevitably characterized greenstone belts (Boyle, 1979; Colvine, 1983). The tendency of vein-type gold deposits to form during deformational events in greenstone belts is well illustrated by the vein deposits in the Barberton greenstone belt, South Africa (Viljoen et al., 1969). Here, the majority of gold vein deposits occur where fracture systems cross the Middle Marker Horizon (see Fig. 2, Viljoen et al., 1969), an auriferous, iron-rich unit of wide areal extent. Karvinen (1981) has documented similar relationships between more local syngenetic auriferous units and vein gold deposits in the Timmins area, Ontario, and Kerrich (1981) has reported stable isotope and geochemical data that support the two-stage development of many gold vein deposits in greenstone terrains.

Most large tonnage gold deposits in greenstone belts, however, exhibit a marked stratigraphic association with lean, sulfide-bearing carbonate iron formation (Ridler, 1970). Sawkins and Rye (1974) termed these Homestake-type deposits, and included the important Morro Velho, Brazil, and Kolar Goldfield, India deposits in this category. In the case of the Brazilian deposits the grade of regional metamorphism is low, and thus in many places the orebodies can be recognized as merely auriferous, sulfidic facies of either carbonate iron formations or a distinctive ferriferous dolomitic rock known locally as "Lapa

Seca" (personal observations). In the case of the Kolar Goldfields of India, grades of regional metamorphism are much higher and most gold ores now occur within an en echelon series of quartz gash veins (Narayanaswami et al., 1960). However, the exceptional stratigraphic control of the ores and the iron-rich nature of associated metamorphic silicate minerals, seem to provide compelling evidence that they represent reworked auriferous iron formation. Fripp (1976) has also demonstrated that many of the gold deposits of the Rhodesian craton in Zimbabwe are of this type. The association of gold with Precambrian iron formations, is, however by no means universal. Furthermore, it has recently been demonstrated that some of the smaller gold deposits associated with iron formations in the Superior Province of Canada are of replacement origin (Mason and McConnell, 1983; Fyon et al., 1983).

Barnett et al. (1982) have described volcanic-hosted massive sulfide lenses that contain economic quantities of gold, but negligible amounts of base metals. The ores occur within a sulfide-silicate-carbonate-oxide facies iron formation and appear to represent a particularly iron sulfide rich variant of Homestake-type gold mineralization.

4.6.1 The Homestake Gold Mine, South Dakota

The Homestake mine has produced over 35 million ounces of gold since it began production in 1877. The Precambrian metasediments that host the deposit occur in the northern extremity of the Black Hills dome, a window of Precambrian rocks surrounded by Phanerozoic sediments. The small areal extent of this window does not readily permit the assignment of the exposed units to a greenstone belt environment, but the ores bear a striking similarity to other Homestake-type deposits, virtually all of which do occur within greenstone belt terrains.

The orebodies are restricted to the Homestake Formation, a thin (< 100 m), auriferous, quartz-sideroplessite schist unit within a thick sequence of metasedimentary and minor metabasaltic rocks (Fig. 4.14) (Slaughter, 1968). It is noteworthy, however, that where lithologies similar to the Homestake Formation occur higher up in the section (Flagrock Formation), they are gold bearing. The Poorman Formation, which underlies the Homestake Formation, is a graphitic, ankeritic carbonate unit containing minor amounts of phyllite and recrystallized chert. Its base is not exposed and it is thus of unknown thickness. The Ellison Formation, overlying the Homestake Formation consists mainly of dark phyllite, but contains many lenses of graphitic quartzite. Some mafic amphibolites occur locally within the Poorman Formation, and probably represent metamorphosed basalts, and similar rocks are present higher in the section within the Flagrock Formation.

The package of rocks that hosts the gold deposits has been metamorphosed and deformed into a set of complex folds plunging 10 to 45 degrees to the southeast, with axial planes dipping to the east. In the extreme northeast, metamorphism reaches staurolite grade but decreases to biotite grade over a distance of

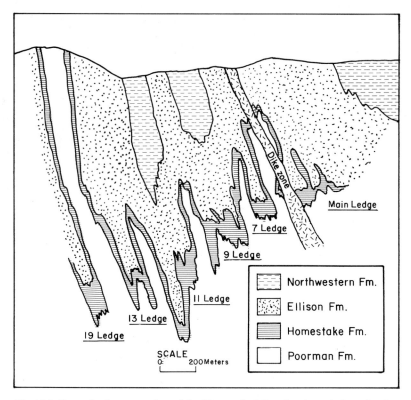

Fig. 4.14. Generalized cross section of the Homestake Mine showing relation of major orebodies to areas of Homestake Formation thickened by folding (from Rye and Rye, 1974).

about 6 km towards the southwest. The entire section is intruded by early Tertiary dikes, sills and stocks of granitic, monzonitic, phonolitic, and syenitic porphyry. Some of these felsic dikes cut through the center of the mine area.

The Homestake orebodies are elongate spindle-shaped zones that appear to be localized, at least in part, by dilatant zones formed by super-position of F_1, and F_2 fold structures. The orebodies consist essentially of quartz, chlorite and ankerite in various proportions, accompanied by pyrrhotite and arsenopyrite. The quartz occurs as both metamorphic segregations which form irregular masses or short veins, and recrystallized chert. Most of the chlorite appears to have formed at the expense of cummingtonite or sideroplessite of the metasediments. Arsenopyrite, commonly as euhedral crystals, is typically developed in the chlorite adjacent to quartz segregations, whereas pyrrhotite occurs with ankerite clots, and in more broadly disseminated form. The sulfide content of nonore Homestake Formation is about 2 percent, but can reach 8 percent within orebodies.

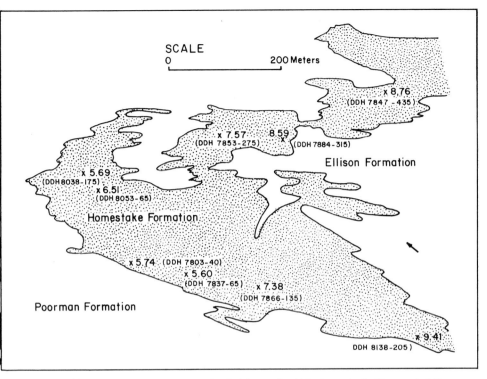

Fig. 4.15. $\delta^{34}S$ values of sulfides in the 5900 level of the number 13 Ledge orebody, Homestake Mine. Note progressive reduction of $\delta^{34}S$ values as the nose of the fold structure is approached from each limb (from Rye and Rye, 1974)

The genesis of the Homestake ores was obscured for a long time by the presence of small amounts of unequivocal Tertiary age gold mineralization associated with the Tertiary igneous rocks. Furthermore, Lindgren (1933) had designated the Homestake ores as a type example of his class of hypothermal replacement ore. The stable isotope studies of Rye and Rye (1974), however, demonstrated convincingly that the sulfide sulfur and the oxygen in quartz from the orebodies were indigenous to the Homestake Formation and distinctive from Tertiary vein mineralization. Furthermore, they found that $\delta^{34}S$ values of sulfides tended to decrease from fold limbs to dilatant areas where sulfides were now more concentrated (ore zones) (Fig. 4.15). These results all indicated that the components of the Homestake ores, including the gold, were original (syngenetic) constituents of the Homestake Formation, but were redistributed and concentrated to some extent during folding and metamorphism. This concept was in agreement with that proposed earlier by Ridler (1970) for certain gold ores in the Abitibi greenstone belt, and later by Fripp (1976) for conformable gold ore zones in greenstone belts of Zimbabwe.

4.6.2 Discussion and Suggestions for Exploration

One important characteristic of Homestake-type gold deposits is their stratigraphic continuity, although the mineralized zone typically contains a series of
discrete orebodies. Thus, the Morro Velho mine in Brazil and the Champion
mine in the Kolar goldfields have produced considerable amounts of gold, and
are amongst the deepest metal mines in the world.

Recent studies of mineralized vent systems and associated silicification of
sedimentary and volcanic rocks in the southern part of the Barberton greenstone belt (de Wit et al., 1982) have documented startling similarities of certain
structures in these 3.3 b.y.-old rocks to features of modern hotspring systems.
Significant amounts of gold are present locally in these ancient silicified structures, and they appear to have fundamental similarities to some Tertiary hot-
spring-type gold deposits.

Recognition of the hotspring-related, essentially stratabound nature of
Homestake-type gold ores, and their tendency to occur within siliceous, sulfide-
bearing, carbonate iron-formation provides an initial guide for exploration. In
many of the known deposits strong deformation and recrystallization during
metamorphism has reconcentrated and coarsened the gold, aiding its recognition. It seems possible, therefore, that some chemical sediments in less deformed
and metamorphosed greenstone belts may contain substantial reserves of fine-
grained, essentially unrecognizable, gold ore. No examples of such situations
are known to the author, but it would require carefully conceived exploration
programs to find such deposits. Clearly carbonate iron-formations should be
the primary lithology sought, but interflow sediments and certain tuffs also deserve attention. In geochemical terms arsenic is the best pathfinder element.

4.7 Overview of Arc-Related Metallogeny

In the foregoing chapters we have seen that the spectrum of metal deposits generated in arc systems is a broad one, but that many of the different ore types
can be keyed to specific tectonic environments within arc systems. Thus, the recognition by Dewey (1980) that different arcs can be characterized as tensional,
neutral, or compressional can be used to explain the incompatibility of two important classes of arc-related deposits, porphyry coppers, and Kuroko-type deposits (Uyeda and Nishiwaki, 1980; Sillitoe, 1980c).

4.7.1 Relation of Arc Metallogeny to Subduction Style

The most fundamental process operative at convergent plate margins is the subduction of oceanic lithosphere, and therefore, as argued cogently by Sillitoe
(1981a), it is logical to seek an explanation for variations in arc metallogeny in

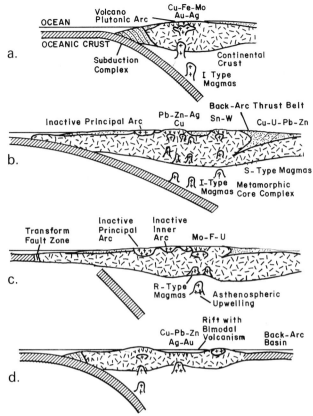

Fig. 4.16. Schematized relationships between styles of subduction and arc metallogeny. (**a**) Moderate to steep subduction with emplacement of Cu-Fe-Mo-Au-Ag deposits in principal arc; neutral stress regime. (**b**) Shallow subduction with emplacement of Pb-Zn-Ag-Cu deposits and Sn-W-U in inner arc belts; compressional regime. (**c**) Rapid steepening of detached, freely sinking slab due to transition from subduction to transform margin, with emplacement of lithophile element-type deposits; extensional regime. (**d**) Steep subduction and commencement of intra-arc rifting with emplacement of Kuroko-type deposits in a submarine setting; extensional regime. (from Sillitoe, 1981 a)

terms of variations in subduction style and its control on the stress regime in the overriding plate (Dewey, 1980). Thus, principal arcs, with their characteristic Cu, Fe, Mo, Au ($\pm$Ag) metal suite form as linear belts above steep- to moderate-dipping Benioff zones (Fig. 4.16a) either in oceanic or near-trench Cordilleran settings. Such ores appear to be essentially restricted in time and space to the emplacement of shallow-level, I-type, magnetite series granitoids (Takahashi et al., 1980).

An increase of the relative convergence vectors along Cordilleran margins results in a decrease of subduction angle, and it is under these conditions that the inner arc suite of silver-lead-zinc ($\pm$copper) deposits are generated (Sillitoe,

1981b; Clark et al., 1982). However, as noted earlier (see Chap. 2). the demarkation of the boundary between principal arc and inner-arc regimes is difficult, especially in complex Cordilleran systems such as that of the western U.S. where migration of the principal arc has occurred in response to subduction angle changes.

The generation of belts of tin-tungsten deposits on the innermost side of inner-arc terrains appears to involve deeply penetrating, shallow subduction that is somehow capable of generating S-type magmas (Sillitoe, 1981a), perhaps in connection with the formation of metamorphic core complexes (Armstrong, 1982) and/or development of back-arc thrust belts (see Fig. 4.16b). The fact that tin-tungsten deposits of this type occur only within restricted segments of Cordilleran arcs (e.g., Bolivia, Northern British Columbia and Yukon) is puzzling, for S-type igneous rocks apparently lacking such mineralization are now being found in a belt stretching from Idaho to Baja California (Miller and Bradfish, 1980).

The high-silica rhyolites and associated Climax-type porphyry molybdenum deposits that were generated after 30 m.y. ago in the western U.S. appear to relate to rapid slowing and cessation of subduction as discussed by White et al. (1981) (see Fig. 4.16c). This change in subduction regime in the western U.S. about 30 m.y. ago had a profound effect on the complex metallogeny of that region, which can be best understood, I believe, in terms of westward expansion of the mid- to late-Cenozoic tensional regimes as the principal arc withdrew towards its current position in the Cascades (Eaton, 1982).

The development of volcanic-hosted massive sulfide deposits in arc systems is closely associated with rifting events above relatively steeply dipping Benioff zones, which tend to develop caldera-style submarine volcanism (Sillitoe, 1980c, 1982b) (Fig. 4.16d). The absence of lithophile-element deposits in ensimatic arcs characterized by extension may be due to limited crustal thickness of such arcs and their lack of material suitable for partial melting and generation of S-type magma (Sillitoe, 1981a). The segmentation of arc systems and its influence on along arc variations in magmatism and metallogeny, as noted by Sillitoe (1974), is presumably also controlled by segmentation of the subducting plate (Dewey, 1980).

The metal deposits associated with I-type, magnetite series granitoids (e.g., porphyry copper, polymetallic skarn and limestone replacement deposits) appear, together with such igneous rocks, to be essentially restricted in time and space to subduction-related arc terrains. This is less true with respect to other groups of arc deposits (e.g., tin-tungsten, volcanogenic massive sulfide, and porphyry molybdenum deposits) which, as we shall see in later chapters, are not unique to arc settings. This is primarily due to the fact that igneous rocks with which such deposits are associated can be generated in tectonic settings other than those involving the subduction process.

In the preceding chapters I have not placed strong emphasis on the genetic problems associated with arc deposits. It is clear, however, that the large major-

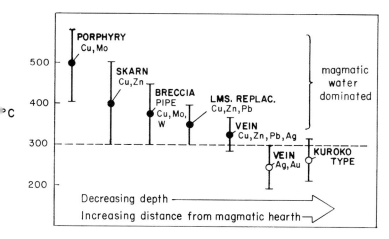

Fig. 4.17. Generalized temperature-deposit type relationships for the major hydrothermal ore types found in arc systems emphasizing the essential coherence of arc metallogeny despite variations in the metal content of individual deposits

ity of metal deposits in arc systems are closely related in time and space to the emplacement at shallow levels within the crust of intermediate to felsic intrusions. Some workers cling to the notion that such intrusives act mainly as heat engines to drive convective flow of non-magmatic fluids, that garner and concentrate metals from the surrounding rocks (Norton, 1978, 1979). The most compelling argument against this concept is the complete disregard deposits such as porphyry coppers exhibit towards the lithochemistry of the varied country-rocks in which they are emplaced. Even in the case of Kuroko-type deposits it can be argued, albeit contrary to the conventional wisdom, that the major source of the metals are cooling magmas (Henley and Thornley, 1979; Sawkins, 1982b, 1983). The only arc-related metal deposits that seem to be keyed to specific countryrocks are epithermal gold deposits, which exhibit a strong tendency to occur within andesites (Silberman et al., 1976). Finally, the mere fact that I-type and S-type magmatic systems are consistently associated with deposits of distinctive metal composition (Ishihara, 1981) argues strongly for a magmatic source of those metals.

Figure 4.17 shows the typical ranges of fluid inclusion temperatures obtained from base and precious metal deposits in arc systems. These data emphasize the essential coherence of copper and polymetallic Cordilleran deposits as a group and their distinction from lower temperature ores formed from fluids dominated by waters of non-magmatic origin. The extent to which countryrock leaching is a factor in the generation of these latter ore types remains to be resolved, but in most instances the presence of a small, but perhaps critical, magmatic water component in the ore fluids cannot be ruled out.

Part II
Divergent Plate Boundary Environments

Chapter 5   Metallogeny of Oceanic-Type Crust

5.1 Generation of Oceanic-Type Crust

The volumes of magma generated per year along the current > 50,000 km long system of oceanic spreading ridges are estimated to exceed those generated on the remainder of the earth by about an order of magnitude (Menard, 1967). Oceanic crust and lithosphere are mainly formed at so-called mid-ocean ridge systems, but essentially similar oceanic crust is also generated during the earlier stages of continental separation (e.g., Red Sea), and during the formation of marginal basins behind some subduction-related arc systems (Karig, 1971).

The nature of oceanic crust and underlying mantle material was little known until the realization that certain mafic-ultramafic complexes (ophiolites) embedded in many of the younger orogenic belts of the world exhibited thicknesses, and seismic and petrologic features that closely matched those known from oceanic areas (Coleman, 1977). The ophiolite model for the crust of the deep ocean basins needs to be approached with some caution, however, because most major ophiolite complexes may well represent either fore-arc limbs of island arc complexes (Gealey, 1980), marginal basin material (Harper, 1980; Hawkins, 1980), or former oceanic crust adjacent to fracture zones (Karson and Dewey, 1978). Emplacement of major ophiolite complexes inevitably involves an arc-continent or continent-continent collision event, and under normal conditions of subduction only thin slivers of ophiolite material tend to be incorporated in imbricate, fore-arc melange terrains (Gealey, 1980).

Considerable research effort has been focussed in recent years on the petrology and petrochemistry of ophiolite complexes (see Panayiotou (ed), 1980, Proceedings of International Ophiolite Symposium, Cyprus, 1979). However, Fox et al. (1980) emphasize that, although a generally acceptable model of oceanic crust via ophiolite studies is at hand, there are many puzzling first order variations in the structure, thickness and composition of ophiolite complexes. For example, the ophiolite complexes of the western Tethyan area (Italy to Turkey) are distinctive in regard to some aspects of their trace element geochemistry to those of eastern Tethyan regions, which in turn exhibit certain differences from typical mid-ocean ridge basalts (MORB) (Pearce, 1980). For example, the lavas of the complete ophiolite complexes in this area (Troodos Massif, Semail Nappe) are strongly depleted in Cr and contain much lower Ce/Sr ratios than

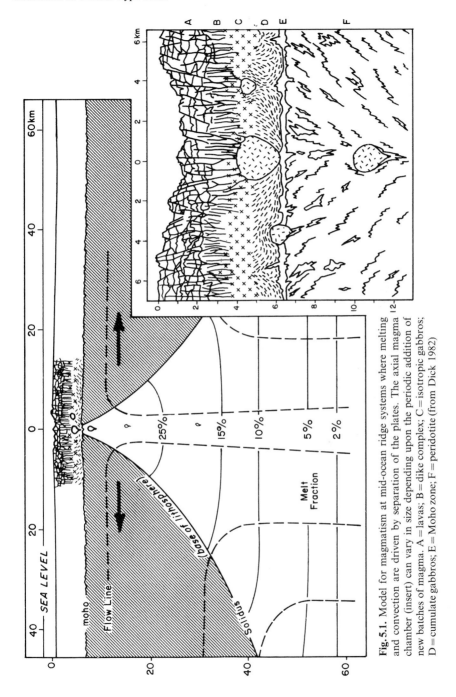

Fig. 5.1. Model for magmatism at mid-ocean ridge systems where melting and convection are driven by separation of the plates. The axial magma chamber (insert) can vary in size depending upon the periodic addition of new batches of magma. A = lavas; B = dike complex; C = isotropic gabbros; D = cumulate gabbros; E = Moho zone; F = peridotite (from Dick 1982)

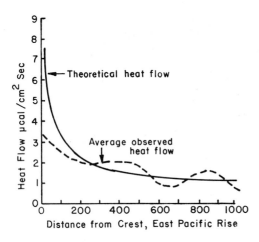

Fig. 5.2. Theoretical and average observed heat flow-distance curves for the Pacific Ocean. Similar relations are also found in the Atlantic and Indian Oceans (from McKenzie 1967)

MORB. These and other trace element data suggest the lavas and their associated ophiolite units formed in marginal basins. Unfortunately, complexities abound in detail, and the hope that clear trace element discriminants for tectonic settings would be found has not fully materialized.

Uncertainty also exists regarding the precise nature of the Moho discontinuity in oceanic-type crust, but Clague and Straley (1977) have suggested it marks the boundary between partially serpentinized harzburgite (compressional wave velocity 7.4) and fresh tectonized harzburgite (compressional wave velocity 8.2). The mechanisms of magma generation and crystallization during formation of oceanic crust and lithosphere are also somewhat contentious, but recent models proposed by Duncan and Green (1980) and Dick (1982) (Fig. 5.1) appear capable of explaining many of the subtleties of ophiolite petrology. It is noteworthy that small bodies of plagiogranite are observed in many ophiolite complexes, and small volumes of rhyolite are generated in Iceland and have been recorded, albeit rarely, from oceanic ridge samples (Melson et al., 1976). The significance of these felsic igneous rocks in this setting is not fully understood.

As newly-formed oceanic lithosphere moves away from ocean ridges it cools, thickens, and decreases in elevation, attaining normal oceanic depths after a time interval of approximately 50 m.y. Slow spreading ridge systems such as the mid-Atlantic Ridge are characterized by steep topography, whereas the fast spreading East Pacific Rise is a much broader, but topographically smoother feature (see Fig. 4). The elevation of oceanic ridge systems reflects their underlying thermal structure, and the steeper topography of slow spreading ridges is probably related to the longer residence time of newly formed crust over the area of magma bodies.

It is now recognized that these accretionary plate boundaries tend to be the sites of intense local hydrothermal activity. In fact, it was the observation that empirical and theoretical heatflow patterns at oceanic spreading systems were markedly disparate (Fig. 5.2), that led to the realization that convecting seawater must remove substantial amounts of heat from these areas.

5.2 Contemporary Mineralization at Oceanic Spreading Ridges

The observation that the empirical heatflow patterns associated with spreading ridge systems were markedly disparate from those predicted by theoretical considerations (Lister, 1972, 1980; Sclater et al., 1974; Wolery and Sleep, 1976) led to a search for evidence for hydrothermal activity and eventually the actual sites at which thermal springs were debouching on the seafloor were discovered (Corliss et al., 1979).

Hydrothermal activity, leading to localized greenschist and amphibolite facies metamorphism, is primarily concentrated in new ocean crust at spreading centers, whereas zeolite facies metamorphism and low-temperature alteration persists away from ridge crest until the excess heat of the young oceanic crust is dissipated. Whether hydrothermal processes at mid-ocean ridges can develop fluids sufficiently enriched in metals to create ore deposits, depends critically on the magnitude and rate at which these fluids ascend through the oceanic crust. A highly permeable region of oceanic crust overlying a magma chamber may be required to permit metal-rich fluids to reach the seafloor in amounts necessary to form economically significant ore deposits. Thus, although high-temperature hydrothermal alteration of basalt by seawater may be a dominant and widespread process at mid-ocean ridges, it is perhaps only those sub-systems characterized by tectonic features conducive of locally high permeability that generate seafloor heavy metal deposits. However, given the high heat energy inputs, tensional stress environments, and omnipresence of a chloride fluid (seawater), it is puzzling that a broader spectrum of metal deposits is not formed in this setting.

The hydrothermal activity at spreading ridge systems can be categorized as being of either low or high intensity type. The low intensity type is characterized by high water/rock ratios and leads to iron-rich and manganese-rich encrustations on pillow basalts, each with distinctive Fe/Mn ratios (Rona, 1978). In contrast, ferromanganese seafloor nodules of hydrogenous origin have Fe/Mn ratios in the order of 1, and are characterized by much higher contents of trace metals (Ni, Co, Cu and Zn). The distribution, composition, and economic potential of such manganese nodules are discussed in Horn et al. (1973). The hydrothermal encrustations have been found in many of the closely investigated sectors of the North Atlantic and East Pacific ridge systems (Rona, 1978) and, where manganese-rich, contain mainly birnessite, todorokite and pyrolusite, and, where iron-rich, goethite and nontronite predominate. In addition to these iron and manganese encrustations, a thin layer of metalliferous sediments commonly separates layer 2 basaltic crust (pillow lavas) from overlying pelagic sediments in all major ocean basins.

The high intensity hydrothermal activity of spreading centers is of far more interest in terms of the ore deposits found in the upper parts of ophiolite complexes. Recent direct observations and sampling of the hydrothermal activity at 21° N on the East Pacific Rise have generated considerable research activity (MacDonald et al., 1980; Edmond et al., 1982). Some warm springs sampled from the Galapagos Ridge apparently represent high-intensity systems that have undergone near surface cooling by admixture with shallow convecting seawater. Certain aspects of their chemistry, however, indicate an original high temperature, low water/rock interaction with deeper levels of oceanic crust (Edmond et al., 1979; Edmond et at., 1982). Mottl (1983) demonstrates that the rate of heat loss from underlying magmatic systems achieved by the high temperature discharges is such that both they, and the magmatism that drives them, must be episodic in nature. The amount of deep seated water, carbon dioxide and other volatile components in these high temperature discharges is as yet unknown, but may not be negligible.

The high intensity discharges at 21° N on the East Pacific Rise (East Pacific Rise Study Group, 1981) are of two types, termed black and white smokers. The black smokers represent discharges that upon entry to ambient seawater produce clouds of pyrrhotite particles. Samples of the columnar vent structures themselves indicate they are composed of sulfides that exhibit surficial oxidation to ochrous iron oxides. Two main types of sulfide 'ore' are present: a zinc-rich material containing about 25 percent Zn and an iron-rich material with 20–40 percent Fe and 2–6 percent Cu. Additional metals present in minor amounts are Co, Pb, Ag, and Cd. The white smokers contain little sulfide material, and the precipitate formed on admixture with seawater is predominantly barite.

Hydrothermal activity with formation of iron, zinc, and copper sulfide mounds scattered over an area 7 km long and 2 km wide has recently been discovered in the Guaymas Basin, Gulf of California (Lonsdale et al., 1980; Scott et al., 1983). Although the Gulf of California primarily represents a transform plate boundary, it contains a number of short seafloor spreading centers that link en echelon transform faults (Fig. 5.3). The Guaymas Basin is underlain by one such actively spreading segment, but because of relatively high sedimentation rates, the Basin contains considerable sediment fill and the sulfides are accumulating in a sedimentary environment well above oceanic basement. Scott et al. (1983) have suggested that this situation may well be representative of that in which the sediment-hosted Zn-Cu Besshi-type deposits formed (see Chap. 4).

Recently, contemporary hydrothermal activity and base metal sulfide accumulations have also been discovered on the Galapagos ridge (copper) and the Juan de Fuca Ridge (zinc) (Normark et al., 1983). Together with the East Pacific Rise activity, these occurrences are of major interest, not only in terms of providing actualistic examples of processes of 'ore' formation, but data gained from these systems impact on our resolution of problems as diverse as the formation

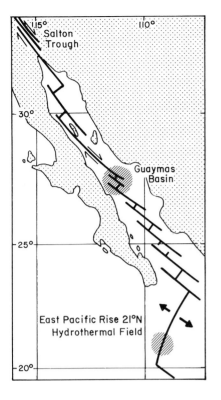

Fig. 5.3. Location of the Guaymas Basin above two short segments of spreading in the Gulf of California. The hydrothermal activity and sulfide deposits occur in the northern trough at depths of approximately 2000 m. Note positions of the 21° N hydrothermal field and position of Salton Trough along this same plate boundary system (modified from Lonsdale et al. 1980)

of oceanic crust, its subsequent metamorphism, the chemistry of seawater, and the global magnesium flux (Mottl, 1983). Study of these systems has also allowed for a particularly intriguing marriage of the empirical, experimental and theoretical approaches to the solution of geologic problems. Active circulation of metalliferous brines and recent precipitation of economically interesting sulfide layers within a marine environment are also known from the axial portions of the Red Sea (Degens and Ross, 1969). These will be discussed in a later chapter.

5.2.1 The Salton Sea Geothermal System

The Salton Sea geothermal system has attracted considerable attention, not only as a potential source of geothermal power in southern California, but because it contains significant quantities of metals in its deep fluids (White et al., 1963; White, 1974; Skinner et al., 1967). Although its setting is hardly oceanic, it does lie along a 'leaky' transform plate boundary where offsets in the transform faults are connected by short segments of actively rifting crust (Menard and Atwater, 1969) (see Fig. 5.3).

Data available from this hydrothermal system indicate fluids of meteoric origin have been heated to temperatures of 360 °C, and acquired elevated salinities (35% total dissolved salts) and metal contents (Mn 1400 ppm, Fe 2290 ppm, Pb 102 ppm, Zn 540 ppm, Cu 8 ppm, and Ag 1.8 ppm). Discharge fluids from wells deposited an opaline silica containing a suite of fine grained copper and other minerals characterized by high metal/sulfur ratios. The metals have apparently been mobilized in large part from subsurface pelitic formations now hydrothermally altered to greenschist facies rocks. The extent to which some of the brine constituents may have been generated from the underlying magmatic heat source is unclear, and the suggestion (Craig, 1966) that the chlorine in the system has come from the country rocks remains unsubstantiated.

5.3 Massive Sulfide Deposits of the Troodos Ophiolite, Cyprus

The precise tectonics of emplacement of the Troodos ophiolite massif is still a somewhat contentious subject (e.g., Gealey, 1980; Robertson, 1977; Bortolotti et al., 1976), but there is little doubt that this sequence of mafic and ultramafic igneous rocks and overlying pelagic sediments was originally formed at a submarine spreading center during later Cretaceous time. The scenario in which the Troodos massif is seen as a segment of outer arc oceanic basement uplifted due to a collision event involving continental material moved in from the (present) southwest as a result of northdipping subduction (Fig. 5.4) seems to best fit the regional geologic relationships.

The Troodos Massif proper forms a elongate domal uplift exhibiting roughly concentric zones of sheeted dike complex surrounding pillow lavas around a plutonic core complex consisting of gabbros and ultramafic rocks (Fig. 5.5).

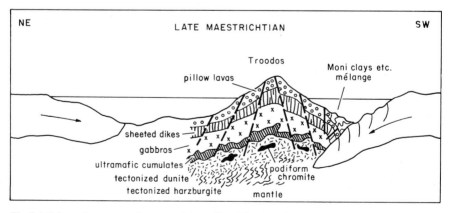

Fig. 5.4. Schematic cross-section to explain uplift of the Troodos ophiolite complex to its present position (from Searle and Panayiotou 1980)

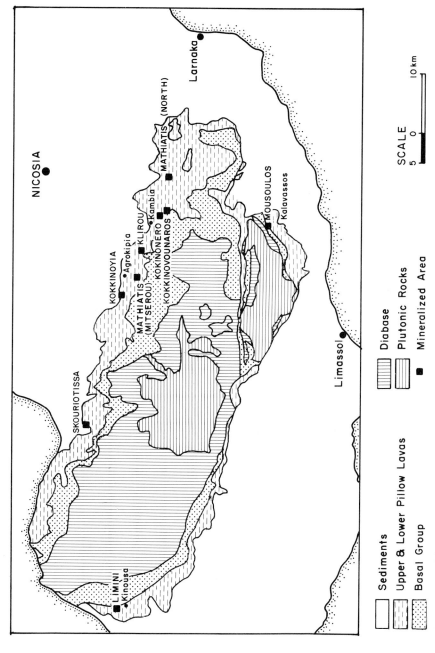

Fig. 5.5. Map of the Troodos complex showing crude anular structure with plutonic ultramafic rocks in central regions, and restriction of massive sulfide deposits to pillow lavas (from Maliotis and Khan 1980)

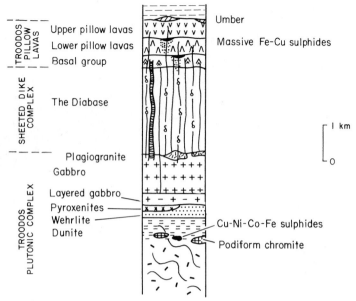

Fig. 5.6 Lithostratigraphic section of the Troodos Ophiolite (from Searle and Panayiotou 1980)

The complex is cut by numerous normal faults that trend mainly north-south, and a major east-west structure, the Arakapas Fault that exposes additional plutonic igneous rocks on its south side (Searle and Panayiotou, 1980). For a review of the geology of the Troodos massif see Gass (1980 and references therein).

The massive sulfide deposits of the Troodos massif are all within or at the top of the ower pillow lava sequence (Fig. 5.6). Many deposits are known (>90) but only six exceed 1 million tons in size, and only the Mavrovouni orebody (15 million tons) exceeds 10 million tons of ore. In a number of instances, groups of small (<1 million tons) deposits occur in relatively close proximity to each other (Adamides, 1980) (Fig. 5.7). A typical deposit consists of a zone of massive pyrite, containing variable amounts of marcasite and lesser chalcopyrite and sphalerite, sandwiched between an overlying ochre horizon and a basal siliceous ore zone (Constantinou, 1980). Below this are stringer zones consisting mainly of quartz and quartz-sulfide veins cementing chloritized basalt breccia, and in fractures cutting pillows. Disseminated sulfides are also present in the altered pillow lavas. The ochre horizons consist of quartz and goethite with lesser illite and jarosite, and have been interpreted to result from submarine oxidative weathering of sulfide ore exposed to seawater (Constantinou and Govett, 1972).

The massive sulfide ores typically consist of porous blocks of iron sulfides set in a friable sulfide matrix (Constantinou, 1976). This conglomeratic texture is more pronounced in the lower portions of orebodies and is thought to have

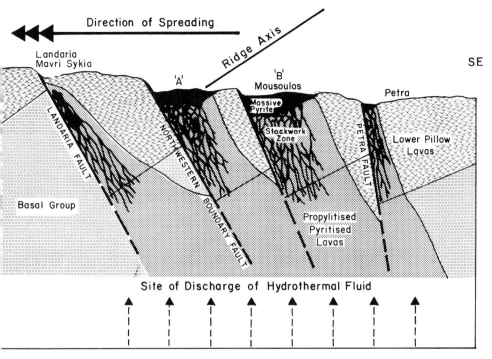

Fig. 5.7. Diagrammatic illustration of the environment of formation of the Kalavasos ore deposits (from Adamides 1980)

resulted from intense leaching of the sulfides, presumably due to passage of later fluids. The copper contents of massive ores are usually from 1 to 6 percent, with zinc contents somewhat lower. However, substantial amounts of zinc (approaching 10 percent) are present in certain orebodies (Bear, 1963).

Chemical, fluid inclusion, and isotopic studies have all tended to support the concept that the ore fluid responsible for the formation of these deposits was seawater that had circulated deep into the newly formed oceanic crust. For example, fluid inclusion data from stringer zone quartz indicates temperatures of close to 350 °C with salinities close to that of seawater (Spooner and Bray, 1977). Similarly, studies of strontium (Chapman and Spooner, 1977) and stable isotopes (Heaton and Sheppard, 1977) in the stringer zones and the adjacent altered rocks have tended to confirm the seawater origin of the ore fluids.

5.4 Additional Examples of Cyprus-Type Massive Sulfide Deposits

In many parts of the world where ophiolite complexes with their uppermost portions still intact are known, massive sulfide deposits similar to those of the

Troodos massif have been discovered (Sillitoe, 1972b; Franklin et al., 1981). This pertains particularly to the Ordovician ophiolite complexes of northeastern Newfoundland (e.g., Upadhyay and Strong, 1973; Duke and Hutchinson, 1974), where in the Betts Cove area, for example, massive sulfide deposits occur within the lowermost pillow lavas overlying a sheeted dike complex. The largest deposit, Tilt Cove, contains 6.8 million tons grading 3% copper and lesser zinc. Most of the deposits in Newfoundland ophiolites are spatially associated with chloritized fault zones and occur close to the base of pillow lava sequences.

The Semail ophiolite of Oman is a very large, well exposed ophiolite complex emplaced during Tethyan collision events. Coleman et al. (1978) report that over 150 cupriferous massive sulfides prospects have been discovered within it. However, the most important of these are spatially associated with a series of volcanic centers (Fig. 5.8) strung out along the uppermost part of the complex. These volcanic centers (Lasail Unit) appear to represent 'seamounts' superimposed on a base consisting of typical non-vesicular aphyric basaltic pillow lavas up to 1.5 km in thickness (Geotimes Unit). The centers are atypical of ophiolites in that they contain significant amounts of felsic and andesitic volcanics and, locally, high level trondhjemite plugs. Intense hydrothermal alteration is associated with these centers and it is of no small significance that the major massive sulfide bodies also occur within them (Alabaster et al., 1980). The largest known orebody lies within the Jizi center and contains 12 million tons of 2.4 percent Cu. These volcanic centers, superimposed on more normal upper ophiolite sequences, are petrochemically similar to island arc volcanics (Alabaster et al., 1980), and such observations serve to emphasize the complexities of ophiolite metallogeny, and the possible pitfalls of oversimplistic models for Cyprus-type ore genesis.

Additional examples of Cyprus-type deposits are known along much of the Tethyan suture zone, in particular in the Mesozoic ophiolites of Italy (Zuffardi, 1977), the ophiolite zone of Turkey, the Sevano-Alceron zone of the USSR, and the Zagros Ranges of Iran (Jankovic, 1980). A large number of massive sulfide deposits are known along the length of the Uralian suture in the USSR (Hamilton, 1970). At least some of these appear to have typical ophiolitic associations, although others are associated with calc-alkaline volcanic sequences (Gealey, 1980). The orebodies themselves are cupriferous pyrite lenses that commonly overlie sulfide disseminations in silicified altered footwall rocks (Smirnov, 1970).

In the Philippines, especially on Balabac Island (John, 1963) and in the Zambales Range of southwest Luzon, a number of cupriferous massive sulfide deposits within mafic pillow lava sequences are known. The spatial association of these volcanics with ultramafic rocks, gabbros, and trondhjemite in many areas indicates they constitute parts of ophiolite complexes, and thus the massive sulfides within them qualify as Cyprus-type deposits.

The recognition of Cyprus-type deposits, and for that matter ophiolite complexes themselves, in metamorphic terrains, is not an easy matter. In such

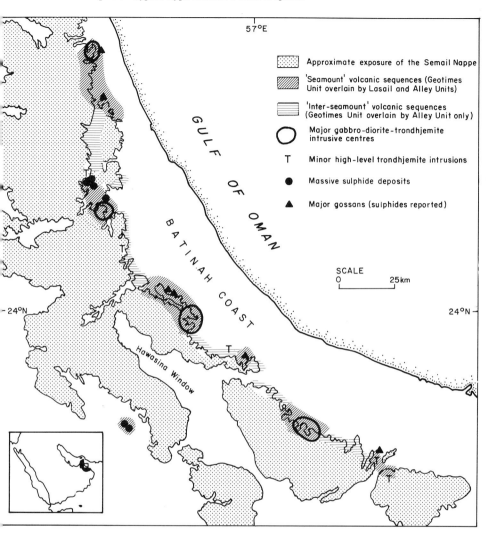

57°E

Approximate exposure of the Semail Nappe

'Seamount' volcanic sequences (Geotimes Unit overlain by Lasail and Alley Units)

'Inter-seamount' volcanic sequences (Geotimes Unit overlain by Alley Unit only)

Major gabbro-diorite-trondhjemite intrusive centres

T   Minor high-level trondhjemite intrusions

●   Massive sulphide deposits

▲   Major gossans (sulphides reported)

SCALE
0   25km

G U L F

O F

O M A N

B A T I N A H   C O A S T

Hawasina Window

24°N

24°N

Fig. 5.8. Map of the Semail Nappe Ophiolite showing 'seamount' volcanic sequences. Note that massive sulfide deposits are mainly associated with these more felsic volcanics (from Alabaster et al. 1980)

situations recourse can and is generally made to patterns of immobile trace elements in the associated mafic rocks. On this basis, Grenne et al. (1980) have suggested that the massive sulfide deposits of the Trondheim area (see Chap. 4) are of Cyprus-type. A similar designation may be appropriate for many of the early Paleozoic massive sulfides of the Norwegian Caledonides.

5.5 Discussion

The broad similarities between oceanic-type crust and ophiolite complexes, and between modern ocean ridge hydrothermal activity and Cyprus-type massive sulfide deposits, are without doubt impressive, but some intriguing problems remain. For example, are ophiolite complexes an average representative of typical oceanic crust, or is the very fact of their incorporation into continental crust indicative of an atypical origin? As Coleman (1977) states "The actual comparison of ophiolite complexes with oceanic crust is incomplete." He also points out that somewhat less than 0.001% of the total oceanic crust has been incorporated into the continents and notes that most ophiolites are much thinner than average oceanic crust. What does seem to be clear is that collision events, especially those involving island arcs and continental blocks, are an important factor in the emplacement of many major ophiolite complexes (Gealey, 1980).

Immobile trace elements such as rare earth elements, titanium, yttrium, and zirconium have been widely used to categorize the tectonic settings in which mafic rocks are generated. The problem with such methods is not the concepts upon which they are based, but that no elements are totally immobile and that mafic rocks can be subject to alteration shortly after formation and at various later stages in their history. Some ophiolitic rocks, for example, may experience alteration at the time of their initial formation, during transport across ocean basins, at the time of their tectonic emplacement, during later regional metamorphic events, and finally upon surface exposure. Others may go through formation and emplacement largely unscathed by significant alteration events. These variations, compounded upon by inherent trace element fluctuations due to inhomogeneities in mantle source regions, provide ample reason why trace element discriminants for mafic rocks produce patterns that are of times markedly less than tidy.

The extent to which the black smokers discovered on the East Pacific Rise are analogous to the systems that produced Cyprus-type deposits in ophiolites is also unclear. The major sulfide mineral precipitating from the black smokers is pyrrhotite, a phase that is uncommon in unmetamorphosed Cyprus-type deposits. Furthermore, Mottl (1983) points out that the alteration zones beneath high intensity ocean-ridge hotsprings should be quartz and chlorite poor rather than quartz and chlorite rich. This is the reverse of that found in the stringer systems below the Cyprus deposits, although it should be noted that many Cyprus-type deposits in other areas have less pronounced quartz-chlorite zones beneath them.

Another question of interest is: What is the typical areal density of Cyprus-type deposits in normal oceanic crust and how variable is it? Although the average size of the massive sulfide deposits within the Troodos pillow lavas is small, a large number of deposits and deposit clusters are known. Solomon (1976) has observed that these exhibit spacing-size relationships that are probably related to the size of the convective systems whose fossil discharge points they now mark. Modern subaerial hydrothermal convective systems, such as those in the Taupo Volcanic Zone, New Zealand, tend to exhibit diameters of approximately 5 km and this dimension is apparently reflected in the average spacing of Cyprus deposits and deposit clusters.

The concept that metalliferous deposits in the upper portions of oceanic crust may influence the eventual metallogeny of arc systems formed in relation to subduction of that crust is probably erroneous. Firstly, the formation of metal deposits in layer 2 pillow lavas and metalliferous sediments above them does not represent any net increase in the metal budget of oceanic crust, merely a redistribution thereof, and secondly, whether actual slab melting occurs to any significant extent during the subduction process remains questionable (Gill, 1981). What is probably more important in terms of arc metallogeny is the extent to which water, and perhaps marine sulfur and chlorine, is fixed in oceanic crust during ridge-related hydrothermal processes. The subduction of relatively highly altered oceanic crust may thus be a more fundamental factor in generating arc systems that are well endowed with metal deposits.

From the viewpoint of exploration, the pillow lava sequences of ophiolite complexes, especially in areas where early faulting can be recognized, deserve attention for the possible presence of Cyprus-type ores. Recognition of favorable levels within pillow lava sequences is probably not possible, inasmuch as massive sulfide lenses are known to occur at all levels within ophiolitic pillow lava sequences. In many Newfoundland ophiolites the massive sulfides occur near the base of the pillow lavas, in Troodos most ore bodies occur at the boundary between the lower and upper pillow lavas (Constantinou, 1980), and in the Semail ophiolite the major ores are in local volcanic centers superimposed on the pillow lava sequences. In Cyprus a variety of geophysical techniques, including induced polarization and resistivity (Maliotis and Khan, 1980), have been used to locate subsurface massive sulfide lenses, but with respect to interpretation of geophysical data in general, it is important to remember that most deposits are relatively small (< million tons, see Adamides, 1980).

5.6 Chromite Deposits in Ophiolite Complexes

The deeper, plutonic portions of ophiolite complexes tend to contain economic deposits of chromite. Chromite is a common accessory mineral in virtually all ultramafic rocks, but in certain instances the chromite grains can become sufficiently concentrated to form economic chromite deposits. Due to their tendency to form lensoid bodies, such deposits in ophiolite complexes have been termed podiform deposits (Thayer, 1964). In 1975, over 60% of world chrome production was from this source, although about 97% of world chromite reserves occur as stratiform deposits within large non-ophiolitic, layered mafic and ultramafic intrusives (see later).

Podiform chromite deposits occur as tabular, elongate, or irregular masses
that invariably exhibit evidence of some degree of metamorphic deformation
(Thayer, 1969). Important examples of these deposits are known from Yugos-
lavia, Greece, Turkey, Iran, and Pakistan along the Alpine-Himalayan collision
belt, and from the Philippines, and New Caledonia in the western Pacific (Coleman, 1977 and references therein). The ophiolite belts in Cuba also contain important deposits (Thayer, 1942). Analysis of the lithologic environments of podiform chromite deposits indicate that they occur within the upper mantle (ultramafic) portions of ophiolite complexes, but generally not far below the cumulate gabbroic rocks thought to equate with the lower portions of layer III of
modern oceanic crust (Fig. 5.9). These upper mantle portions of ophiolite complexes consist predominantly of harzburgite (>95%), but locally dunite bodies
are present and it is with these that the podiform chromite concentrations are
primarily associated. Although these ultramafic rocks invariably exhibit tec-
tonite fabrics, in some instances of considerable complexity (Coleman, 1977),
evidence for gravitational crystal accumulation of chromite grains within local
Mg-rich (dunitic) melts is indicated for some deposits (Burgath and Weiser,
1980; Brown, 1980) and the chromite concentrations of the Orhaneli ophiolite
massif, Turkey, for example, (Tankut, 1980) exhibit well-defined layering.

Recently, Lago et al. (1982) have suggested that podiform chromite concentrations form within convecting dike-like bodies of basalt magma that cross-cut
harzburgite within peridotite diapirs (Fig. 5.10). Collapse of the accumulated

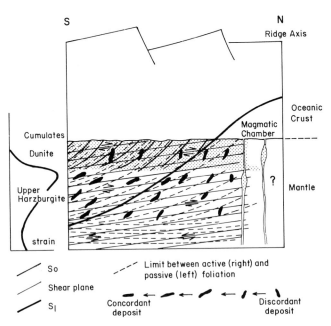

Fig. 5.9. Sketch to illustrate one concept of
podiform chromite ores
in uppermost oceanic
mantle beneath an active
spreading ridge (from
Lago et al., 1982)

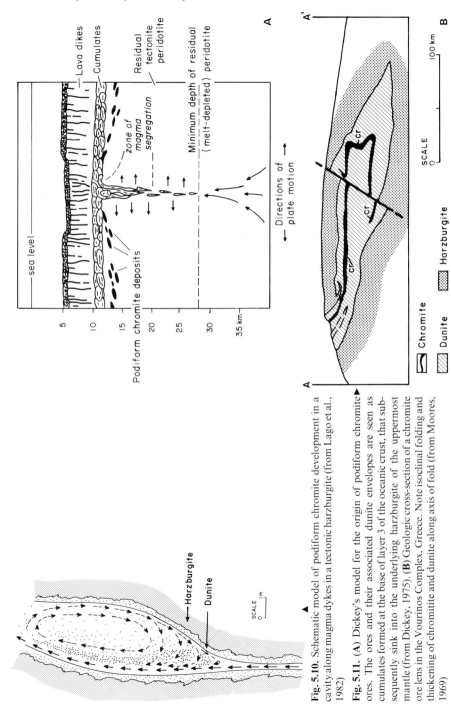

Fig. 5.10. Schematic model of podiform chromite development in a cavity along magma dykes in a tectonic harzburgite (from Lago et al., 1982)

Fig. 5.11. (A) Dickey's model for the origin of podiform chromite ores. The ores and their associated dunite envelopes are seen as cumulates formed at the base of layer 3 of the oceanic crust, that subsequently sink into the underlying harzburgite of the uppermost mantle (from Dickey, 1975). (B) Geologic cross-section of a chromite ore lens in the Vourinos Complex, Greece. Note isoclinal folding and thickening of chromitite and dunite along axis of fold (from Moores, 1969)

chromite grains and nodules formed along one side of the magma chamber would produce brecciated, massive, or irregularly layered ore. Subsequent deformation during shearing of the enclosing dunite and more pervasive harzburgite would produce the wide variety of stretched and deformed shapes that podiform chromite bodies tend to exhibit. Whether the above scenario is adequate to explain all features of podiform chromite bodies, including observed variations in Cr and Al contents of the chromite grains (Brown, 1980) remains to be seen. Dickey (1975) envisages the formation of podiform chromite bodies in the lowermost layer of cumulate activity during the formation of new oceanic lithosphere and the subsequent gravitational settling of these dense chromite-dunite autoliths into underlying harzburgite, itself a crystal mush (Fig. 5.11). This would explain the tendency of podiform chromite ores to occur within the upppermost portions of the harzburgite portions of ophiolites (Cassard et al., 1981). Recently, Nicolas and Violette (1982) have suggested that spreading at ocean ridge systems may be of either horizontal or diapiric type. The former (Table Mountain type) is less favorable to generation of economic chromite deposits, than the latter (Acoje type) which is characterized by inhomogeneous plastic flow patterns, deformed paleo-Moho, and large scale folds (Fig. 5.12).

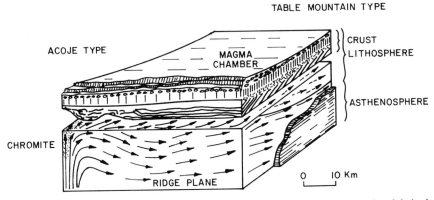

Fig. 5.12. Model for accumulation of chromite ores based on relationships observed mainly in the Zambales Ophiolite, Philippines. *Full arrows*, flow lines in asthenosphere; *dashed arrows*, fossil flow lines in lithosphere; *thick lines*, chromitite layers in cumulate gabbros (from Nicolas and Violette 1982). See text for further details

5.6.1 The Chromite Deposits of the Vourinos Complex, Greece

The Vourinos Complex forms part of a broad band of Tethyan ophiolites that runs from the Alps through the Balkan Peninsula to Turkey and beyond. It is emplaced in crystalline Jurassic limestones and exhibits a full suite of ophiolitic rock types from pelagic sediments down through pillow lavas, dikes, gabbros, and ultramafics (Moores, 1969).

In the northern part of the complex a cluster of podiform chromite deposits occur at Voidolakkos, within a dunitic host rock that cross-cuts the ambient harzburgites (Zachos, 1969). The orebodies are present as steeply dipping pipes of podiform massive chromite that appear to have segregated from a mushroom-shaped intrusion of chromite-bearing dunite. Lineation and foliation within the ores and surrounding dunite are also steep and differ from that of the harzburgites. Individual orebodies tend to be small (< 10,000 tons), but the chromite contains 40–50% Cr_2O_3 and is low in alumina and iron. As such it represents good metallurgical grade ore.

Distinctive from this mineralization are the schleiren type podiform ores of the Xerolivado area in the southern part of the complex (Zachos, 1969). Here again dunite and serpentinized dunites form the immediate hostrocks, and orebodies are mainly steeply dipping and in some cases attain vertical extents of 100–150 meters and range up to 15 meters in thickness. Strike lengths of the orebodies are difficult to determine due to faulting. As at Voidolakkos, geologic relationships indicate a late intrusion of chromite-rich dunite from which the deposits formed. These chromite ores of the Vourinos Complex are typical of podiform deposits and, given the effects of later deformation, would seem to support the genetic model of Lago et al. (1982) discussed earlier.

5.6.2 The Chromite Deposits of Selukwe, Zimbabwe

Highly altered chromiferous ultramafic rocks near Selukwe, Zimbabwe contain important chromite deposits. In this area a large sheet of ultramafic rocks has been emplaced in a thick sequence of early Archean (Sebakwian) arkoses and greywackes, containing lesser units of chemical sediments and volcanics. The ultramafic unit has been dismembered by faulting and thrusting, possibly at the time of its emplacement, and has undergone intense hydrothermal alteration to serpentinite, talc schist, talc carbonate, and silicified talc-carbonate assemblages (Cotterill, 1969). From relict textures the ultramafics appear to have originally been dunites and harzburgites. Stowe (1974) indicates that the ultramafic sheet is over 600 meters thick locally, and that the whole succession of rocks in the area has undergone complex structural dislocation, including recumbent folding and major thrusting.

The orebodies of Selukwe are mainly large elongated lenses parallel to the original layering of the ultramafic hostrocks. An average orebody exhibits dimensions of roughly $60 \times 300 \times 10$ m (Cotterill, 1969) and most occur within definite zones within the various ultramafic slices. In addition, seams of stratiform cumulate chromite up to 3 meters thick have been traced for up to 100 meters, and pipe-like orebodies are well developed at the Selukwe Peak Mine. The lower margins of larger ore lenses are mostly sharp and all the ores exhibit cumulate settled textures, and, where it can be ascertained from serpentinite textures, the original immediate hostrocks were apparently dunitic.

Overall, these Archean chromite ores at Selukwe exhibit strong similarities to the podiform ores described from Phanerozoic ophiolite complexes, although cumulate features are perhaps more pronounced. Inasmuch as chromite accumulations survive the effects of disruption and hydrothermal alteration much better than their host ultramafic rocks, and podiform chromite ores are virtually restricted to ophiolite complexes thought to form at sites of ocean spreading, it seems reasonable to suggest that the Selukwe ultramafic sheet may in fact represent parts of an Archean ophiolite complex. As such it would represent an example of ores providing clues to tectonic settings (Guilbert, 1981).

5.7 Additional Minor Mineralization in Ophiolite Complexes

Cyprus-type massive sulfide deposits and podiform chromite deposits are the only hypogene metal concentrations of any significant economic consequence in ophiolite complexes, but important concentrations of nickel in the form of garnierite, a hydrated magnesium nickel silicate, tend to form in the lower soil horizons of ophiolitic ultramafic masses subjected to tropical weathering. Such lateritic nickel deposits have been extensively mined in New Caledonia and the Dominican Republic, and similar deposits are known in Colombia and Brazil.

Minor hypogene mineralization, containing mainly copper and nickel sulfides, has been described from ultramafic rocks in the Luzon ophiolite complex in the Philippines (Bryner, 1969), in gabbroic rocks of the Semail ophiolite, Oman (Hassan and Al-Sulaimi, 1979), and in the Limmasol Forest area of the Troodos ophiolite (Panayiolou, 1980). In this latter case veins, massive pods, and disseminations of Cu, Ni, Co, and Fe sulfides and arsenides occur within serpentinized harzburgite along fault zones. Although these deposits were probably worked in a small scale by the ancients, recent investigations have failed to establish their economic viability.

Gold in economic concentrations occurs in serpentinized ophiolitic rocks at Ovado, western Liguria, Italy (Zuffardi, 1977; Pipino, 1980). It is not clear, however, whether these gold deposits were inherent to the formation of the ophiolites themselves, or emplaced at some later time. Apart from the high gold in some Cyprus-type deposits, this is the only example of gold mineralization in ophiolites known to the writer and, given the active convective circulation of seawater in the basaltic portions of oceanic crust and the background gold contents of such rocks, it is perhaps surprising that epithermal gold deposits are not a significant facet of spreading ridge, and by analogy, ophiolite metallogeny.

Although outside of the province of this volume, mention can be made of the important non-metallic mineral resources present in some ophiolite complexes. These include major deposits of magnesite, talc, and chrysotile asbestos. Economic concentrations of these minerals tend to develop within the highly serpentinized portions of ultramafic ophiolite complexes, and deposits of this type have been worked in the Mediterranean area and elsewhere. Two particularly important asbestos deposits of ophiolitic affinity in North America are those at Thetford, Quebec (Laurent, 1980) and Coalinga, California (Mumpton and Thompson, 1975).

Chapter 6 Intracontinental Hotspots, Anorogenic Magmatism, and Associated Metal Deposits

It is probably safe to say that the tectonics of plate interiors (see Geodynamics Series Volume 1, 1980, Am. Geophys. Union) are less well understood than those of plate margins. In particular, we have much to learn about the forces responsible for the creation of broad intracontinental basins and plateau uplifts (Crough, 1979). The latter are of interest at this juncture because, although enigmatic, it is generally agreed that they are connected with thermal perturbations of the underlying mantle (McGetchin et al., 1980). In fact, it has been argued by Thiessen et al. (1979) that the pronounced basin and swell nature of the African continent is related to down and upwelling mantle currents, the latter marked in many instances by surface manifestations of igneous activity.

Even before the formulation of an integrated theory of plate tectonics, Wilson (1963, 1965) had suggested that linear volcanic chains in the oceans were related to movement of oceanic lithosphere over mantle hotspots. Almost a decade later, Morgan (1972) proposed that hotspots were the crustal manifestations of rising mantle planes. Despite their conjectural aspect, it is becoming increasingly clear that mantle plumes, or at least areas of anomalously hot mantle, are a fundamental aspect of the lithosphere-asthenosphere interactions that in a broad sense comprise plate tectonics. In continental settings, the manifestations of an underlying hotspot on the upper crust depend critically on the rates of relative motion between the asthenospheric source of the hotspot and the overlying continental lithosphere (Burke, 1977). Where continental lithosphere drifts across a potent hotspot, lines of basaltic volcanoes will be formed that mark its passage. Such appears to be the case with respect to the basaltic lavas of Cenozoic age in eastern Australia (Wellman and McDougall, 1974). A similar explanation has been proposed by Smith and Christiansen (1980) to explain the basaltic and rhyolitic magmatism of the Snake River Plain and Yellowstone areas.

Where the relative motions of hotspots and overlying continental crust are negligible or very small, mantle hotspots impinge more substantially on overlying continental areas and appear capable in specific instances of generating an array of igneous rocks. These can include basalts, peralkaline mafic rocks and carbonatites, and per-alkaline and per-aluminous felsic suites. Studies of the initial $^{87}Sr/^{86}Sr$ ratios of these igneous rocks indicate that some are of direct mantle derivation, whereas others are of largely crustal anatectic origin. Caution is required in interpretation of the initial strontinum data however, because at least some hotspots appear to be related to patches of mantle with an enhanced budget of heat-producing elements such as rubidium and uranium (Anderson, 1975). In addition, the strontium isotopic systems of hotspot magmas can be disturbed by interaction with meteoric waters (Bonin et al., 1979).

Recently, Mohr (1982) has questioned the widely accepted notion that broad domal uplifts are the precursors to rifting events (Burke and Whiteman, 1973), and demonstrated that the major updoming in the East African rift system occurred only subsequent to the initiation of rifting. As is so commonly the case, modern studies of rifting environments and their relationship to hotspot activity, both past and present, are revealing far more variability and complexity than originally envisaged. Despite these problems, there are certain types of metal deposits that exhibit a clear relationship to hotspot activity and others for which such an association can be reasonably suggested.

6.1 Tin Deposits Associated with Anorogenic Granites

A clear association of certain tin districts, especially in Africa, and granites emplaced in stable intracratonic, environments is evident (Sillitoe, 1974b). Burke and Dewey (1973) explain the generation of such granites in terms of underlying mantle plume activity. In Nigeria and Niger in West Africa several groups of granitic ring complexes in a crude north-south array are known (Turner and Webb, 1974) (Fig. 6.1), although it needs to be emphasized that those at the northern extremity of the belt of Niger are considerably older (mid-Paleozoic) than the Jurassic complexes of the Jos Plateau at its southern extremity. Although many of the intrusives in this diachronous belt of alkali granites exhibit some evidence of tin mineralization, the major tin deposits occur within the Jos Plateau area.

In the Jos Plateau region over 40 granitic ring complexes intrude the surrounding Precambrian igneous and metamorphic country rocks, and in some cases cut local felsic volcanics and minor basalts (McLeod et al., 1971; Bowden and Kinnaird, 1978). Per-alkaline albite-riebeckite granites are a major rocktype in these complexes, but the tin mineralization is associated with certain of the less alkaline biotite granites (Bowden, 1982). Within these latter intrusives, cassiterite and tantalum occur both as disseminations, and within greisen zones and quartz veins containing pyrite and base metal sulfides. Mineralization occurs most commonly along horizontal roof sections of biotite granites, which were probably emplaced at depths of less than 1 km below the original surface.

The cassiterite deposits of Rondonia, western Brazil, exhibit very strong similarities to those of the Jos Plateau, as noted by Kloosterman (1969). This important tin province is associated with a broad, approximately northeast-southwest, 250 km long zone that contains eighteen single or multiple alkali granite complexes that cut sharply across older basement complex rocks (Fig.

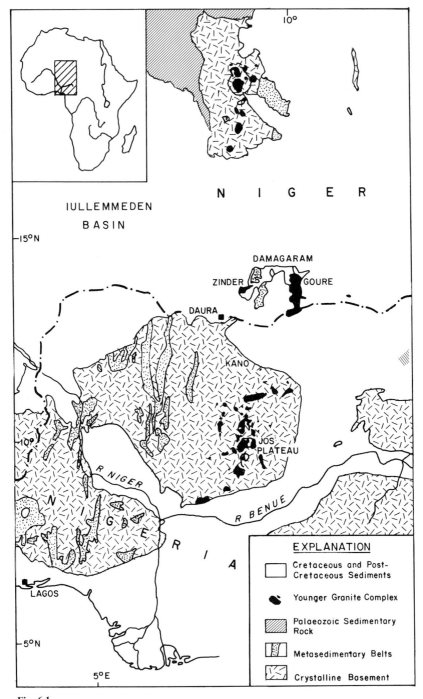

Fig. 6.1

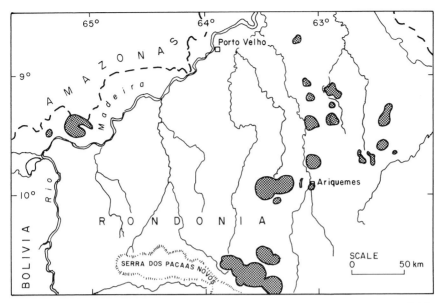

Fig. 6.2. The late Proterozoic anorogenic granites of the Rondonia Province, western Brazil. Note circular shape and considerable dimensions of many of these tin-bearing intrusive complexes (modified from Kloosterman 1969)

6.2). The largest individual ring complexes attain diameters of over 20 km. Priem et al. (1971) have reported a rubidium-strontium isotopic age of close to 1,000 m.y. for these intrusives and, based on high initial strontium ratios (>720), concluded that they were of crustal anatectic origin. It was also noted by Sawkins (1976b) that the Rondonia granites coincide with a major and widespread episode of hotspot activity that affected many continental areas about one billion years ago.

Detailed descriptions of the Rondonia mineralization are not available to the writer, but according to Kloosterman (1969) both quartz-cassiterite and quartz-cassiterite-wolframite veins, and greisen bodies cut by veinlets are present in many of the mineralized areas. The most common type of greisen contains quartz and green mica, with or without topaz. In both the Jos Plateau and Rondonia districts the predominant method of cassiterite recovery consists of removal and washing of cassiterite concentrated in weathered overburden or within gravels overlying decomposed bedrock. These gravels exhibit little evidence of having been transported more than a few tens of meters. Clearly, in both the Jos Plateau and Rondonia, concentration of cassiterite by tropical weathering processes is an important factor in the economics of tin recovery,

◄ **Fig. 6.1.** Map of Nigerian anorogenic granites. Note north-south array of alkaline granitic complexes (from Turner and Webb 1974)

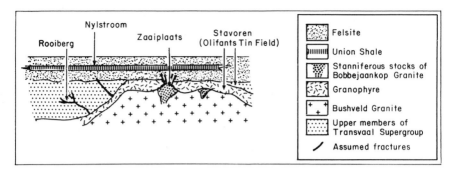

Fig. 6.3. Schematic cross-section showing relationships of certain tin deposits to the Bushveld Granite and associated intrusive units (from Hunter 1974)

but unfortunately, under such circumstances the details of hypogene mineralization tend to be sketchy.

Additional examples of tin mineralization associated with Phanerozoic anorogenic granites of postulated hotspot origin include a number of minor occurrences scattered across northern Africa and in Transbaikala-Mongolia (Sillitoe, 1974b). A series of tin deposits are also associated with the Proterozoic Bushveld Granites in South Africa (Hunter, 1973) (Fig. 6.3). These granites are considered to have resulted from crustal melting triggered by the emplacement of the huge Bushveld Igneous Complex. Whether the emplacement of this suite of igneous rocks was related to a meteor impact event, as suggested by Rhodes (1975), or is a manifestation of a mantle hotspot, large scale melting of the subjacent mantle is indicated by its mere size.

The Bushveld tin deposits had yielded almost 70 thousand tons of tin metal by 1971 (Lenthall, 1974). The tin ores occur either as pipes or sheet-like disseminations in coarse-grained porphyritic granites, or as fissure veins, breccia zones, or replacements in the granites or their volcanic and sedimentary roof rocks (see Fig. 6.3) (Hunter, 1973). Associated minerals include sericite, quartz, fluorite, chlorite and tourmaline.

It is probable that certain of the tin deposits of the U.S.S.R., are of hotspot-related type, but the available descriptions (see Smirnov, 1977) do not provide adequate details on which to base any meaningful speculations. One possible exception is the Kitelya deposit (Materikov, 1977) which is confined to the contact zone of the Salma massif consisting of late Proterozoic rapakivi granites. Tin mineralization is also associated with rapakivi granites in Finland (Haapala, 1977). The overall geology and associations of rapakivi granites, especially those of late Proterozoic age are suggestive of hotspot activity (Windley, 1978).

Finally, tin mineralization, albeit minor, is associated with a group of Proterozoic granite complexes in the St. Francois terrain, Missouri, that have been ascribed to mantle hotspot activity (Lowell, 1976). Kisvarsanyi (1980) has accumulated the available surface and subsurface data and demonstrates that granitic magmatism and coeval felsic volcanism occurred in relation to ring fracturing and cauldron subsidence approximatley 1.5 b.y. ago. The last phase of magmatic activity involved emplacement of two-mica microcline granites and albite granites as central plutons in resurgent cauldrons. Many of these exhibit strong enrichment in Sn, W, Nb, U, and rare earth elements.

Most authors have favored a crustal origin for these anorogenic alkali granites and their associated tin deposits described in the foregoing section, but Sillitoe (1974b) suggests that the tin may be, at least in part, of mantle origin. He also notes the linear arrays exhibited by the host granites in several instances, and suggests that this could have implications in terms of exploration for hotspot-related tin deposits.

6.2 Iron-Titanium Deposits Associated with Anorthosites

The origin of anorthosite bodies of massif-type has long represented an intriguing problem to petrologists (Wiebe, 1980). Not only are these igneous rocks highly distinctive in terms of their composition, but they exhibit a relatively limited time control (1600–1000 m.y.), and most occur within two linear belts on pre-Permian drift reconstructions; one in the southern hemisphere and one extending across North America through Scandinavia to the USSR (Herz, 1969). Many anorthosite massifs have been involved in high grade metamorphic events, but those in the Nain Province of Labrador are virtually unaffected by post-emplacement metamorphism and deformation. With respect to these Emslie (1978a,b) notes that they were emplaced about 1450 m.y. ago in an anorogenic setting, and may have been precursors to crustal attentuation or rifting.

Wynne-Edwards (1976) has noted that the anorthosite massifs of Labrador and the Grenville province occur as a series of roughly north-south linear arrays (Fig. 6.4), that exhibit younging from north to south within each array. Also, the intrusion arrays tend to exhibit progressively younger ages eastward (down to 1050 m.y.) through the Grenville province. Whether these younger ages are true crystallization ages, or represent a partial resetting of isotopic systems during Grenville metamorphism, is not entirely clear at this point. It is significant, however, that anorthosites occur both within the Grenville province and in the stable continental area to the north of it, indicating that coeval high-grade metamorphism is not a prerequisite for anorthosite emplacement, but more likely a phenomenon that tends to follow the events of anorthosite generation. No doubt many insights to the petrogenesis of massif-type anorthosites remain to be gained, but it seems likely that they represent manifestations of mid-Proterozoic hotspot activity (Bridgwater et al., 1974) rather than normal products of deep crustal processes in collision orogens (Dewey and Burke, 1973). Many

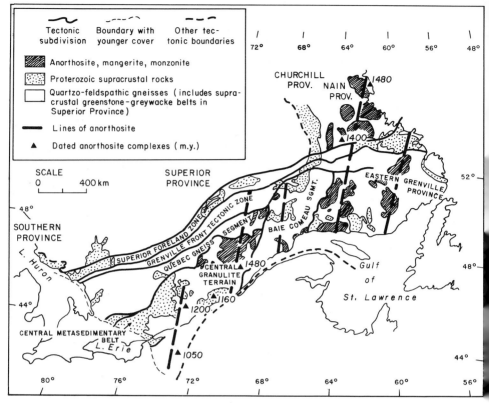

Fig. 6.4. Map of the Grenville province and adjacent areas showing anorthosites and related rocks. Note that anorthosite complexes are not restricted to the Grenville orogen, but also occur in anorogenic settings in the Nain province to the northeast (from Wynne-Edwards 1976)

reconstructions indicate the presence of a Proterozoic supercontinent at that time (e.g., Piper, 1982), and thus, the broad development of hotspot activity during this period, and the widespread, tensional and rifting events that followed (Sawkins, 1976a) may represent a prolonged series of attempts by the subcontinental mantle to rid itself of excess heat.

Certain of the anorthosite bodies of the Grenville province and others in southern Norway have important iron-titanium ores associated with them (Gross, 1967; Bugge, 1978). Disseminated iron and iron-titanium oxides are a common feature of anorthosite bodies, but in some instances lenses or irregular bodies of massive ilmenite are present. Those at Allard Lake, Quebec (Hammond, 1952), and in the Egersund anorthosite complex in southern Norway are the largest known. The Tellnes deposit in the Egersund district, for example, contains over 300 million tons of ore grading 18% TiO_2 and production of il-

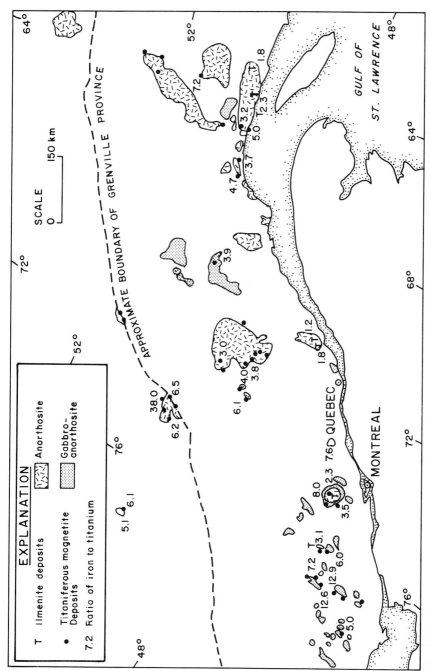

menite concentrate amounts to over 800,000 tons per year (Bugge, 1978). Lesser amounts of magnetite concentrate containing 0.6% V_2O_5 are also produced, as well as relatively minor amounts of nickel, copper, and cobalt sulfides. The Lac Tio deposit, Quebec contains in excess of 125 million tons averaging 32% TiO_2 and 36% Fe.

Within the Grenville province the iron-titanium deposits vary according to specific rock-type association and regional distribution (Fig. 6.5). Thus, ilmenite deposits, essentially devoid of magnetite, are associated with anorthosites, whereas gabbroic anorthosites tend to have deposits of titaniferous magnetite associated with them (Gross, 1967). In addition, the major ilmenite deposits are concentrated in the southeast of the Grenville belt whereas those deposits in the central and western portion of the belt contain titaniferous magnetite and, in general, exhibit significantly higher Fe:Ti ratios (Gross, 1967).

The Kunene anorthosite suite (Simpson, 1970; Vermaak, 1981) occupies an area of over 17,000 km^2 in southwest Angola and northernmost Namibia, and may be as much as 14 km thick. Unfortunately this huge anorthosite complex is poorly exposed and has been mapped in any detail only locally. It intrudes early Proterozoic metamorphic rocks and is thought to have been emplaced approximately 1.5 b.y. ago, although the isotopic age data are somewhat variable (Vermaak, 1981). The complex consists of over 70 percent of anorthosite, and has a minor ultramafic border facies. Granitic rocks make up the rest of the suite. Titaniferous magnetite bodies containing on average 49.5 percent Fe and 18.7 percent TiO_2 are scattered through the northcentral parts of the complex. It is not at present known whether these oxide bodies occur mainly in layered or plug-like form, but they appear to be typical of the iron-titanium oxide segregations known from the Grenville terrains.

The general relationship of these iron-titanium ores to their anorthositic host rocks suggests that they represent immiscible oxide segregations (Hargraves, 1962), and there is little evidence of concentration of oxides by gravity settling of early crystallized phases in a silicate melt.

6.3 Hotspot-Related Layered Mafic Complexes and Associated Ores

Layered mafic complexes of basaltic composition commonly are emplaced in association with rifting events (Sawkins, 1976b, 1982a) and can be considered as intrusive equivalents of tension-related flood basalts such as the Siberian Traps, Parana Basalts, and the Deccan Traps. However, at least two important ore-bearing, layered mafic intrusive bodies, the Bushveld Complex and the Sudbury Norite were emplaced in anorogenic environments where no prior or subsequent rifting occurred, and it is thus perhaps appropriate to relate them to the presence of underlying mantle hotspots. A meteorite impact origin has been suggested for both the Sudbury and Bushveld complexes (French, 1970; Rhodes, 1975), but the scale of magmatism in each case, especially the latter, indicates that any impacts that may have occurred served only to trigger the rise of basaltic magma from underlying mantle that was already in a thermally perturbed or hotspot mode.

6.3.1 The Geology and Ores of the Bushveld Igneous Complex, South Africa

The Bushveld Complex (Fig. 6.6) represents a major storehouse of minerals and contains the world's largest deposits of chromite, platinoid minerals, and vanadiferous magnetite (Willemse, 1964, 1969; von Gruenewaldt, 1979). The layered mafic portion of the Bushveld Complex represents a hugh lopolith that outcrops over, or underlies, an area of 67,000 km². It has a thickness in its central portions of about 8 km, and has been subdivided into five zones: the Chill Zone, and Basal Zone, the Critical Zone, the Main Zone, and the Upper Zone (Fig.

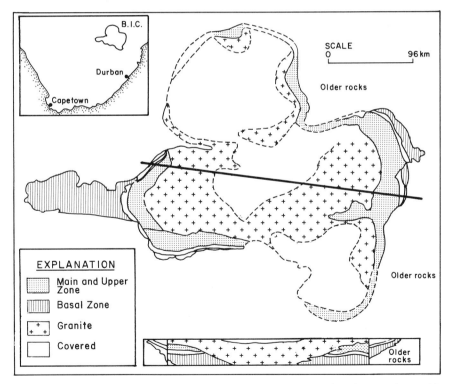

Fig. 6.6. Simplified map and cross section of the Bushveld Igneous Complex. The extensive granitic rocks probably represent, in large part, melted crustal material, and are distinct from the mafic rocks, which have the average composition of basalt

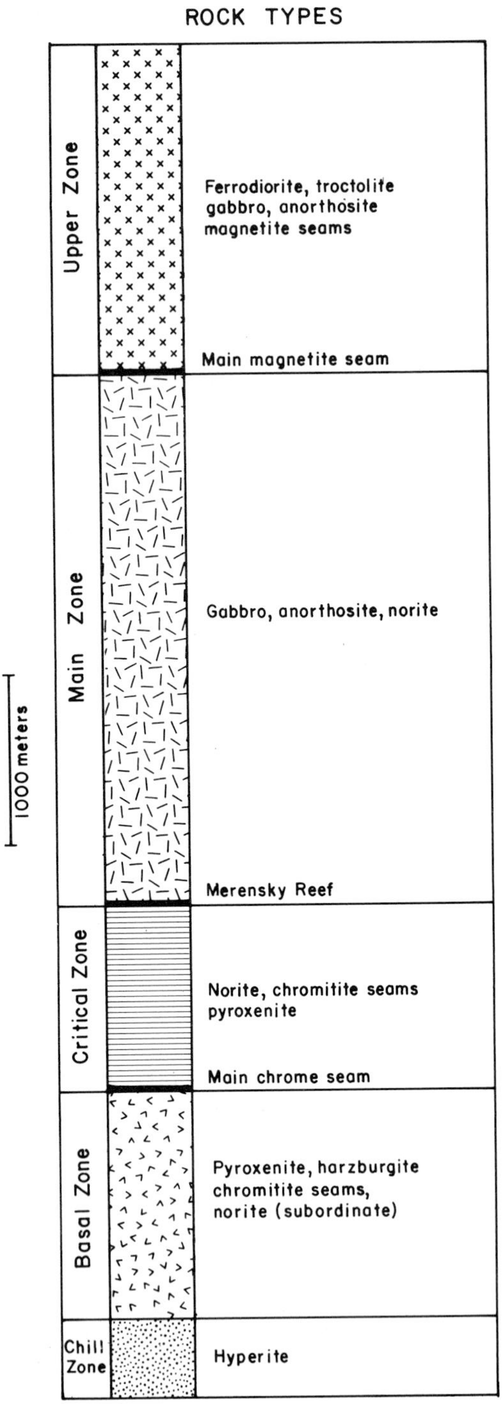

ROCK TYPES

Fig. 6.7. Generalized cross section of the eastern portion of the Bushveld Igneous Complex, showing main subdivisions of the mafic rocks, their constituent lithologies, and the main concentrations of chromite, platinum (Merensky Reef), and magnetite (simplified from Willemse 1969)

6.7). The Basal Zone, consisting of norite, is somewhat irregular in thickness and occurrence and has been little studied. It essentially separates the contact-metamorphosed underlying sediments from the ultramafic rocks, largely periodites and pyroxenites, of the Basal Zone. At the top of the Basal Zone, roughly 1400 meters above the Chill Zone norite, is the Main Chrome Seam that marks the base of the Critical Zone, which is approximately 1100 meters thick, and contains most of the chromitite layers within the complex. Chromitite seams also occur in the ultramafic rocks within the westernmost lobe of the complex, a basin-like structure in which the overlying zones are absent. The chromite layers in this area are characterized by relatively lower iron and higher aluminum compositions, and as such represent valuable refractory ores.

Mineral layering is strongly developed within the Critical Zone, which consists mainly of interlayered pyroxenite, norite and anorthosite, in addition to the chromitite seams. The chromite reserves of the eastern Bushveld Complex, where the Critical Zone tends to be well exposed, probably aggregate to more than 1 billion tons. Cumulate layering of pyroxene, olivine, pyroxene plus plagioclase, plagioclase, and chromite has produced the various litho-units in the Critical zone, and individual cumulate chromitite layers vary from less than 1 cm thick in some instances to over 1 meter thick in others (Cameron and Desborough, 1969; Cameron, 1980). Although cumulate concentration is capable of explaining the formation of chromitite seams in broad terms, there are many problems related to a detailed understanding of the processes involved. Cameron (1980) has suggested that changes in oxygen fugacity induced mainly by interaction of magma with wallrock xenoliths were an important control of chromite crystallization.

The top of the Critical Zone is marked by the Merensky Reef, an extraordinary unit of pyroxenite mineralized with sulfides and bands of chromite that can be traced throughout much of the Complex (Cousins, 1969; Vermaak, 1976). It is remarkable not only for its lateral persistence, but for its content of platinoid metals, and represents the greatest ore reserve of these metals known. It is considered to represent the basal portion of a specific increment of magma to the complex that exhibits a clear pattern of magmatic differentiation and gravity accumulation.

The platinoid-bearing reef, which varies from centimeters to meters in thickness, occurs within pegmatitic pyroxenite in the western portion of the Bushveld Complex and pyroxenite in its eastern portion. The small amounts of non-silicate minerals in the Reef include the oxides chromite, magnetite, ilmenite, cassiterite, and rutile and the sulfides pentlandite, pyrrhotite, chalcopyrite, pyrite, cubanite, machinowite, and valleriite. The platinum minerals are mainly sulfides, the arsenide sperrylite, and ferro-platinum (Cousins, 1969), and nickel and copper contents of the Reef exhibit a good correlation with platinum values.

The Main Zone of the Complex is about 3,000 meters thick and consists of noritic rocks towards its base and gabbroic rocks in its upper parts. Due to the limited economic significance of this zone and its somewhat monotonous character it has received relatively little attention from geologists. The Upper Zone is separated from the Main Zone by a unit termed the Main Magnetite Seam (see Fig. 6.7), and consists of about 1,600 m of gabbros and ferrodiorites interlayered with lesser units of anorthosite, troctolite, and magnetite. Up to twenty seams of magnetite containing significant amounts of vanadium occur within this unit, but only a few of the major seams are of economic importance.

A whole series of pipe-like pegmatoid bodies of various types occur at different levels within the complex, and some of them host ore deposits. The most significant are three pipe-like bodies of hortonolite dunite within the Critical Zone that have been mined for platinum (Willemse, 1969). At higher levels within the complex, pipes of massive magnetite occur, but they have not been exploited, mainly because their content of vanadium is relatively low ($<1\%$).

Rb/Sr dating studies of the Bushveld Complex (Hamilton, 1977) indicate it was emplaced close to 2.1 b.y. ago. Initial $^{87}Sr/^{86}Sr$ ratios are relatively high (0.7056–0.7077) and increase in a stepwise manner up through the Complex. This could be taken to indicate progressive incorporation of radiogenic crustal strontium with time during its emplacement history, but it seems clear that the upper mantle source region for the magmas was characterized by a relatively high Rb/Sr ratio (Hamilton, 1977). It is also clear that the Complex represents a whole series of successive magmatic pulses, and that the mantle source regions must have been thermally perturbed in order to produce the requisite volumes of melt without associated rifting.

6.3.2 The Platinum Deposits of the Stillwater Complex, Montana

The Stillwater Complex is a layered mafic intrusion with a thickness of about 6,000 meters that exhibits similarities to the Bushveld in bulk composition, internal form and structure, mineralogy, and texture (Hess, 1960) (Fig. 6.8). A rather precise Sm-Nd age of 2.701 b.y. has been obtained for the Stillwater Complex by DePoalo and Wasserberg (1979), and although the tectonic setting into which the Stillwater Complex was emplaced during Archean time has been obscured by later events, it may well represent a manifestation of hotspot activity in an anorogenic setting.

The major tilting of the Complex which accounts for its present outcrop patterns did not occur until Laramide time. The lowermost portions consist of a thin noritic basal zone and an ultramafic zone 1,200 to 2,000 meters thick, comprising a succession of layers of bronzitite, harzburgite, and chromitite (McCallum et al., 1980). Above this are the Banded and Upper Zones, consisting of layers of norite, anorthosite, troctolite, and gabbro, but the contact between the Ultramafic Zone and these overlying units is not well defined (Jones et al., 1960). The Ultramafic Zone can be divided into two subzones of roughly equal thickness: an upper subzone of bronzitite, and a lower subzone consisting primarily of interlayered harzburgite and chromitite. The zones of chromitite typi-

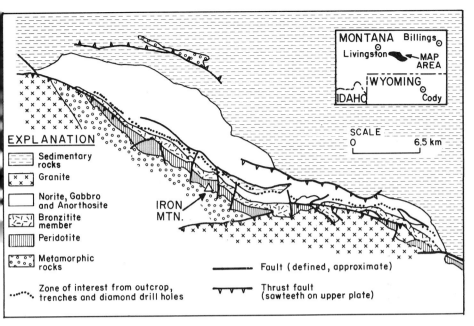

Fig. 6.8. Geologic map of the Stillwater Complex showing position of platinum-rich horizon near base of Banded and Upper Zone (from Conn 1979)

cally contain a lower massive chromitite layer overlain by a series of alternating chromite-rich and olivine-rich layers of cumulate origin (Jackson, 1969), and some of the massive chromitite layers attain thicknesses in excess of 1 meter and can be traced laterally for thousands of meters. Mining of some of these horizons has produced over 5 million tons of ore.

Exploration for platinum deposits stratigraphically higher in the Complex, based on the model of the Merensky Reef, has been successful (Conn, 1979), and a favorable zone containing minor copper-nickel sulfides with associated platinoid minerals has been traced for 39 km in anorthosites within the Banded Zone of the Complex. Estimated average grades range up to 22 gm/ton along significant portions of this zone.

6.3.3 The Copper-Nickel Ores of the Sudbury Irruptive, Ontario, Canada

The sulfide ores associated with the Sudbury Irruptive represent the world's greatest source of nickel (Naldrett, 1981). Mining of these ores has produced over 6 million tons of nickel, equivalent amounts of copper, and a significant amount of platinum and other precious metals. The Irruptive occurs as a roughly elliptical ring over 50 km long and 25 km wide of norite and overlying micro-

EXPLANATION

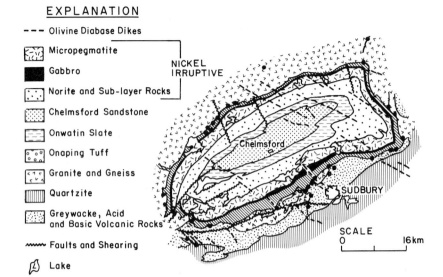

Fig. 6.9. Geological map of Sudbury Irruptive, showing location of nickel deposits (from Naldrett 1981)

pegmatite layers typically several kilometers wide in outcrop (Fig. 6.9). These igneous units separate the overlying sediments and volcanics of the Whitewater Series from the Archean basement rocks into which the Irruptive was intruded. Isotopic ages studies (reported in Pattison, 1979) indicate that the various units of the Irruptive were emplaced between 1.95 and 1.85 b.y. ago. They also exhibit relatively high initial Sr ratios and could thus, as is the case for the Bushveld Complex, have been generated from mantle enriched in radioactive (heat producing) elements.

The suggestions by Dietz (1964) and French (1970), that the Sudbury Irruptive was triggered by a meteorite impact, have gained wide, although by no means universal, acceptance. Nonetheless, it is generally agreed that the rocks and their associated nickel ores are of mantle provenance. The copper-nickel sulfide ores are not within the basal zone of the main norite as was originally supposed, but are associated with a series of sublayer intrusions along the basal zone, and dike-like bodies radiating outward from it (Souch et al., 1969; Naldrett et al., 1972; Pattison, 1979). Relationships between the sublayer intrusions, leucocratic breccias, and sulfide accumulations are complex and puzzling in detail, and the timing of the various intrusive events is still a matter of contention. Many orebodies occur within depressions or embayments within the floor of the Irruptive, and at such sites a sequence of massive sulfide containing mafic inclusions is typically succeeded upward by sulfides containing inclusions, and disseminated sulfides (Fig. 6.10). Significant orebodies also occur in the dike-like offsets within the underlying basement rocks (see Fig. 6.9).

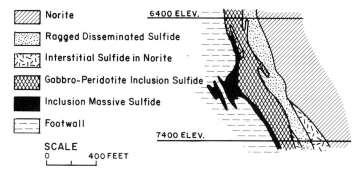

Fig. 6.10. Detailed section through the Creighton ore zone, Sudbury, showing relationships of massive and disseminated ores (from Souch et al. 1969)

Sudbury ores consist of varying proportions of pyrrhotite, pentlandite, and chalcopyrite accompanied by lesser amounts of pyrite, cubanite, and millerite. Many orebodies exhibit an increase in $Cu/Cu + Ni$ ratio toward the footwall and some exhibit marked increases in $Cu + Ni/Fe$ in the same direction (Naldrett and Kullerud, 1967).

6.3.4. Discussion

A number of other major mafic intrusive bodies are known, some of which contain metal deposits, but most of these can be more appropriately related to rifting events (see next chapter) as opposed to mere hotspot activity. The very large Dufek intrusion in Anarctica (Ford, 1975) may represent another example of a hotspot-related mafic intrusion, but its precise setting and ore potential are unknown. The three important mineralized complexes described above have been singled out as hotspot related because no evidence exists in each case that a rifting phase developed. Their suggested relationship to hotspot activity is admittedly speculative, but it is noteworthy that the mafic rocks of each are characterized by relatively high initial strontium ratios, suggesting the local presence of mantle unusually enriched in incompatible elements. The postulated hotspot activity that gave rise to them may thus represent some combination of structural or impact triggering mechanisms and anomalous conditions in the underlying mantle.

6.4 Metal Deposits Related to Carbonatites

Carbonatites, and their not too distant relatives kimberlites, represent a miniscule fraction of the total volume of igneous rocks, but they are of interest on a number of counts. Many, together with their associated alkaline rocks, exhibit

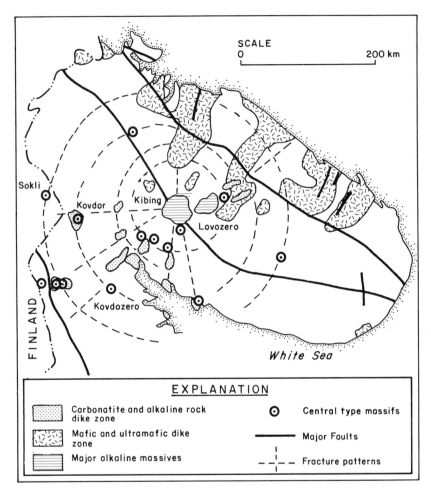

Fig. 6.11. Geologic map of main alkaline and mafic complexes, and structures of the Kola Peninsula, U.S.S.R. (modified from Belyayev and Uvad'yev 1978)

a broad spatial relationship to areas of hotspot-induced rifting (LeBas, 1977; Bailey, 1980), and Herz (1977) has related Brazilian carbonatites and their associated igneous rocks to the events preceding and accompanying creation of the South Atlantic. The older (Paleozoic) carbonatites and alkaline massifs of the Kola Peninsular (Fig. 6.11) also appear to represent direct products of hotspot activity (Mitchell and Garson, 1981). Despite their limited volume, carbonatites and their associated mafic alkaline rocks are widely scattered on most continents and embrace an age span of from 2 b.y. ago until the present.

Numerous metals, elements and non-metallic minerals, are enriched and locally concentrated in carbonatites (Semenov, 1974). These include niobium,

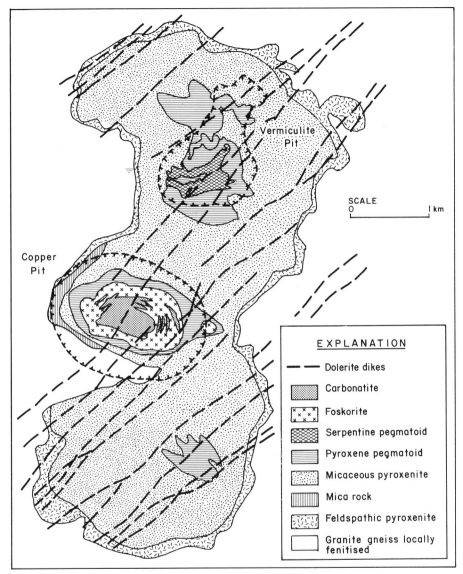

Fig. 6.12. Generalized geologic map of the Palabora Igneous Complex. The disseminated copper ores are mined by open-pit methods from the Loolekop carbonatite area (from Palabora Mining Company Staff 1976)

iron, titanium, copper, rare earth elements, apatite, fluorite, and vermiculite. However, only a few carbonatite complexes contain significant deposits of the more conventional metals, notably the Kovdor alkalic/ultramafic complex in the Kola Peninsula and the Palabora Complex in South Africa. The Kovdor complex contains relatively small amounts of carbonatite, but iron ore reserves of about 700 million tons and apatite reserves of 110 tons are being actively mined from it (Northolt, 1979).

The Palabora carbonatite in South Africa contains 300 million tons of copper ore grading 0.69% Cu, in addition to important economic deposits of apatite and vermiculite (Palabora Mining Company Ltd staff, 1976). The Palabora igneous complex consists primarily of a large, irregularly elongate body of micaceous pyroxenite (~ 6 km $\times 2.5$ km) intruded in its central portion by various phases of carbonatite (Fig. 6.12). The disseminated copper mineralization is associated with the last phase of an irregular dike-like carbonatite intrusion and occurs also as numerous veinlets within the surrounding carbonatites and pyroxenites. Chalcopyrite and bornite are the major sulfide minerals in the orebody, but some cubanite, pyrrhotite and various nickel, cobalt, copper, lead, and zinc sulfides occur in very small amounts. Valleriite, an interlayered copper-iron sulfide and magnesium-aluminum hydroxide mineral, was formed as a late stage phase, mainly along broad shear zones cutting the orebody. It replaces all other ore and gangue minerals, and its presence is detrimental to good copper recovery in the concentrator.

The age of the Palabora complex is thought to be essentially the same as that of the Bushveld Igneous Complex, and thus it can be viewed as a manifestation of the same episode of hotspot activity that gave rise to the Bushveld. The Bukusu carbonatite complex in Uganda contains small amounts of chalcopyrite (Baldock, 1969), but the Palabora deposit is unique as a major carbonatite-related copper resource. It should be emphasized that this deposit, although of disseminated type, is quite distinct from porphyry copper deposits in terms of its tectonic setting and igneous rock associations.

6.5 Afterword

The various deposits and their associated igneous rocks that have been suggested as having a relationship to mantle hotspot activity in this chapter are indeed diverse, and it could be argued that this diversity seriously impairs the credibility of much of the foregoing. However, the precise manifestation of mantle hotspot activity on overlying crust will surely depend on a number of parameters. For example, some hotspots may represent mantle plumes (Morgan, 1972), whereas others may be generated by a surfeit of heat-producing elements within a particular patch of subcontinental mantle (Anderson, 1975). Other factors, such as supercontinental assemblies and distance from spreading ridges (Sawkins, 1976a), longevity and intensity of hotspot activity, and access routes to the surface can all vary in individual cases. When all these possible variables are acknowledged, it is less surprising that the final manifestations of hotspot activity display considerable heterogeneity.

Chapter 7   Metal Deposits Associated with
the Early Stages of Continental Rifting

7.1 General Considerations

As we have seen in previous chapters, rifting activity in oceanic and arc environments can be associated with the generation of certain types of metal deposits, but in this chapter I will consider metal deposits that tend to form in continental rift settings. As stated so aptly by Mohr (1982), "sufficient unto rift valleys are the existing models thereof." Mohr stresses the complexity and variability of rift systems and the need to re-examine some of the notions regarding rifting that have become entrenched in the minds of many workers. He demonstrates, for example, that the stratigraphic record, where legible, does not always support the notion of prior updoming, and that the development of suites of exotic alkaline rocks is not a universal feature of rift development.

The plethora of rifting models that have been proposed are perhaps an indication that extensional tectonics and rifting in continental environments can be manifest in a variety of ways. McKenzie (1978), for example, has suggested that formation of all large sedimentary basins must involve some degree of crustal thinning and therefore necessitate tensional tectonics.

Burke et al. (1981) provide an excellent brief summary of continental rifts, and stress that they are both more common than previously recognized and can develop in a variety of tectonic settings. Four basic types of rifts are recognized: (i) rifts formed by continental rupture, (ii) failed rifts at Atlantic-type margins, (iii) aulacogens, and (iv) impactogens. Given the continuum of plate tectonic processes, the first three of these rift types represent variations on a single theme, and due to either Wilson Cycle or ensialic collision events (see Chap. 9), most rift sequences developed by continental rupture eventually become enmeshed in orogenic belts and may be difficult to recognize. Aulacogens, defined originally by Shatski (1947), are rifts striking into fold belts, but must have originally been failed rifts at Atlantic-type margins (Burke, 1977). Impactogens also strike into fold belts, but differ from aulacogens in that they form as a consequence of a collision event, rather than during initial rifting that is eventually followed by collision (Sengor et al., 1978).

Two basic concepts of mantle involvement in continental rifting and its associated volcanism have been advanced. One envisions rifting as a result of differential stresses in plates resulting from their interaction. The initiation of rift-

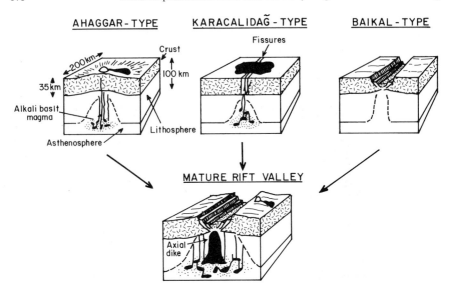

Fig. 7.1. Sketches illustrating how a mature rift valley may evolve from three different origins. In the Ahaggar-type, the mantle is active and uplift and volcanism precede rifting. In the Baikal type, the mantle is passive and rifting is not preceded by doming or volcanism. The Karacalidag-type is more complex with fissure formation and magmatism prior to major down-faulting (from Burke et al. 1981)

ing perturbs the underlying mantle and volcanism, generally limited in extent, follows rifting. This situation fits observations available from impactogens such as the Rhine Graben and the Baikal Rift rather well. The other concept of rift initiation envisions an active rather than passive role for the underlying asthenosphere and volcanism predates the initiation of rifting. Such appears to have been the case with rift systems of East Africa where a combination of underlying mantle convection and reactivation of old structures (McConnell, 1974) controlled rift development. This mechanism, by which the coincidence of mantle hotspots or convection and older flaws in the continental lithosphere result in rifting, is probably the more general cause of continental breakup and the formation of failed rifts that eventually become aulacogens (Burke and Dewey, 1973; Dewey and Burke, 1974). It must be appreciated, however, that a mature rift valley can originate from either active, passive, or more complex crust-mantle involvement (Fig. 7.1). Finally, the outstanding feature of rift systems is the great thickness of sediments and volcanics that they tend to contain.

Despite the systematics outlined above, rift systems are complex objects and dichotomies abound in their interpretation. The Keweenawan Rift System (Wold and Hinze, 1982) and associated Mid-Continent Gravity High in the United States, for example, has long been considered a classic example of Proterozoic continental rifting, and Chase and Gilmer (1973) presented an elegant plate tectonic model for its origin. Recently, however, Green (1983) has claimed a marked lack of evidence for any rift-type faulting along this system, and has attempted to demonstrate that plateau basalts filled an elongate basin formed by downwarping rather than faulting. Another problem, exemplified by the Devonian to Carboniferous terrains of central and western Europe (Ziegler, 1978), is the differentiation between true intracontinental rifting events and those related to behind-arc rifting. This is particularly the case in Europe because the terrains in question have been deformed and metamorphosed by subsequent tectonothermal events and are largely covered by younger formations (see later).

The difficulty inherent in any meaningful attempt to relate metal deposits to rifting environments through much of earth history is thus the recognition of such environments in terrains where much of the critical evidence is obscured by later tectonic events. Furthermore, rifting has to be viewed in a broader context than merely the development of graben or parallel-sided rift valleys, and should include all environments resulting from attentuation of continental crust. On the other side of the coin it is all too tempting in some cases to interpret certain lithologic sequences in terms of rifting where the available evidence does not warrant this. An understanding of the spectrum of rift-related metal deposits can help in this regard, for it has become abundantly clear that metallogenesis is an important facet of rifting activity (Vokes, 1973; Russell, 1968; Sawkins, 1976b, 1982a). Thus, the presence of a metal deposit similar to others of clear rift association justifies the search for additional evidence of rifting within the surrounding terrain.

Dewey and Burke (1973) have emphasized that continental rifting is a necessary initial step in the operation of Wilson Cycles, but whether all the ancient orogenic belts that now lie in continental interiors are the products of Wilson Cycle tectonics, or whether the concept of ensialic orogeny has validity, is a matter for considerable debate (Kroner, 1977a; Martin and Porada, 1978) (see Chap. 9). If a supercontinent did exist for a significant portion of Proterozoic time, as argued by Piper (1982), then the operation of Wilson Cycle tectonics involving large ocean basins during that period becomes problematic. However, many of the orogenic belts now locked into the fabric of the continents, whatever their precise evolutionary history, were demonstrably initiated by continental rifting events, and thus represent viable terrains for exploration for rift-related metal deposits.

I have attempted to divide continental rift-related deposits into those that tend to be formed during the early stages of rifting and those formed during the more advanced stages of rifting. The division is somewhat arbitrary, especially when dealing with older deposits, but in general the basins formed by rifting or tensional events tend to evolve from an initial terrestrial sedimentation stage through a shallow marine to a deeper marine stage. The transition from shallow marine to deeper marine roughly coincides with a break in the spectrum of metal deposits associated with rifting environments.

7.2 Hydrothermal Copper Deposits

Copper deposits of clear epigenetic hydrothermal origin are relatively rare in continental rift environments, but they do represent a recognizable facet of rift-related metallogeny. Examples of minor hydrothermal copper mineralization are known from the Zambian copper belt (Darnley, 1960) and the Coppermine River area, Canada (Kindle, 1972), and more substantial deposits occur within the Keweenawan rift province (Robertson, 1975; Norman, 1978) and in the Messina district, South Africa (Sawkins, 1977). These rift-related copper deposits differ significantly from those in arc systems not only in their tectonic setting, but also in terms of their mineralogy and associated host rock alteration.

7.2.1 The Messina Copper Deposits, South Africa

The breccia pipe and replacement copper deposits that are mined in the vicinity of Messina have to date produced over 300,000 tons of copper metal from ores that, on average, grade close to 3% Cu. The district lies within the third (failed) arm of the Lower Limpopo triple junction of Burke and Dewey (1973) (Fig. 7.2). The deposits occur in a linear array more or less along the Messina Fault that cuts across high grade metamorphic rocks of the Limpopo mobile belt. These metamorphic rocks form a horst block within the broader confines of the Limpopo rift structure.

The geology of the Messina copper deposits has been described by Bahnemann (1972) and Sohnge (1946). More recently, alteration studies were carried out by Jacobsen and McCarthy (1976), and fluid inclusion and isotopic studies by Sawkins (1977) and Sawkins and Rye (1979). During the rifting and igneous events that signalled the breakup of Gondwanaland, voluminous basalts and lesser rhyolites were erupted along the Sabi and Lebombo Monoclines (see Fig. 7.2) and probably covered the entire area of the Limpopo rift. In addition, a line of ring complexes of bimodal character, known as the Nuanetsi igneous province, was emplaced along a northeast-southwest trend (Cox et al., 1965). An age range for these igneous rocks of approximately 210 to 170 m.y. is indicated by rubidium-strontium data (Manton, 1968).

The orebodies of Messina form a linear array, as noted earlier, and occur as either replacement bodies (Artonvilla Mine) or within large breccia pipes (Fig. 7.3). The three replacement orebodies in the Artonvilla area occur as elongate pipes confined to mafic units in a sequence comprising cordierite and pyroxenegarnet granulites. They exhibit structural control by minor warps on the flank of a steeply plunging F_1 fold. Early stage hydrothermal activity caused silica dissolution and formation of a central core of albite surrounded by a sericite envelope, and was followed by intense chloritization, and formation of epidote, copper sulfides, iron oxides, and quartz. As noted by Jacobson and McCarthy (1976), the orebodies exhibit an unusual concentric zoning with chal-

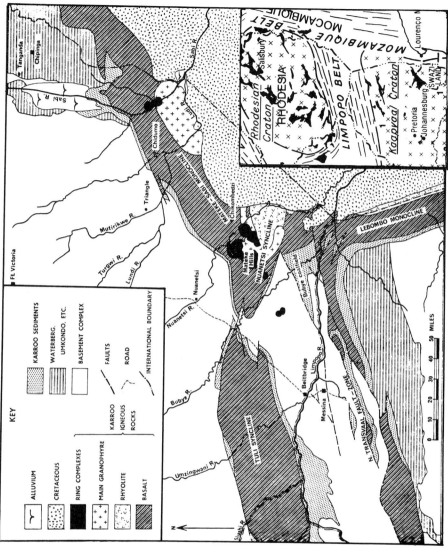

Fig. 7.2. Map of Lower Limpopo triple junction showing Lebombo and Mateke-Sabi Monoclines and the Messina horst within the third (failed) rift arm (from Sawkins 1977)

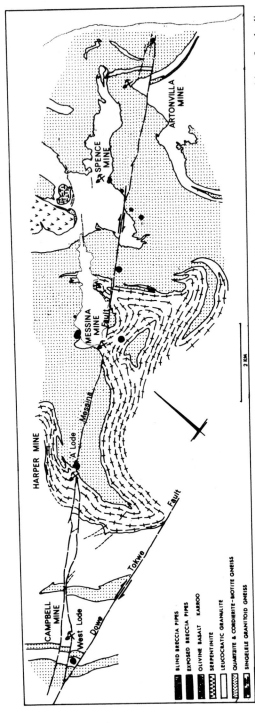

Fig. 7.3. The Messina copper district showing the position of the various breccia pipe and replacement (Artonvilla Mine) deposits. Note position of orebodies along or adjacent to Messina Fault (from Sawkins 1977)

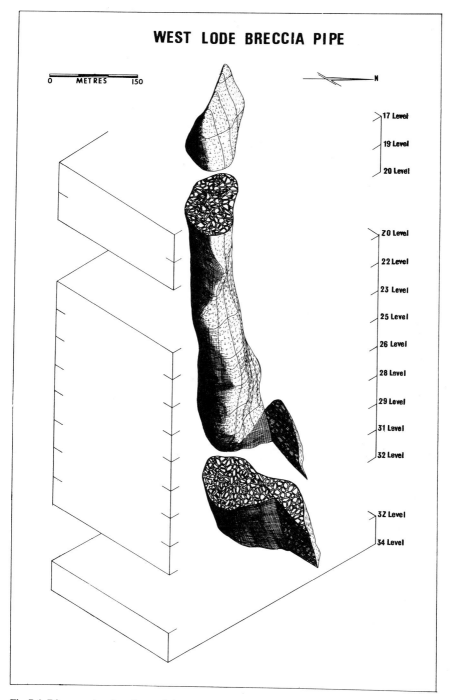

WEST LODE BRECCIA PIPE

0   METRES   150

N

17 Level

19 Level

20 Level

Z0 Level

22 Level

23 Level

25 Level

26 Level

28 Level

29 Level

31 Level

32 Level

3Z Level

34 Level

Fig. 7.4. Diagram showing shape of the West Lode breccia pipe. Note upward termination of the pipe, suggesting formation by a solution-collapse rather than an explosive mechanism (from Jacobsen et al. 1976)

cocite in the central, most altered zone, and succeeded outward by bornite and then chalcopyrite. Pyrite is minor and occurs mainly around the margins of ore-bodies.

The breccia orebodies occupy the uppermost portions of large breccia pipes, most of which terminate prior to reaching the surface (Fig. 7.4). Downward movement of fragments can be demonstrated by comparison of the lithologies of some blocks with those in the surrounding rocks. In general, the breccia fragments are little altered, but pink albite and quartz, accompanied by lesser epidote, clinozoisite, chlorite, and copper sulfides, occupy the intersticies between fragments. Where filling was incomplete, zoned quartz crystals locally containing occluded specularite, epidote, and copper sulfides are developed. Deposition was terminated by local formation of calcite. The copper sulfides within the pipes are zoned, with chalcopyrite present in the uppermost parts and bornite at deeper levels.

Fluid inclusion and stable isotope studies (Sawkins and Rye, 1979) have demonstrated that mineralization was effected by low temperature aqueous fluids (130–210 °C) with salinities that varied from 1 to approximately 26 equivalent wt% NaCl. $\delta^{18}O$ values of the aqueous fluids (calculated from $\delta^{18}O_{qtz}$ values and fluid inclusion temperature data) indicate they ranged from -0.4 to -8.4, whereas δD values obtained directly from inclusion fluids ranged from -39 to -56. These numbers suggest the ore fluids were relatively unexchanged meteoric water.

Sawkins and Rye (1979) suggested a genetic model for the Messina orebodies that envisages the leaching of copper from overlying copper-rich rift basalts (see Sawkins, 1976b) by meteoric fluids, some of which attained high salinities by evaporative concentration of rift valley playa lakes. These fluids were involved in convective geothermal systems in and close to the Messina Fault system. The high heat flow typical of active rift systems was important in providing the thermal energy to drive the convection. This scenario is perhaps an unusual one for the genesis of copper deposits, but it is supported by the unusual temperature, salinity, and stable isotope data available, and the mineralogic and alteration relationships. The breccia pipes are seen as solution collapse features formed by dissolution of hostrocks by initial circulation of convecting alkaline meteoric waters.

7.2.2 Discussion

The copper-bearing breccia pipes of the Tribag mine, Ontario (Blecha, 1965) were formed by higher temperature, more saline fluids and appear to be more closely related to the emplacement of felsic magma at an important structural intersection within the Keweenawan province (Norman, 1977). They also have zones of disseminated molybdenite associated with them, and thus may be transitional to rift-related disseminated molybdenum deposits (see later).

The association of hydrothermal copper deposits with rift environments is a relatively limited one, but the fact that several of the important Messina orebodies are blind upward suggests that important copper deposits of this type may await discovery in other rift terrains.

7.3 Rift-Related Molybdenum Deposits

It has been demonstrated in Chap. 3 that Climax-type molybdenum deposits can be related to rifting events on the innermost side of the North American convergent plate boundary. The Oslo Rift in Norway has long been known to contain vein-type molybdenum mineralization (Ihlen and Vokes, 1977) and recently the presence of porphyry type molybdenum mineralization has been recognized (Geyti and Schonwandt, 1979). Occurrences of generally weak molybdenum mineralization are widespread in the Oslo Rift and are almost exclusively associated with subalkaline granitic intrusives (Fig. 7.5), but the porphyry-type mineralization is restricted to cauldron intrusions or ring structures within batholithic intrusions.

At the Bordvika occurrence within the Glitrevann cauldron, two quartz-feldspar-porphyries and an aplitic granite occupy the central parts of the cauldron and have recently been recognized as ignimbrite units (R.H. Sillitoe, pers. comm.). Broad areas of hydrothermal alteration are developed along the shores of the Glitrevann Lake at the northern extremity of these porphyry and aplite bodies, and involve four alteration types: 1) K-feldspar alteration as a stockwork of millimeter wide veins; 2) sericitic alteration as selvages along veins containing quartz-sericite-pyrite and as pervasive host rock alteration, 3) argillic alteration in the form of intense replacement of feldspar phenocrysts by clay minerals; and 4) propylitic alteration in the form of veinlets and cavity fillings of chlorite plus calcite accompanied locally by epidote and/or fluorite. The K-feldspar alteration is only known from one locality, and the sericitic alteration is the most prominent and widespread type of alteration. The propylitic zone is difficult to map but, as with most porphyry-type mineralization, represents the distal facies of alteration.

Molybdenite occurs as both veinlet fillings and disseminations within the areas of K-feldspar and sericitic alteration, and in some samples attains grades of 0.5 percent Mo. Whether these molybdenum occurrences within the Oslo Rift will ever support viable bulk mining operations remains to be seen, but their presence does indicate that the porphyry molybdenum potential of subvolcanic granitic complexes within continental rift systems elsewhere in the world should not be overlooked. The Malmbjerg porphyry molybdenum occurrence in central East Greenland represents a good example of such mineralization and contains approximately 200 million tons grading 0.25 MoS_2 (Nielsen, 1976). The mineralization occurs within and adjacent to a Tertiary alkali granite associated

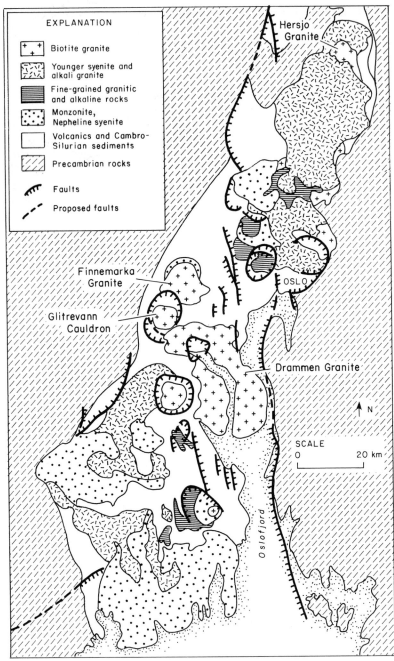

Fig. 7.5. Simplified map of the Oslo Graben showing major granitic intrusives and cauldron complexes. Disseminated molybdenum mineralization is mainly associated with the biotite granites, especially those in the Glitrevann cauldron (modified from Gaut 1981)

with syenites that form part of the East Greenland igneous province associated with Atlantic rifting. Were this deposit less isolated it would represent an important source of molybdenum.

7.4 Rift-Related Stratiform Copper Deposits

Copper deposits in which the ore minerals are confined to specific shale or sandstone horizons represent a well-defined ore type, and are second only to porphyry copper deposits in terms of global resources of this metal (Gustafson and Williams, 1981). They tend, however, to contain ore grades that are distinctly higher than those of typical porphyry copper deposits. I believe that such deposits can be meaningfully differentiated from other sediment hosted copper deposits such as Mt. Isa (see later) on a number of counts. Stratiform copper deposits are disseminated rather than massive in character, tend to have distinctive mineralogy and zoning patterns, and unlike most sediment-hosted massive sulfide deposits contain relatively insignificant amounts of associated lead and zinc sulfides. Lead-zinc deposits can, however, occur in similar settings, but within hostrocks of different lithology (see later). Stratiform copper deposits occur in all the continents and encompass an age range from 2.0 b.y. to Miocene (Table 7.1). There is, however, a significant concentration of deposits in Upper Proterozoic lithologic sequences (Rowlands, 1980; Sawkins, 1983).

7.4.1 Lithologic Setting

Most of the major deposits of this type, such as those of the Zambian copper belt (Mendelsohn, 1961), the Kupferschiefer (Rentzsch, 1974), and at Lubin, Poland (Konstantynowidz, 1973), occur within the first marine transgressive unit laid down after a period of redbed sedimentation. In other deposits, exemplified by Udokan, U.S.S.R. (Samonov and Pozharisky, 1977) and Dzhezkazgan, U.S.S.R. the lithologic settings are somewhat less distinctive, but the deposits occur in shales, sandstones or dolomitic units, typically of drab color, within redbed sequences.

In many instances there is evidence for the former presence of evaporites in the immediate section (Gustafson and Williams, 1981), and, in the case of the Zambian deposits and the Kupferschiefer, carbonate units are present up section. In other cases, such as the stratiform copper deposits in the Adelaide Geosyncline, marine lithologies characteristic of the more advanced stages of rifting are developed up section (von der Borch, 1980).

The general lithoenvironments in which stratiform copper deposits occur can be considered typical of the early stages of rifting in stable continental interiors (Raybould, 1978), and perhaps the clearest example of this is the Miocene Boleo deposit in Baja California (Wilson, 1955), where a clear association between initial rifting of the Gulf of California, deposition of the host sed-

Table 7.1. Stratiform Copper Deposits

Deposit or District	Age	Host rocks	Lithology	Rifting	Reference
Basal Cretaceous, Angola	Cretaceous	Cuvo-formation	Mudstone and siltstone	Association with South Atlantic rifting	Van Eden (1978)
Mansfeld copper deposits, Central Europe	Permian	Kupferschiefer	Black shale	Basin and range type faulting, basalt-rhyolite (see reference)	Lorenz and Nicholls (1976)
Aynak copper deposits, northeastern Afghanistan	Infracambrian	?	Metasandstone metadolomite	Association with formation of Tethys Ocean	Sillitoe (1980d)
White Pine, Michigan, U.S.A.	1.0 b.y.	Nonesuch Shale	Gray-marou shale	Keweenawan basaltic magmatism	White (1968)
Spar Lage, Montana U.S.A.	Late Proterozoic	Revett Formation	White quartzite and siltite	Thick sedimentary sequence, basaltic magmatism	Harrison (1972, 1974)
Seal Lake, Labrador, Canada	Late Proterozoic	Adeline Island Formation	Gray-green shales	Thick clastics, associated basalts	Gandhi and Brown (1975)
Coppermine River N.W.T. Canada	Late Proterozoic	Rae Group	Gray-green glauconitic sandstone	Thick clastics, associated basalts	Kindle (1972)
Redstone Copper Belt N.W.T. Canada	Late Proterozoic	Redstone River Formation	Siltstones and carbonates	Normal faulting, associated basalts	Eisbacher (1977)
Zambian Copper Belt Central Africa	Late Proterozoic	Ore shale, Lower Roan Formation	Argillite and impure dolomite	Sediment thickness changes, time equiv. Bukoban basalts	Mendelsohn (1961)
Witvlei and Klein Aus mines, Namibia	Late Proterozoic	Wituki Formation, Nosib group	Greenish-grey argillite	Thick clastics, underlying basalts	Toens (1975)
Adelaidean copper province, South Australia	Late Proterozoic	Lower Willouran, Adelaidean System	Dolo-siltstones carbonaceous dolo-arenites	Thick clastics underlying basalts	Rowlands (1974)
Kilembe Mine Uganda	Early Proterozoic	Kilembe Series	Meta-siltites	Thick meta-clastics, underlying metabasalts	Davis (1967)
Udokan, U.S.S.R.	Early Proterozoic	Udokan Series	Siltstones, sandstones	Thick clastics	Samanov and Pozharisky (1977)

iments, and their mineralization can be postulated. Igneous rocks, where present in these rift related sequences, are invariably basaltic in composition and in some instances, especially in the Keweenawan area, underly the sedimentary section in which the stratiform deposits are hosted (Norman, 1978). In fact, in virtually all cases known to the writer, some evidence of basaltic magmatism is present within or near the basins in which stratiform copper deposits occur.

7.4.2 Mineralization

As stated earlier, a characteristic feature of stratiform copper deposits is the disseminated nature of the mineralization. Another characteristic feature is the high copper:iron ratios in the ores, and in many deposits chalcocite and bornite are significant ore minerals whereas pyrite is typically minor or absent within the orebodies. In fact, the distribution of copper and iron sulfide minerals in stratiform copper deposits in many cases exhibits well-defined zonal characteristics. At the White Pine Mine, Michigan (Brown, 1971), and in the Kupferschiefer in the Mansfield district (Rentzsch, 1974), an upward zoning of copper minerals from chalcocite, and even native copper, to digenite, bornite and finally chalcopyrite is manifest (Fig. 7.6). Above the chalcopyrite zone any lead, zinc, and cadmium present in the ores tend to occur together with syngenetic pyrite in the reduced shale hostrocks (Brown, 1980).

In other deposits, especially those of the Zambian copper belt, somewhat similar zoning patterns are found, but here the transition from chalcocite to bornite to chalcopyrite has been interpreted in terms of zoning outward from paleoshorelines. In detail, however, mineralogical zoning in many Zambian orebodies is complex and not easily understood solely in terms of paleoshorelines (see later). Certain stratiform copper deposits tend to contain notable amounts of silver and cobalt in their ores, and the silver exhibits a close correlation with copper minerals rather than with galena, which is present in both the Kupferschiefer and Dzhezkazgan ores. Cobalt is particularly important in the central African stratiform copper deposits of Zambia and Zaire and this region represents a major world source of that metal.

7.4.3 Ores of the Zambian Copper Belt

The Zambian copper belt and the related deposits of neighboring Zaire represent an extraordinary concentration of copper metal in this portion of the African continent. In Zambia well over 1.5 billion tons of ore, containing on average approximately 3 percent copper and locally significant cobalt, have been discovered, and there are also major amounts of sub-economic copper mineralization known in the area. Orebodies are of tabular shape and typically about 2,000 meters long and tens of meters thick. Hostrocks for the disseminated ores are of two types, shales and arenites, with about 60% of the ores occurring in shales.

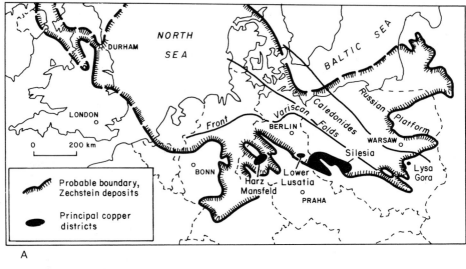

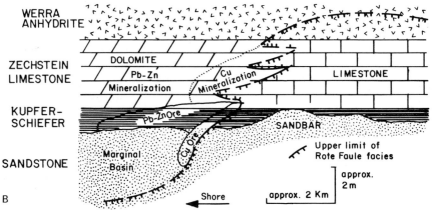

Fig. 7.6 (A) Map of the present extent of the marine Zechstein deposits in western and central Europe showing position of the principal known copper districts (modified from Rentzsch 1974). **(B)** Generalized cross section to illustrate transgressive metal sulfide zoning within and adjacent to the Kupferschiefer. Note extreme vertical exaggeration of section (modified from Rentzsch 1974)

The ores occur predominantly within the Lower Roan sedimentary rocks of the Katanga Supergroup, and are arrayed in two roughly linear belts separated by the Kafue anticline along the southeastern extremity of the Lufilian arc (Fig. 7.7). To the west, this fold belt swings westward and probably connects with the Damarides of Namibia. These Katangan sedimentary sequences are preserved in synclines and basins formed by northward directed compressive forces between the Kibaran massif to the west and the Bangwenlu massif to the north-

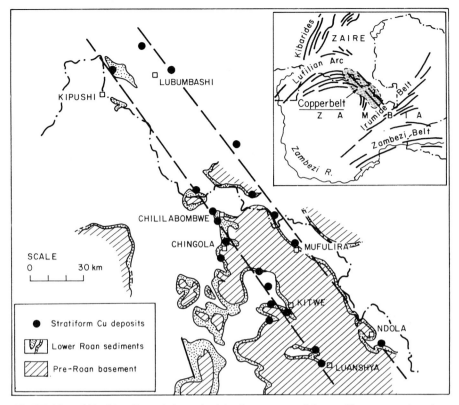

Fig. 7.7. Map of Zambian Copperbelt emphasizing linear arrays of the stratiform copper deposits. Within Zambia the deposits in the eastern trend tend to be sandstone-hosted (e.g., Mufulira), whereas those in the western trend tend to be shale-hosted deposits (from Raybould 1978)

east. The development of crossfolds produced a series of roughly equant domes and basins in the region. Metamorphism decreases in intensity towards the northeast, and the epidote-amphibolite isograd slices at a low angle across the southwestern line of copper deposits.

The Katangan sedimentary successions are separated from the basement schists, arenites and granites by a major unconformity (Mendelsohn, 1961) (Fig. 7.8). The lowermost units above the unconformity consist of conglomerates, talus scree, and presumed aeolian sandstones, and their distribution and textures attest to a rugged basement topography. Subsequently, shallow marine and littoral deposits and local algal bioherms formed as a northeastward directed marine transgression occurred. These pass upward into sandstones and shales, and most of the former contain carbonate and sulfate minerals. Broadly speaking, the Lower Roan clastics are overlain by Upper Roan dolomites and dolomitic argillites containing some anhydrite beds, and in some areas these

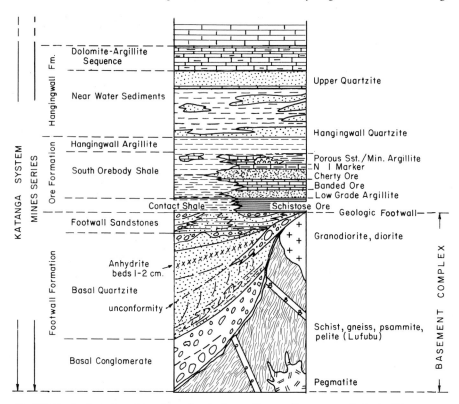

Fig. 7.8. Idealized stratigraphic column for the Lower Roan sedimentary rocks in the Kitwe area, Zambia. The stratiform copper mineralization in this area is restricted to the shaly and carbonate units of the Ore Formation (modified from Clemmey 1974)

Upper Roan units have been invaded by massive gabbro sills. Up section are dolomite and carbonaceous and pyritic shale, a diamictite of probably glacial origin, limestones and dolomites and finally pyritic shales grading upward into massive arenites.

Although evidence for synsedimentary faulting has yet to be described, the succession is typical of a magmatically 'dry' continental rift system. It is of some significance, in terms of the possible origin of the copper, that at the time the Lower Roan sediments were accumulating (~ 1.0 b.y., Cahen et al., 1971), the copper-rich Bukoban basalts and associated sediments were probably undergoing erosion in southern Tanzania (Harris, 1961; Cahen, 1970). These basalts and sediments contain abundant evidence of copper mineralization and were originally probably considerably more extensive than their present area of outcrop. Some authors (e.g., Pienaar, 1961; Wakefield, 1978), however, have noted the copper-rich nature of the basement rocks, and suggested them to be the source of the copper in the Katangan sediments.

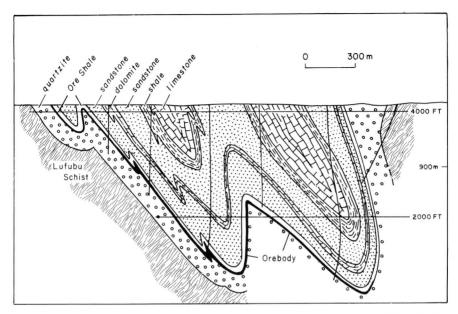

Fig. 7.9. Section through part of the Roan extension orebody showing marked restriction of mineralization to the lower portions of the ore shale and its considerable extent (from Fleicher et al. 1977)

The orebodies of the Roan Antelope mine (Fig. 7.9) are typical of copper mineralization hosted in shales. The Ore Shale unit here varies in thickness from 17–55 m. It is not uniformly mineralized, but in some localities the lowermost two thirds of the Ore Shale contains disseminated chalcocite and bornite, whereas in some others two separate orebodies, the Lower and Upper Orebodies, are separated by barren pyritic shales. These orebodies extend for many kilometers and exhibit sulfide mineral zoning patterns that have been interpreted in terms of transgressive and regressive events superimposed on a basic shoreline control (Fig. 7.10).

The Mufulira ores provide good examples of sandstone hosted mineralization. Here, three main orebodies, A, B, and C, occur in a sandstone unit 30 to 80 m thick (Fig. 7.11). These host sandstones contain quartz and feldspar and each appears to represent an initial high energy sedimentation event followed by quieter conditions. Margins of orebodies are controlled by changes in sediment type (upward), and by changes from clean mineralized arenites to dirty barren ones (laterally).

The mineralogic zoning patterns in these sandstone ores are quite distinctive from those of shale ores, and basement topography apparently exerted a significant control on the sites of orebody development. Sandstones containing only pyrite occur over paleohighs, whereas the richest orebodies occur on the flanks

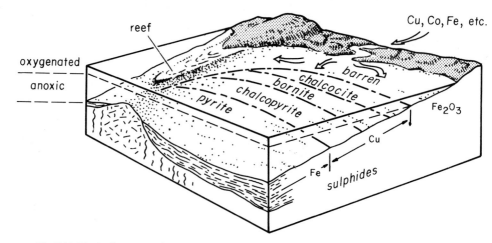

Fig. 7.10. Block diagram to show one suggested explanation for the mineralogic and metal zoning patterns observed in shale-hosted Zambian copper deposits (from Fleischer et al. 1976)

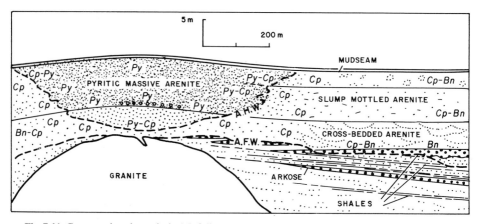

Fig. 7.11. Cross section through the Mufulira west ores. Note that the mineralogic zoning patterns of sulfides in these sandstone-hosted ores are essentially the reverse of those observed in shale-hosted Zambian deposits. A.H.W. and A.F.W. refer to assay hanging wall and assay foot wall respectively (from Fleischer et al. 1976)

of these highs (Fig. 7.12). Clearly, such zoning patterns cannot be explained in terms of the same shoreline control claimed for the shale-hosted ores.

The important ores of the Shaba Province of Zaire occur in the northwestern extremity of the Katangan belt, and further west in the essentially similar rocks of the Mines Series. Cahen (1970) has demonstrated that deposition of these sedimentary rocks probably occurred close to 1 b.y. ago. The Mines Series is dominated by dolomitic units, however, and this led earlier works to correlate

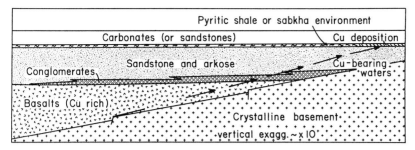

Fig. 7.12. Conceptual model linking copper-rich rift basalts and the formation of stratiform copper deposits. The basalt source-rocks may lie below the host rocks of the copper ones (White Pine) or could be exposed nearby (Zambian copper belt)

it with Upper Roan units in Zambia. Stratiform copper ores, containing significant cobalt, occur in siliceous dolomites (Francois, 1974), but in addition important uranium-copper-cobalt-nickel ores (e.g., Shinkolobwe) occur in vein-type ores in faulted and brecciated areas. It seems possible that these ores represent remobilization of originally stratiform metal concentrations (Cahen et al., 1971).

7.4.4 Discussion and Suggestions for Exploration

Although concrete evidence for rifting during the accumulation of the Katangan sedimentary successions in Zambia and Zaire is not available, many of the analogous stratiform copper deposits listed in Table 7.1 have clearly formed in environments controlled by rifting (Sawkins, 1976b). The Adelaide Geosyncline, for example, has been shown to have strong parallels to post-Permian rifts in terms of its tectonic evolution (van der Borch, 1980), and the stratiform copper deposits of the Kupferschiefer and the Dzhezkazgan region, U.S.S.R., that are related to Permian rifting events, are essentially similar to stratiform copper deposits of Proterozoic age. Small stratiform copper deposits also tend to occur in continental redbeds deposited in non-rift settings (e.g., Creta, Oklahoma; Ripley et al. 1980; Coro-coro, Bolivia; Petersen, 1970), but these are of little consequence in comparison with rift-related examples.

The reason that rift environments are so favorable for the generation of stratiform copper deposits appears to stem from the coincidence of four features that tend to be common to rifting environments: 1) the copper-rich nature of rift basalts (Table 7.2); 2) the presence of sharp Eh boundaries in rift sedimentary environments; 3) the operation of tensional faulting during rift sedimentation; and 4) the enhanced heatflow characteristic of rift environments. Thus, not only are suitable copper sources and traps available, but permeability factors, both in terms of the sediments and the structures, are such that the copper can readily migrate from sources to traps. The enhanced heatflow can be

Table 7.2. Copper in Hotspot and Rift-Related Basalts

Locality	Average Cu content in basalts (ppm)	References
Kilauea, Hawaii	207	Prinz (1967)
Kap Stosch, Greenland	197	Noe-Nygaard and Pedersen (1974)
Faeroes Islands	> 200	Bollingberg et al. (1975)
Columbia River		
(1) Picture Gorge	160	McDougall (1976)
(2) Grande Ronde and Imnaha Valley	57	
Dolerite sills, Tasmania	Up to 160	McDougall and Lovering (1963)
Keweenawan, Michigan	126	Cornwall and Rose (1957)
Coppermine River, N.W.T.	126 (excluding Cu-rich flow tops)	Baragar
Parana traps, Brazil	149	Ruegg (1976)

Modified slightly from Sawkins (1976b)

expected to promote both the leaching of the copper and the migration of the fluids that transport it.

Another interesting aspect of stratiform copper deposits is the strong concentration of this type of mineralization in late Proterozoic sedimentary sequences (see Table 7.1). The prime cause of this concentration is probably mainly a function of the widespread rifting events that occurred about a billion years ago (Sawkins, 1976a). However, it may also in part reflect atmospheric evolution. The solubility of copper in natural waters, especially the chloride and sulfate brines predictable in rift environments (Robbins, 1983), is controlled by redox reactions, and prior to about 1 b.y. ago most circulating groundwaters may not have been sufficiently oxidizing to effect significant redistribution of copper. The approximately 2 b.y. age of the very large Udokan stratiform copper deposit (Kratz and Mitrofanov, 1980), however, belies this latter argument.

The precise mode of genesis of stratiform copper deposits is still a matter of contention in many instances. However, Brown (1971) has demonstrated rather convincingly that the sulfide mineral zoning patterns of the White Pine deposit, Michigan, can be interpreted in terms of the flushing of copper-rich formation water across the overlying pyritic Nonesuch Shale, probably shortly after its deposition. Geologists working on the Zambian Copper Belt, however, have largely remained adamant in their support of a purely syngenetic deposition of the copper minerals (e.g., Garlick and Fleischer, 1972). This is questioned by Annels (1974), who noted an antipathetic relationship between anhydrite and sulfides in both shale and sandstone hosted ores, and suggested the sulfides formed by replacement of anhydrite. Renfro (1974) has emphasized the role of evaporite minerals such as anhydrite in many stratiform copper deposits, and proposed a model involving deposition of the copper by replacement in a sabkha environment. In actuality, both synsedimentary and/or syndiagenetic depositional processes probably occur in the formation of individual stratiform copper deposits.

In terms of exploration, two major points can be extracted from the data base. Firstly, stratiform copper mineralization is a relatively common feature of early rift sedimentary sequences, and secondly, the first reduced sedimentary unit above an oxidized clastic sequence overlying the basement tends to host such mineralization. In addition, the early sedimentary sequences of late Proterozoic rift environments should be carefully prospected for stratiform copper deposits. In areas where outcrops are sparse, such as the Zambian Copper Belt, applied geochemical techniques involving soil, and in some instances geobotanical, samples have been used with considerable success to locate mineralized horizons (Ellis and MacGregor, 1967).

7.5 Rift-Related Magmatic Copper-Nickel Deposits

As discussed in Chap. 6, certain large, layered mafic intrusions can be related to subcontinental mantle hotspots. Other mafic intrusions, however, provide evidence of emplacement during rifting events, and some important copper-nickel deposits occur within such complexes. As Naldrett (1981) and Naldrett and MacDonald (1980) have pointed out, the two most significant examples of such magmatic copper-nickel ores are those of the Noril'sk-Talnakh region of the U.S.S.R. (Glaskovsky et al., 1977) and the mineralization associated with the Duluth Complex, Minnesota, U.S.A. (Weiblen and Morey, 1980). A rift-related origin is also indicated for the mafic and ultramafic intrusions and associated copper-nickel mineralization of the Pechanga Belt of the Kola Peninsula, U.S.S.R. (Glaskovsky et al., 1977).

A rift setting for the important copper-nickel deposits of the Thompson Belt, Manitoba Canada (Peredery and Geological Staff, 1982), the copper-nickel mineralization of the Ungava Belt, Canada (Barnes et al., 1982), and the ores of the Limpopo Belt, Botswana (Gordon, 1973) is more tenuous. However, the Ungava Belt represents a thick pile of basaltic volcanics and minor sediments between the Churchill Province gneisses to the north and the Superior Province gneisses to the south and thus a rifting environment seems probable (Hynes and Francis, 1982). A series of ultramafic komatiitic intrusions has invaded this sequence and many of these contain disseminated oregrade copper-nickel sulfides along their basal contact (Barnes et al., 1982).

The copper-nickel deposits of both the Thompson and Limpopo Belts occur within high-grade linear orogenic belts, and thus original tectonic environments are obscure. It is noteworthy, however, that in both areas emplacement of the ore-bearing mafic intrusions was restricted to sedimentary cover rocks. In the case of the Thompson Belt, this occurred at 2.0 ± 0.1 b.y., based on Rb/Sr isotopic studies (Brooks and Theyer, 1981). Such patterns of cover rock sedimenta-

tion and subsequent major tectonism and metamorphism involving remobilization of crystalline basement rocks are thought to be a common feature of rift-
ing-initiated intracratonic orogenic belts (Sawkins, 1982a).

7.5.1 Copper-Nickel Deposits of the Noril'sk-Talnakh Region, U.S.S.R.

Clearer and more important examples of rift-related magmatic copper-nickel
deposits are those of the Noril'sk-Talnakh region in the northwest corner of the
Siberian Shield. Here the mafic hostrocks are related to the extensive intracratonic igneous events that produced the Siberian Traps, a late Permian to
Triassic effusion of flood basalts. The mafic host intrusions were emplaced
along a north-northeast trending zone of active blockfaulting adjacent to the
deep Yenisei and Khatanga Troughs, to the west and north respectively
(Glaskovsky et al., 1977). Both these troughs contain about 10,000 meters of
sedimentary fill and are underlain by thinned continental crust (Tamrazyn,
1971).

The ore-bearing intrusions, many of which are associated with the Noril'sk-
Kharadakh Fault (Fig. 7.13), typically consist of differentiated picrite and picrite dolerite grading upwards to slightly more felsic compositions. They are sill-
like in form and attain lengths of 12 km and thicknesses of 30–350 m. The cop-
per-nickel-platinoid mineralization occurs in relatively persistent ore horizons,
and consists of disseminated and massive accumulations of pyrrhotite, pentlandite, and chalcopyrite in the lower portions of these mafic intrusions. Sulfide
disseminations and veins are also present locally in footwall rocks. The ores in
the Noril'sk area are lower grade than at Talnakh and mining operations are
now concentrated in this latter area.

The sedimentary country rocks in the region are Carboniferous and Permian
continental sediments and coal measures underlain by Devonian and Carboniferous limestones and evaporites. The evaporites are thought to have played an
important role in ore formation in terms of providing a source of sulfur for the
mafic magmas (Naldrett, 1981). This notion is strongly supported by $\delta^{34}S$ data
on ore sulfides which indicate values of $+7$ or greater (Godlevskii and Grinenko, 1963; Kovalenko et al., 1975). The incorporation of sulfur from sedimentary
sources has also been demonstrated as a factor in the development of copper-
nickel mineralization near the base of the Duluth Complex, Minnesota (Mainwaring and Naldrett, 1977).

7.5.2 Discussion

The geologic settings of the copper-nickel deposits of the Thompson Belt,
Manitoba, and the Limpopo Belt, southern Africa appear vastly different from
those of the Noril'sk-Talnakh, U.S.S.R. and Duluth, Minnesota areas. The major differences, however, may be essentially due to differences in their histories
subsequent to the rifting environments in which they formed.

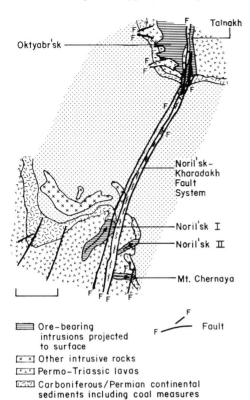

Oktyabr'sk

Talnakh

Noril'sk –
Kharadakh
Fault
System

Noril'sk I

Noril'sk II

Mt. Chernaya

Fig. 7.13. (A) Schematic geology of the Noril'sk-Talnakh nickel districts, U.S.S.R. (from Naldrett and Macdonald 1980). **(B)** Cross section through the Noril'sk I deposit (modified from Glaskovsky et al. 1977)

Ore-bearing intrusions projected to surface

F Fault

Other intrusive rocks

Permo-Triassic lavas

Carboniferous/Permian continental sediments including coal measures

Devonian/Carboniferous evaporites and limestones

A

West   East

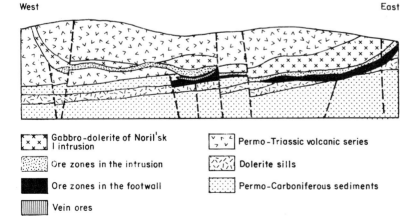

Gabbro-dolerite of Noril'sk I intrusion

Ore zones in the intrusion

Ore zones in the footwall

Vein ores

Permo-Triassic volcanic series

Dolerite sills

Permo-Carboniferous sediments

B

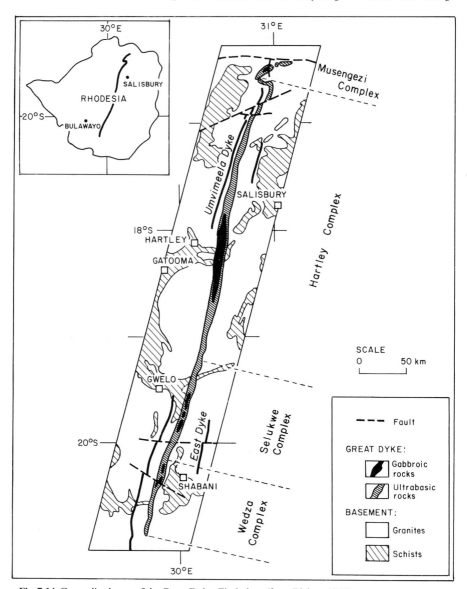

Fig. 7.14. Generalized map of the Great Dyke, Zimbabwe (from Bichan 1969)

It is perhaps interesting that the proportion of mafic meta-igneous rocks in high grade orogenic terrains such as the Thompson and Limpopo Belt is relatively small. Furthermore, no extensive terrains of high-grade mafic rocks have been described (at least to the knowledge of this writer). This in turn suggests that magmatically 'wet' intracontinental rifts (e.g., Keweenawan Rift, Cape

Smith-Wakeham Bay) have less tendency to develop at a later stage into high grade metamorphic belts than magmatically 'dry' rifts. This observation may be invalid due to erosional factors, but the possibility that large scale basaltic magmatism somehow defuses later orogenic activity perhaps merits further investigation.

The tendency of sulfur-rich sedimentary rocks such as evaporites to form in rift environments is well established, as is the tendency for basaltic magmatism. It thus seems possible that additional situations where the juxtaposition of these two elements has occurred in a rift setting (e.g., Noril'sk-Talnakh), may await the attention of the exploration geologist.The Great Dyke, Zambia (Vail, 1977) (Fig. 7.14) is not noted for its copper-nickel mineralization, but deserves mention at this juncture as the oldest (2.6 b.y.) known example of a failed continental rift system. It is, however, the host for important stratiform chromite deposits (Bichan, 1969).

7.6 Carbonate-Hosted Lead-Zinc Deposits in Relation to Rifting

This broad group of sulfide deposits is a diverse one and includes Mississippi Valley-type deposits, Alpine-type deposits, and Irish-type deposits (Sangster, 1976). Many workers would claim that this group of deposits manifests no relationship to either plate tectonics or magmatic activity, and although this may be true in a number of instances, in others a persuasive connection with rifting events can be made (Sawkins, 1976b). Mitchell and Garson (1981) point out that carbonate-hosted, lead-zinc deposits most commonly occur in sedimentary successions deposited either on shelf areas (passive continental margins) or in intracratonic areas.

While readily acknowledging the tenuous nature of possible connections between most groups of carbonate-hosted lead-zinc deposits and plate tectonics, I intend in the following sections to review their occurrence and distribution, and at least explore the possible connections they may exhibit to plate tectonics.

7.6.1 Mississippi Valley-Type Deposits

Lead-zinc deposits of this type are, not surprisingly, widely distributed within the stable central region of the United States, but important examples (Guild, 1974) are also known in Arctic Canada (Kerr, 1977), northwest Canada (Kyle, 1981), northern England (Sawkins, 1966), Poland (Sass-Gustkiewicz et al., 1982), and in the U.S.S.R. (Smirnov, 1977). In addition important carbonate-hosted zinc deposits occur in the south Appalachians (Kyle, 1976; Hoagland, 1976) outside of the Mississippi Valley proper. A variant of Mississippi Valley-

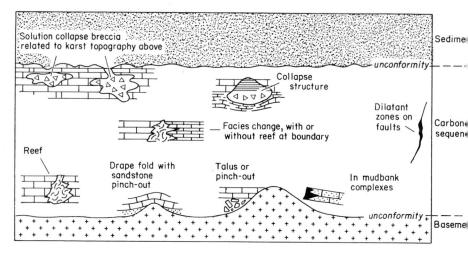

Fig. 7.15. Illustraton of the various types of geologic situations in which carbonate-hosted lead-zinc deposits of Mississippi Valley-type can occur (modified from Callahan 1967)

type deposits are sandstone-hosted lead deposits (Bjorlykke and Sangster, 1981), but these will be discussed briefly in the following chapter. The U.S. deposits occur within essentially undeformed cover rocks ranging in age from Cambrian to Carboniferous and are unequivocally epigenetic in origin. Despite their broad similarity in lithologic setting, low temperature of formation (Roedder, 1976) and basic lead-zinc composition, Mississippi Valley-type deposits display considerable variability. For example, zinc-lead ratios in some ore districts are > 10 and in others < 1, some deposits contain important amounts of copper, and the association of the lead and zinc sulfides with barite and/or fluorite is pronounced in some instances and essentially nonexistent in others. Despite these variables and variations in the morphology of individual orebodies (Fig. 7.15), Mississippi Valley-type deposits do form a distinctive ore type.

Although much remains to be learned about the precise details of their genesis (Ohle, 1980), several important points can be extracted from the available data base on Mississippi Valley-type deposits. For example, they tend to form on the flanks of or above basement highs, and from fluid inclusion studies it is clear that saline connate waters expelled out of adjacent basins form a major component of the ore-forming fluids. In addition, the deposits in many districts occur in carbonate rocks adjacent to either sandstone beds, paleokarst features, or faults; all capable of acting as aquifers for large scale fluid movement.

A clear time-space relationship to rifting can be indicated for the lead-zinc deposits in Cretaceous sediments of the Benue Trough (Farrington, 1952; Grant, 1971), and for the minor deposits of lead and zinc in Miocene sediment along the Red Sea (Dadet et al., 1970) (Fig. 7.16). Such cannot be claimed for the deposits within the Mississippi Valley area proper, but many of these lie

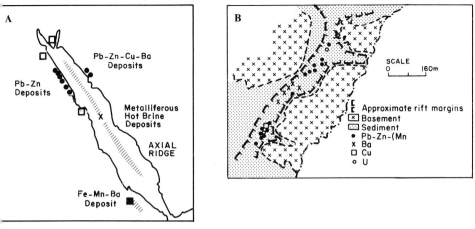

Fig. 7.16. Distribution of Mississippi Valley-type and manganese deposits adjacent to the (**A**) Red Sea and within the (**B**) Benue Through rift systems. These are perhaps the best examples of a relationship between rifting and generation of Mississippi Valley-type deposits (from Olade 1980)

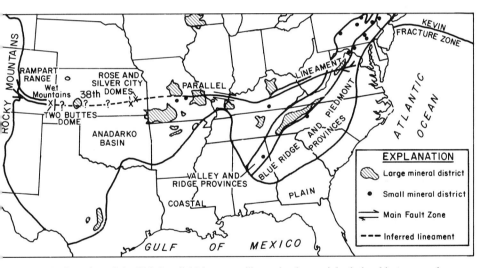

Fig. 7.17. Location of the 38th Parallel Lineament illustrating its spatial relationship to a number of major Mississippi Valley ore districts (from Heyl 1972)

along the 38th parallel lineament (Heyl, 1972) (Fig. 7.17) a zone characterized by numerous alkalic and mafic-alkalic centers. Similarly, the Mississippi Valley-type deposits of the Pennines in England (Dunham, 1948; Sawkins, 1966) apparently developed during latest Carboniferous time (Moorbath, 1962), when mafic and alkali magmatism was prevalent in the Midland Valley of Scotland just to the north (Francis, 1968).

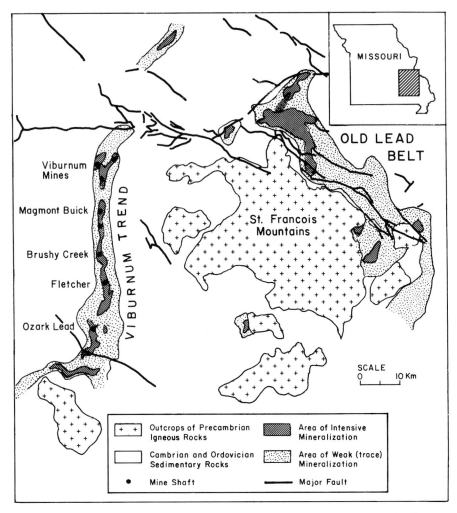

Fig. 7.18. Generalized map of southeast Missouri showing location of major Mississippi Valley ore districts surrounding the St. Francois Mountains basement high. The entire Viburnum Trend, which currently accounts for major lead, zinc, and lesser copper production, lies entirely in the subsurface (modified from Kisvarsanyi 1977)

In economic terms the most important Mississippi Valley ore district is that of the Viburnum Trend, southwest Missouri (see Econ. Geol., v. 72, no. 3). Here, over 100 million tons of lead-zinc ore have been discovered, mainly within the last two decades, and the Viburnum Trend is currently the world's most productive lead district (Vineyard, 1977). In 1974, the district accounted for 85 percent of U.S., and 15 percent of world lead production. The district consists of

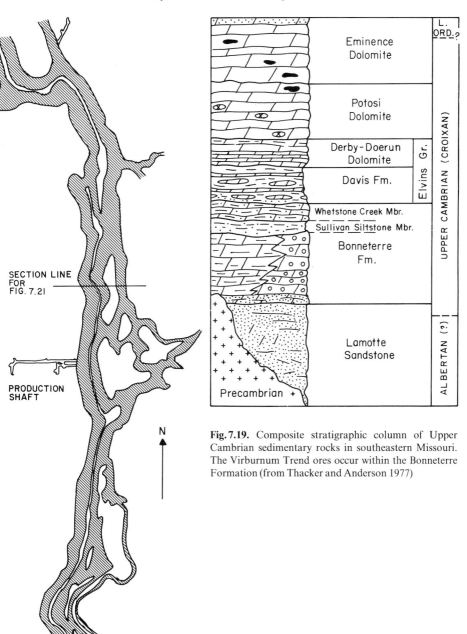

Fig. 7.19. Composite stratigraphic column of Upper Cambrian sedimentary rocks in southeastern Missouri. The Virburnum Trend ores occur within the Bonneterre Formation (from Thacker and Anderson 1977)

Fig. 7.20. Plan of the breccia ore bodies, Buick Mine, Viburnum Trend (from Rogers and Davis 1977)

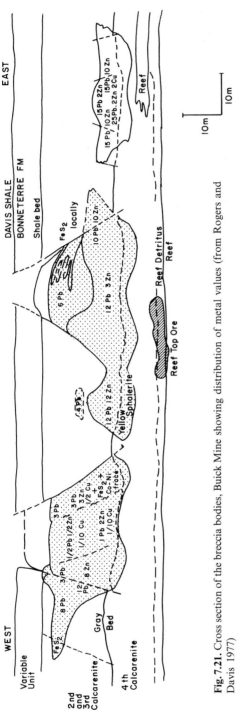

Fig. 7.21. Cross section of the breccia bodies, Buick Mine showing distribution of metal values (from Rogers and Davis 1977)

a virtually continuous, narrow, north-south trending belt of mineralization west of the St. Francois Mountains, a Precambrian basement high (Fig. 7.18).

The ores are distinctly lead rich and lead/zinc ratios vary from about 3 to > 10, and locally, they contain significant amounts of copper and minor nickel- and cobalt-bearing sulfides. The ore trend occurs within the Cambrian Bonneterre Formation, a complex unit consisting mainly of calcareous micrites and calcarenites. Algal reef facies are present in the Bonneterre Formation along parts of the Viburnum Trend and are locally important as an ore-bearing lithology. Below the Bonneterre Formation is the Lamotte Sandstone, lying unconformably on the Precambrian volcanic and crystalline rocks (Fig. 7.19). This unit is a typical transgressive basal sand of irregular thickness, consisting primarily of fine- to medium grained rounded quartz particles (Thacker and Anderson, 1977).

The Buick ore zone (Rodgers and Davis, 1977) runs for over 8 km along the north-central portion of the Viburnum Trend, and is demarcated to the north and south by property lines rather than grade considerations. The sulfide ores occur largely in solution-collapse breccias within dolomitized calcarenites of the upper Bonneterre Formation, which, in the mine area, overlies algal stromatolite reef facies of the lower Bonneterre.

The main orebodies within the Buick Mine consist of narrow, continuous zones of sulfide mineralization developed in breccia bodies that are sinuous and locally branch or rejoin along the trend (Fig. 7.20). These collapse breccias are thought to have developed along lithologies representative of paleointratidal, drainage channels, and they attain dimensions of almost 100 m in width and 25 m in thickness (Rodgers and Davis, 1977). A typical section across the mineralization trend in the Buick Mine indicates three breccia ore zones, each with distinctive metal content and zoning characterizations (Fig. 7.21). In detail, paragenetic relationships are complex and include evidence of periodic sulfide leaching.

Fluid inclusion data on sphalerites from Viburnum Trend ores (Roedder, 1977) indicate the ore fluids were very saline brines at temperatures mainly in the range 94–120 °C, and as such, they appear to be typical Mississippi Valley-type ore fluids. Sverjensky (1981) carried out detailed studies on the Buick ores, including sulfur and lead isotopic work, and found that $\delta^{34}S$ values for sulfides exhibit a range of values from 21.3 to 0.9% and exhibit covariance with lead isotopic data. These results led Sverjensky to conclude that both the sulfur and lead were transported by the same ore fluids, and that much of the sulfur was of evaporitic (sulfate) origin. Ultimate sources of the base metals in these and most other Mississippi Valley-type deposits remain conjectural, however.

7.6.2 Alpine-Type Lead-Zinc Deposits

The series of lead-zinc deposits hosted by mid-Triassic carbonate units in the eastern Alps (Maucher and Schneider, 1967) have come to be known as Alpine-

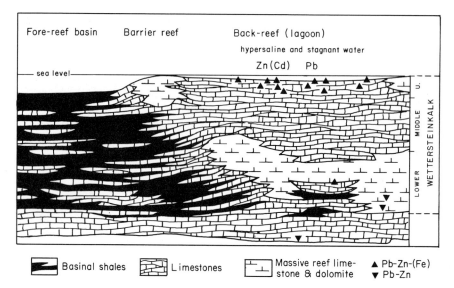

Fig. 7.22. Generalized cross section to illustrate geologic setting of many of the Alpine lead-zinc deposits (simplified from Maucher and Schnieder 1967)

type deposits, and essentially similar deposits also occur in the Atlas Mountains in north Africa. These deposits appear to be of fairly typical Mississippi Valley affiliation, but their tectonic setting can be related to widespread rifting events in the area.

From early Triassic times until the early Cretaceous the Mediterranean area was characterized by a series of continental rifting events, followed by oceanic rifting (D'Argenio and Alvarez, 1980), and although the precise age of Alpine-type mineralization is not known, the deposits must have formed during this time interval. Furthermore, they typically occur in reef or back-reef facies carbonate units that developed on highstanding crustal blocks adjacent to deep shale basins (Fig. 7.22), and it appears probable that fluids migrating upward from these basins to the adjacent reefs formed the deposits. While more remains to be learned about these deposits, they do appear to represent a good example of carbonate-hosted lead-zinc deposits generated in an environment characterized by rifting.

7.6.3 Irish-Type Lead-Zinc Deposits

The series of important lead-zinc-barite ($\pm$ copper) deposits in Ireland are hosted in lower Carboniferous carbonate units, and include the Navan orebody which contains 10 million tons of zinc and lead metal. Studies of these deposits, notably by Russell (1968, 1975, 1978), have demonstrated that the ores are

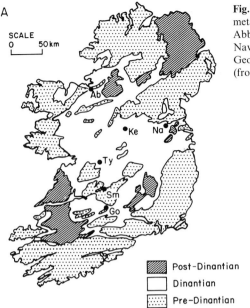

A

SCALE
0   50 km

Post-Dinantian
Dinantian
Pre-Dinantian

Fig. 7.23. (A) Map showing principal base metal deposits of Ireland. Ty, Tynagh; Ab, Abbeytown; Go, Gotdrum; Ke, Keel; Na, Navan; Ke, Keel (from Boast et al., 1981). **(B)** Geologic cross-section of the Tynagh deposit (from Boast et al. 1981).

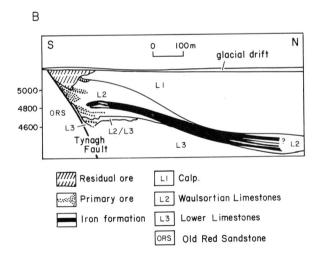

B

Residual ore   L1   Calp.
Primary ore   L2   Waulsortian Limestones
Iron formation   L3   Lower Limestones
                     ORS   Old Red Sandstone

largely of synsedimentary or syndiagenetic origin, and formed near reef complexes adjacent to active portions of major faults in a shallow, saline marine environment (Fig. 7.23).

Russell and Smythe (1983) propose that the ores formed during a sudden onset of rifting and local basaltic magmatism that occurred 360 million years ago.

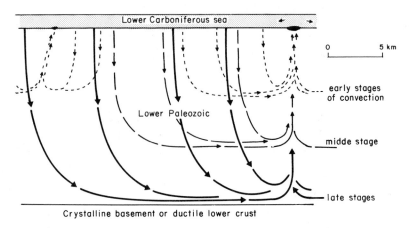

Fig. 7.24. Russell's concept of development of geothermal systems that progressively impinge deeper into the underlying sedimentary column. Fault control of the discharge plumes is envisaged (from Russell 1978)

The metals involved are thought to have been garnered from the thick underlying lower Paleozoic geosynclinal prism by downward-penetrating convection cells of saline seawater, and then brought to the surface to form 'exhalative' deposits (Fig. 7.24). These Irish-type deposits are thus distinctive in many respects from Mississippi Valley-type deposits, and are perhaps best viewed as a deposit type intermediate in character between Mississippi Valley-type deposits and the sediment-hosted massive sulfide deposits described in the following chapter.

This suggestion is strengthened by recent studies of the Tynagh deposit (Boast et al., 1981, and references therein) which support a mode of formation of the Tynagh lead-zinc-silver ores by forceful injection of metalliferous fluids into coherent Waulsortian carbonate mudbanks during their diagenesis. Boast et al. recognize four stages in the development of ores: (1) formation of colloform and granular pyrite clots during early diagenesis, (2) precipitation of microcrystalline sphalerite, galena, barite, and dolomite within a dilatant fracture system developed by hydrofracture within the mudbanks, (3) veining and replacement of tennantite, chalcopyrite, bornite, arsenopyrite, and coarse galena and barite, and (4) calcite precipitation and dolomitization of Waulsortian limestones. The fluids responsible for mineralization are considered to have risen along the contemporaneously active Tynagh fault (Fig. 7.23) prior to spreading outward to the north.

Stable isotope data reported by Boast et al. indicate that local seawater provided the sulfate for barite precipitation, and that the sulfides of stages 1 and 2 were precipitated by isotopically light sulfur apparently derived from bacterial reduction of seawater sulfate. During stage 3, however, an influx of heavier reduced sulfur ($\delta^{34}S \leqq 0\%$) of deepseated origin which mixed with bacteriogenic sulfur is indicated. Oxygen isotope data pertaining to stage 3 mineralization suggest mixing of an isotopically heavy ($\delta^{18}O = 10.5\%$) water from the Tynagh fault with isotopically lighter water present in the bank limestones.

7.6.4 Discussion and Suggestions for Exploration

It is clear from the foregoing that carbonate-hosted lead-zinc ores represent a widespread, somewhat diverse group of deposits. They are largely restricted in their occurrence to Phanerozoic cover-rocks in stable continental interiors, but some Proterozoic examples are known (Sawkins, 1983; Clayton and Thorpe, 1982; Hewton, 1982). The important lead-zinc $\pm$ copper deposits of northern Namibia (Anhaeusser and Button, 1974), for example, include both replacement and breccia-filling types, similar to those of the Mississippi Valley, and also types similar to the Irish deposits. These different groups have been shown recently to be distinguishable on the basis of lead isotope studies (M. Hughes, pers. comm.). Similarly, certain small epigenetic lead-zinc deposits of Proterozoic age in the McArthur River area, Queensland, Australia have been designated as Mississippi Valley-type (Williams, 1978), and both these, and the important Proterozoic Nanisivik deposit, northern Baffin Island (Clayton and Thorpe, 1982), can be related to rifting environments.

Carbonate-hosted lead-zinc deposits in metamorphic terrains, such as the Balmat-Edwards orebodies in Grenville marbles (Lea and Dill, 1968) and the Black Angel Mine, Greenland (Pedersen, 1980) cannot be assigned to specific tectonic environments at their time of formation, but the low silver contents of their ores, their dolomitic host rocks, and the absence of nearby intrusions all suggest mineralization of Mississippi Valley- or Irish-type (Sawkins, 1983).

Precise models for the genesis of Mississippi Valley-type and other carbonate hosted lead-zinc deposits have remained elusive, but it does seem clear that the ore fluids are, at least in major part, basinal brines. This concept is reinforced by reports of lead- and/or zinc-rich formation waters at Cheleken, USSR (Lebedev, 1972), in central Mississippi (Carpenter et al., 1974), and in Alberta, Canada (Billings et al., 1969). Whether the development of such brines and their migration to basin edges is a normal part of basin evolution, or special attendant circumstances are required to create the ores is not clear at present. Thermal perturbation of the basins involved may be necessary and, in this regard, Ohle (1980) states that "The existence of heat plumes cannot be doubted." Furthermore, Hanor (1979) demonstrates that, although saline brines essentially similar in chemistry to Mississippi Valley ore fluids will tend to evolve in the deeper portions of intracratonic basins, thermal events are probably necessary to cause their migration to basin edges. Some connection with alkaline igneous rocks is supported by the well-documented enrichment of barium and fluorine in alkaline magmas, and a similar connection to mafic igneous rocks is suggested by the presence of minor cobalt and nickel in many Mississippi Valley ores.

Exploration for carbonate-hosted lead-zinc deposits involves careful evaluation of carbonate cover-rock sequences, mainly in continental interiors where topographic and structural relief are typically small and outcrops limited. In particular, carbonate units adjacent to potential aquifers that lie on the flanks of basement highs deserve consideration as potential target areas. It is also worth noting that many districts (e.g., Upper Mississippi Valley, Viburnum Trend) occur near the interface between limestone and dolostone in the host unit, the dolostone occurring on the structurally higher, basin-edge side of the mineralization.

Chapter 8   Metal Deposits Related to
           Advanced Stages of Rifting

8.1 General Observations

The variability in styles of rifting makes generalization of the more advanced stages of rifting a hazardous exercise. Nevertheless, broad patterns can be recognized. If the rifting is destined to result in creation of a new ocean basin, it will at a certain point produce a narrow seaway similar to that of the present Red Sea. Other rifts that fail may only do so after they have evolved from an early stage of subareal and very shallow marine sedimentation to deep, starved basin type environments. Still others may receive sufficient supplies of sediment

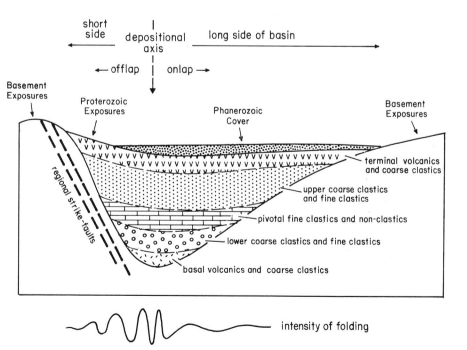

Fig. 8.1. Geometry and gross mirror-image stratigraphic succession of a typical Proterozoic sedimentary-volcanic basin on the Southern African Craton (from Pretorius 1981a)

to build up great thicknesses of sedimentary rocks (> 10 km) without acquiring deep marine environments.

Pretorius (1981a) has argued that many Proterozoic basins have resulted from half-graben development, and demonstrated that such basins tend to have a sedimentary fill that is symmetrical about a pivotal fine clastic and chemical facies developed roughly at the midpoint of the total succession (Fig. 8.1). Although such basins cannot perhaps be considered rifts *sensu stricto*, they do represent a manifestation of extensional tectonics in continental environments.

Another variable in terms of continental rifting and basin development is that of time, and many of these features appear to have existed as at least intermittent repositories for sediment accumulation for hundreds of millions of years. The most logical explanation for such gradual, long-lived subsidence is gradual cooling and contraction of the athenospheric wedge postulated by many to be the initial cause of rifting or extension (e.g., Sleep and Snell, 1976).

8.2 Metalliferous Deposits of the Red Sea

The discovery of hot brine pools in the median valley of the Red Sea in the mid-sixties generated considerable interest (Degens and Ross, 1969), especially when it was shown that sulfide-rich muds of considerable economic potential existed below one of these pools (Hackett and Bischoff, 1973). Thirteen occurrences of either brine pools and/or metalliferous sediments are known scattered along the northern and central segments of the Red Sea (Fig. 8.2). All are located along the axis of spreading where the median valley is best developed, and Bignell (1975) has pointed out that most of these occurrences are located where faults, inferred either from bathymetric data or from continuation of continental fracture lines, cross the median valley.

Studies of the history of the Red Sea (Girdler, 1969) have shown that the main Red Sea graben formed in earliest Miocene time and that a sequence of clastics and evaporites were deposited within it. Opening of the Red Sea to its present width has been a somewhat episodic process, but indications are that spreading has been occurring at about 1 cm/yr over the last 3 million years (Vine, 1966). Micropaleontologic analysis of cores taken from the Red Sea (Berggren, 1969) suggest that increased salinity episodes occurred several times during the last 85,000 years, and that these probably correlate with times when circulation with the Indian Ocean was restricted.

Although a number of occurrences of hot brines are known in the Red Sea axial trough, it should be emphasized that they exhibit considerable variation in terms of chemistry and brine temperature, and their associated metalliferous sediments vary in mineralogy, and sulfide and metal content. Of those known, only the metalliferous sediments of the Atlantis II deep are of possible economic interest (Bignell et al., 1974).

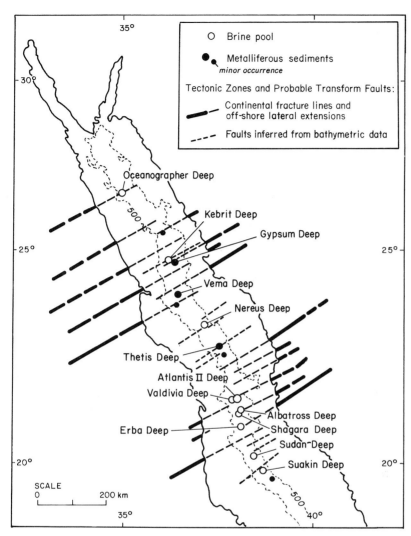

Fig. 8.2. Location of brine pools, metalliferous sediments, and probable transform faults and related structures in central and northern Red Sea (from Bignell 1975)

8.2.1 Metalliferous Deposits of the Atlantis II Deep

Core sampling of the sediments below the Atlantis II hot brine pool, which lie at close to a depth of 2,000 m, has demonstrated that metalliferous sediments averaging 20 m in thickness occur over an area of approximately 50 km² (Hackett and Bischoff, 1973) (Fig. 8.3). The sulfide-rich layers are one meter to several meters thick, but form beds several kilometers long, and are estimated to con-

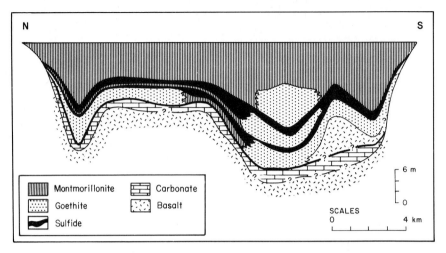

Fig. 8.3. Generalized cross-section of the geothermal deposits in the Atlantis II Deep, Red Sea. Note strong vertical exaggeration (from Hackett and Bischoff 1973)

tain 100–200 million tons of material grading 3.5 percent zinc, 0.8 percent copper and significant silver values, on a dry, salt-free basis. The overlying brines have a salinity of 256 g/kg, and exhibit maximum temperatures of about 60 °C. It is believed that subsurface brine temperatures are above 200 °C (Shanks and Bischoff, 1977).

The metalliferous sediments within the Atlantis II Deep form a relatively thin veneer above the basaltic basement (see Fig. 8.3), and consist of fine-grained thin bedded oxides, silicates, sulfides, sulfates, and carbonates, although two main sulfidic layers contain the bulk of the zinc and copper. The oxidized units contain geothite, Fe-montimorillonite, manganese oxides, and carbonate. Radiocarbon dating reported by Shanks and Bischoff (1980) indicates that the oldest sediments in the Deep were deposited about 28,00 years ago. In addition, a much slower sedimentation rate is indicated for the basal detrital-oxidic-pyritic zone than for the overlying sulfidic, oxidic and silicatic zones (Fig. 8.4).

Isotopic and chemical studies of the hot brines (Craig, 1969; Shanks and Bischoff, 1977, 1980) suggest that the metals and sulfide in the brines were transported by seawater that achieved enhanced salinity from circulation through Miocene evaporites. The heat to drive such convective circulation was probably derived from hot basaltic rocks in the slowly spreading axial zone, and such rocks are also a logical source for the base metals now concentrated in the sulfidic layers of the Atlantis II Deep sediments. The absence of significant amounts of zinc and copper in the sediments below other brine pools is probably due to the fact that circulating brines in those systems did not reach suf-

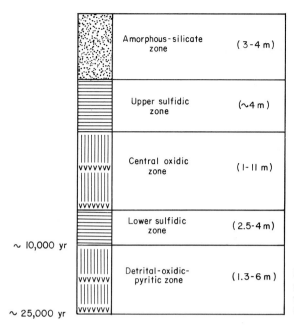

Fig. 8.4. Simplified lithostratigraphic sequence of Atlantis II Deep metalliferous sediments (modified from Baker and Richter 1973)

ficiently high temperatures to effectively leach copper and zinc from the basaltic 'basement'. Some flux of juvenile material into these sites is, however, indicated by the very high He^3/He^4 ratios in the brine pools (Lupton et al., 1977).

8.2.2 Discussion

The slow spreading rate of the Red Sea, and the presence of extensive evaporite beds in the sedimentary sections on each side of the axial rift create a geologic setting that is not directly comparable to that of true ocean spreading systems. Also, the lack of clear analogues of the Atlantis II Deep deposits in the geologic record is puzzling, despite the suggestion of Shanks (1977) that Besshi-type deposits may be representative of this type of mineralization (see Chap. 4). In this respect it is instructive to consider the geologic future of these Red Sea deposits: whether the Red Sea continues to spread or not, the deposits lie approximately 250 km from a passive continental margin and would thus eventually be buried under a thick wedge of miogeoclinal sediments. It follows that their eventual reappearance at or near the surface would require a collision event at that continental margin. By that stage they will have inevitably suffered a certain degree of tectonism and metamorphism and their original setting would be obscure (Sawkins, 1982a).

Tab. 8.1. Sediment-Hosted Massive Sulfide Deposits

Deposit or District	Age	Metal Comp.[a]	Tonnage (10^6)	Hostrocks	Reference
Lik, N.W. Alaska	Miss.	Zn, Pb	25+	Carb. shale, short	Forrest et al. (1983)
Red Dog	Miss.	Zn, Pb	85+	Carb. shale	Northern Miner (1982)
Rammelsburg, Germany	Devonian	Zn, Pb, Cu	22	Carb. slates	Hannak (1981)
Meggen, Germany	Devonian	Zn, Pb	50	Carb. slates	Krebs (1981)
Macmillan Pass	Devonian	Zn, Pb	20	Carb., siliceous shale	Carne and Cathro (1982)
Gataga	Devonian	Zn, Pb	30	Siliceous pyritic shale	MacIntyre (1982)
Howards Pass	Silurian	Zn, Pb	?	Carb. sandstone, chert	Carne and Cathro (1982)
Anvil	Cambrian	Zn, Pb	140	Graphitic pyllite	Carne and Cathro (1982)
Sullivan, B.C.	Prot. (1.4)	Zn, Pb	155	Argillite	Ethier et al. (1976)
Mt. Isa, Aust. (Zn, Pb)	Prot. (1.65)	Zn, Pb	88.6	Carb. shale, dolomite	Mathias and Clark (1975)
Mt. Isa, Aust. (Cu)	Prot. (1.65?)	Cu	181.6	Silica-dolomite	Mathias and Clark (1975)
Hilton, Aust.	Proterozoic	Zn, Pb	35.6	Carb. shale	Mathias et al. (1973)
Lady Loretta, Aust.	Proterozoic	Zn, Pb	8.6	Carb. shale	Loudon et al. (1973)
McArthur River, Aust.	Prot. (1.65)	Zn, Pb	190	Dolomite, shale	Walker et al. (1977)
Metamorphosed Equivalents					
Otjihase, Namibia	Late Prot.	Cu, Zn	?	Biotite schist	Anheusser and Button (1974)
Ducktown, Tennessee	Late Prot.	Cu, Zn	75	Biotite schist	Megee (1968)
					Feiss and Hauck (1968)
Broken Hill, N.S.W.	Prot. (1.7–2.0)	Pb, Zn	180	Felsic gneiss	Johnson and Klingner (1975)
Gamsberg, S. Africa	Prot.	Zn, Pb	93	Meta-pellites	Rozendaal (1980)
Big Syn, S. Africa	Prot.	Zn, Pb	101[b]		
Black Mountain, S. Africa	Prot.	Cu, Pb	82[b]	Mica schist,	Ryan et al. (1982)
Broken Hill, S. Africa	Prot.	Pb, Zn	85[b]	Iron formation	

[a] Metals listed in order of decreasing abundance. Most deposits contain significant silver values

[b] Grades in these deposits are low compared with the others listed

Note: More details on many of these deposits are available in Table 1 of Gustafson and Williams (1981)

8.3 Sediment-Hosted Massive Sulfide Deposits

A number of world class base metal deposits (Table 8.1) can be related, in terms of their lithologic settings, to the more advanced stages of continental rifting. Sawkins (1976c) suggested the name Sullivan-type deposits for this group of sediment-hosted massive sulfide ores, but, in view of the variability exhibited by the different deposits that fall into this category, the more general term 'sediment-hosted massive sulfide deposits' is preferable and has recently achieved wide usage (Large, 1980). The deposits are massive to semimassive, conformable sulfide ores that occur most typically within marine shales or siltstones, or their metamorphic equivalents. Volcanic materials are either minor or absent in the immediate hostrocks, but carbonates and cherts are present in some cases. For a recent compilation of data and concepts relating to the sediment-hosted massive sulfide deposits see Sangster (1983).

8.3.1 Settings of Sediment-Hosted Massive Sulfide Deposits

The deposits tend to occur in settings characterized by very thick sequences of continentally-derived clastics, that are considered indicative of either intracontinental rifting or passive continental margins (e.g., Hoy, 1982a). In both instances we are dealing with linear zones of long-lived subsidence in which contemporaneous tensional faulting can be expected. Large (1980) has suggested that the major first order basins in which sediment-hosted massive sulfide deposits are generated form as either fault controlled embayments in continental margins, or as intracratonic rift basins. The sedimentary facies manifest within such basins can be quite variable and include black shales, siltstones, carbonates, and turbidites (see Table 8.1). Within such first order basins, second and third order basins tend to develop as a result of contemporaneous vertical tectonics during the period of first order basin development. Proximity to the bounding structures of these first, second, and third order basins is reflected by facies and thickness variations in the sediments, and local intraformation breccias.

Although later deformation has generally rendered precise location of basin controlling faults and hinge zones difficult, in most instances the massive sulfide deposits can be inferred to lie close to such structures (see Large, 1980, p. 94–95). The absence of deformation in the terrain that hosts the HYC deposit at McArthur River makes this relationship particularly clear (Fig. 8.5B). It seems very probable that these structures were active at the time of mineralization, and thus may have exerted an important control on the plumbing systems utilized by the ore-generating fluids. Sibson et al. (1975) have suggested that seismic pumping, related to contemporaneous fault movements, is an important mechanism for promoting large scale movement of hydrothermal fluids in such environments.

The relationship of major sediment-hosted deposits to rift environments is particularly apparent in the case of Mt. Isa, Hilton and MacArthur River de-

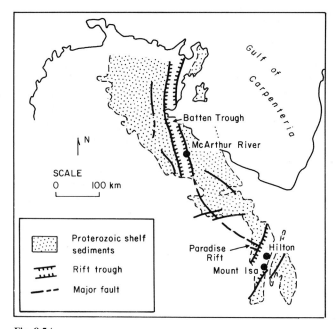

Fig. 8.5 A

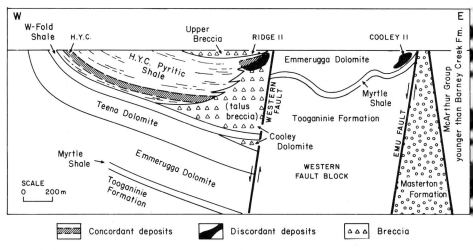

Fig. 8.5 B

Fig. 8.5. (**A**) Map showing locations of Batten Trough, Paradise Rift, and the related sediment-hosted massive sulfide deposits of Mt. Isa and McArthur River (after Dunnet 1976). (**B**) Cross-section of the HYC and related carbonate replacement deposits associated with the Batten Trough, McArthur River (from Williams 1978)

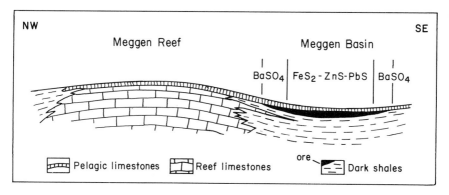

Fig. 8.6. Pre-orogenic position of the Meggen Basin and the Meggen Reef (from Krebs 1981)

posits in Australia, and Dunnet (1976) has pointed out the position of the ore deposits in relation to major Proterozoic rift structures (Fig. 8.5A). The Devonian, Atasu-type sediment-hosted massive sulfide deposits of Central Kazakhstan (Shcherba et al., 1981) occur within dark shales containing chert and carbonate units deposited in troughs related to extensional tectonics. These lead-zinc-barite ores appear to be very similar to European deposits of similar age such as Rammelsberg and Meggen.

The evidence for a rifting environment for Rammelsberg and Meggen, and other Paleozoic massive sulfide deposits in Europe, has been discussed by Sawkins and Burke (1980). More recently, Krebs (1981) has suggested an environment of extensional block faulting during the formation of the Meggen ores (Fig. 8.6), and Hannak (1981) has emphasized the position of the Rammelsberg ore lenses on the hinge zone between the Goslar Trough and the Westharz Rise (Fig. 8.7). It is also noteworthy that both Rammelsberg and Meggen lie close to the hinge zone between the external shelf of the Old Red Continent to the northwest and a mid-Devonian trough to the south. The continental rift setting for these deposits has recently been confirmed by detailed petrochemical studies of Hercynian basalts (Floyd, 1982).

The question of water depth during formation of sediment-hosted massive deposits is largely unanswered. The presence of stromatolitic dolomites in the host Barney Creek Formation at MacArthur River suggests relatively shallow environments, as does the evidence for evaporites in the Mt. Isa sequence (Neudert and Russell, 1981). In all other examples of this type of deposit no valid indicators of water depth are known, although Finlow-Bates and Large (1978) have pointed out that water depths must have been approximately 400 m or more to prevent boiling of the ore fluids and precipitation of metals prior to exhalation. The delicate banding present in many sediment-hosted massive sulfide ores certainly indicates the tranquil bottom conditions associated with deeper marine environments.

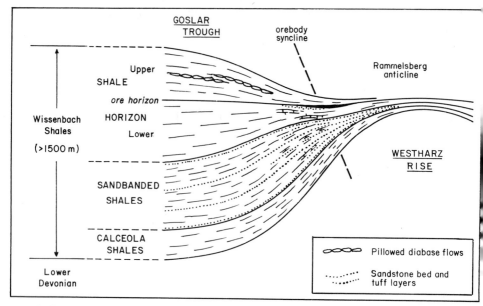

Fig. 8.7. Reconstruction of the structural and stratigraphic relationships pertaining to the Rammelsberg orebody, Harz Mountains, West Germany (from Hanak 1981)

Despite their development in sedimentary sequences lacking significant volumes of volcanic material, it is demonstrable in many cases that some contemporaneous igneous activity was occurring in the general region during the formation of these ores. For example, felsic tuffite horizons have been recognized at Mt. Isa, MacArthur River, Rammelsberg and Meggen (Large, 1980), and at Sullivan intrusion of the Moyie Sills overlaps the time of ore formation (Ethier et al., 1976). No evidence for contemporaneous volcanism has yet been found in connection with the sediment-hosted massive sulfide deposits in the Selwyn Basin, but the sediments that host the Tom deposit are underlain by several mafic volcanic units (Dawson, 1977). Overall, it seems clear that high geothermal gradients, a requisite condition for hydrothermal convection within a sedimentary pile (Solomon, 1976), characterized these environments.

8.3.2 Mineralization

Most sediment-hosted massive sulfide deposits consist of a single or several lenses of pyritic galena-sphalerite ore. Most contain economically significant amounts of silver, and some (e.g., Rammelsberg, Mt. Isa) important amounts of copper. The lateral extent of mineralization is considerable in the larger deposits and ore zones can extend for several kilometers. At Mt. Isa and MacArthur River conformable mineralization occurs over a considerable vertical interval, 650 and 130 m respectively. In such cases shale beds are interlayered with massive or semi-massive sulfides and, inasmuch as the shales at least must have accumulated relatively slowly, time periods over which intermittent mineralization occurred presumably totalled millions of years. This is in strong contrast to many volcanic-hosted massive sulfide deposits where indications are that mineralization occurs relatively rapidly. The iron and lead-zinc sulfides in these ores are typically fine-grained, unless recrystallized as a result of metamorphism. Deformation, both syndepositional and post lithification, has in some instances (e.g., Sullivan and Mt. Isa) produced spectacular fold and flowage structures in thin banded massive sulfide ore.

Certain sediment-hosted massive sulfide deposits have significant amounts of barite associated with them, and this is especially true of Paleozoic examples such as Meggen, Rammelsberg, Tom, and Red Dog. The three very large Proterozoic deposits of sediment-hosted type, Sullivan, Mt. Isa, and McArthur River, lack barite, however. Chert horizons are also present in a number of these massive sulfide deposits and are particularly prominent in association with the ores in northwest Alaska (Red Dog, Lik), the Tom deposit, and at Lady Loretta and MacArthur River. Oxygen isotope and crystallite size studies of the cherts in the Red Dog and Lik area of northwest Alaska (Harrover et al., 1982) have demonstrated that cherts near mineralization exhibit lower $\delta^{18}O$ values and larger crystallite size than cherts distal to mineralization.

Sediment-hosted massive sulfide deposits tend to exhibit zonal patterns of metals in either lateral or vertical directions or both, and at Rammelsberg, for example, a well defined vertical zonation from $Cu \rightarrow Zn \rightarrow Pb \rightarrow Ba$ has been demonstrated (Hannak, 1981). At Sullivan, Mt. Isa and MacArthur River a lateral zonation with increasing Zn/Pb ratios toward the margins of orebodies is manifest (see Large, 1980, Table 9).

Some authors (e.g., Plimer, 1978) have referred to sediment-hosted massive sulfide deposits as being of distal type, apparently in terms of their distance from volcanic or igneous centers. I feel this usage of distal is confusing and the terms proximal and distal should be used in reference to distances from exhalative centers, for in many instances it can be demonstrated that sediment-hosted massive sulfide deposits lie directly above the sites at which the hydrothermal fluids vented. This is certainly true for Sullivan (see next section). Furthermore, the silica-dolomite breccias at Mt. Isa (Mathias and Clark, 1975), the siliceous kneist ores at Rammelsberg (Hannak, 1981), the footwall alteration zones at Meggen (Krebs, 1981) and Tom (Carne, 1979), and the sphalerite veins at Red Dog (personal observation) all suggest the presence of subjacent feeder zones. In all cases breccia textures are associated with these zones.

8.3.3 The Sullivan Massive Sulfide Deposit

This important sediment-hosted metal deposit has been the subject of a number of recent studies (Ethier et al., 1976; Campbell et al., 1978, 1980, Hamilton et al. 1983), and excellent summaries of its geologic setting and features can be found in Hoy (1982a) and Hamilton et al. (1982). The Sullivan mine is located in the Purcell Mountains of southeastern British Columbia and its ores, together with several much smaller conformable massive sulfide deposits, occur within greywackes and argillites of the Lower Aldridge Formation. This unit occurs near the base of the exposed portion of the Purcell Supergroup, a very thick sequence of marine, predominantly clastic rocks that represents the equivalent of the Belt Supergroup in Montana and Idaho (Harrison, 1972). Kanasewich (1968) has noted that the Sullivan deposit occurs close to the northern boundary of an east-west trending buried Precambrian rift structure that can be postulated on the basis of geophysical data.

Volcanic rocks in the Purcell Supergroup are restricted to the Purcell Lavas that occur at least 5,000 m higher up in the stratigraphic succession. The Lower Aldridge is, however, heavily intruded by thick sills of basaltic composition (Edmunds, 1973): in places these account for over half the measured section and their distribution appears to be somewhat concentrated in the general area of the Sullivan deposit. The age of emplacement of these Moyie Sills overlaps that of the emplacement of the Sullivan ores ($\sim$1.4 b.y., see Ethier et al., 1976, Fig. 3).

The orebody (Fig. 8.8), which contains a massive pyrrhotite lens up to 50 m thick in its western portion, consists mainly of massive to poorly banded lead-zinc ore, and is underlain by tourmalinized footwall conglomerate and breccia. At its eastern extremity massive pyrrhotite is not present and the ores consist of well-banded lead, zinc, and iron sulfides, in part interlayered with argillites. The tourmalinization and brecciation that are concentrated under the west end of the Sullivan deposit appear to extend at least 450 m below the sulfide ore lens (Jardine, 1966). There is some tin mineralization in this area and in places the massive ores also contain small amounts of tin. The footwall conglomerates (see Fig. 8.8), which are thought to have resulted from penecontemporaneous faulting and resultant slumping, attain a thickness of 60 m locally, and appear to have filled a newly created seafloor depression. The zone of strong albitization in the hanging wall above the western portion of the ore lens, that caused many to view the deposit as epigenetic, is now thought to have been related to the final, post-ore stages of hydrothermal activity (Hamilton et al., 1983).

Sulfur isotope studies of the Sullivan ores (Campbell et al., 1978, 1980) indicate a range in $\delta^{34}S$ of the sulfides from -10.4 to $+4.7$. These values exhibit variations both laterally and vertically through the ore lens, and are interpreted by the workers involved to indicate both higher temperatures during deposition of the iron sulfide-rich areas in the western portion of the orebody, and an increase in oxygenation of the ambient marine waters toward the final stages of sulfide deposition. They also conclude that the metals were transported by a dense sulfide-deficient brine at temperatures estimated at 150–200 °C. The requisite H_2S for sulfide deposition is thought to have been produced by euxinic conditions in a local seafloor depression. It is noteworthy that a thin car-

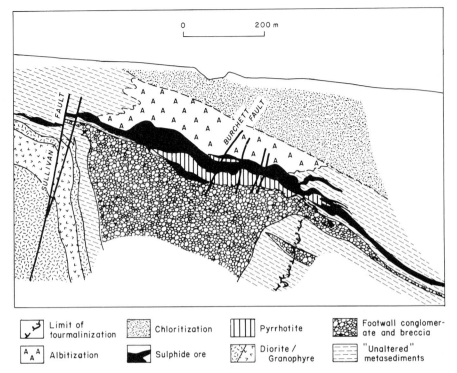

Fig. 8.8. Cross section of the Sullivan lead-zinc orebody at Kimberley, British Columbia (from Hoy 1982b)

bonaceous unit characterized by banded pyrrhotite occurs throughout the Purcell-Belt basin at this same stratigraphic level (Huebschman, 1973), and this indication of widespread stagnant conditions suggests that the Lower Aldridge Formation accumulated in a basin related to rifting, rather than along a continental slope facing a large ocean.

8.3.4 Discussion and Suggestions for Exploration

The considerable size of many sediment-hosted massive sulfide deposits and their relative rarity suggests that a rather special combination of circumstances is required for their generation. Although the precise origins of the metals and ore fluids involved in their genesis remain obscure, the size and protracted mineralization intervals indicated for these deposits are such that metal-rich formation waters (Badham, 1981; Lydon, 1983) or major geothermal systems (Russell, 1983) represent the only logical candidates for the fluids involved in ore generation. In addition, it seems clear that efficient plumbing systems and heat sources must have been available for long periods of time during their formation. The logical explanation for these are the normal faulting and emplacement of mafic magma at deeper levels that characterize active rift environments. With regard to the latter, not only are the rocks of the Lower Aldridge Formation heavily intruded by sills in the Sullivan area, but at Mt. Isa the sedimentary units below the sulfide ores contain numerous north-south trending basaltic dikes. Similarly, more or less contemporaneous basaltic magmatism is associated with the Otjihase massive sulfide ores in Namibia (Anhaeusser and Button, 1974) and the Ducktown deposits in Tennessee (Magee, 1968).

Clearly, carbonaceous units containing syngenetic iron sulfides represent important stratigraphic levels at which sediment-hosted massive sulfides may occur. Whether such euxinic environments are mandatory in terms of a supply of reduced sulfur, as indicated for some sediment-hosted deposits, or whether they merely indicate the locales of second and third order basins within broader rift environments is not apparent. Once such paleoenvironments are recognized, however, the search for sediment-hosted massive sulfides still represents considerable challenge. The presence of intraformational conglomerates, barite lenses, and pyritic cherts can be regarded as encouraging signs in these lithoenvironments, but heavy reliance must still be placed on applied geochemistry and geophysics in exploration for these ores. In recent years the most significant new discoveries of sediment-hosted massive sulfide deposits have been made in the Selwyn Basin of northwest Canada (Carne and Cathro, 1982; MacIntyre, 1983) and the DeLong Mountains of northwest Alaska. Unfortunately, few details of the geology of these groups of deposits have as yet been published.

8.4 Volcanic-Hosted Massive Sulfide Deposits

In a recent review of rhyolite-hosted massive sulfide deposits, Sillitoe (1982b) notes that a significant number of such deposits probably did not form in subduction-related environments (Table 8.2). Such deposits are typically associated with well-defined bimodal basalt-rhyolite volcanic assemblages that essentially lack andesites. They thus appear to have formed in rifting environments distinctive from the intra-arc extensional environments that generate Kuroko-type deposits. Sawkins and Burke (1980) argued that the mid-Paleozoic massive sulfide deposits of Europe can be related to extensional tectonic environments, and it is noteworthy that these massive sulfide deposits, which occur mainly along a complex east-west paleotrough in Germany and Czechoslovakia, include both sediment-hosted (Rammelsberg, Meggen) and volcanic-hosted (Zlate Hory, Horni Mesto) deposits (Pouba, 1971).

The lithosetting of the important volcanic-hosted massive sulfide deposits of southwest Iberia is also atypical of subduction related environments (Sawkins and Burke, 1980; Schermerhorn, 1975; Routhier et al., 1979) and more suggestive of a volcanically active, rift setting. In general terms, volcanic-hosted massive sulfide deposits of apparent rift affinities contain significantly more copper and less lead than sediment-hosted deposits.

Table 8.2. Rifting-Related, Volcanic-Hosted Massive Sulfide Deposits

Deposit or District	Age	Metal Comp.[a]	Associated Volcanics	Petrologic Affiliation	References
Iberian pyrite belt, Spain and Portugal	Early Carboniferous	Cu, Zn	Quartz keratophyres	Bimodal	Soler (1973) Munha (1979)
Jeseniky Montains, Czechoslovakia	Devonian	Zn, Cu, Pb	Quartz keratophyres	Bimodal	Pouba (1971)
Ambler district, Brooks Range, Alaska	Mid-Devonian	Zn, Cu	Rhyolites	Bimodal	Kelsey et al. (1980)
Woodlawn and Captains Flat, NSW, Australia	Mid-late Silurian	Zn, Pb, Cu	Rhyolites	Bimodal	Gilligan et al. (1979)
Bathurst-Newcastle New Brunswick, Canada	Ordovician	Zn, Pb, Cu	Rhyolites	Bimodal	Whitehead and Goodfellow (1978); Harley (1979)
Mt. Lyell-Roseberry, Tasmania, Australia	Cambrian	Zn, Pb, Cu	Rhyolites	Bimodal	Corbett (1981)
Baqf, Iran	Infracambrian	Zn, Pb	Rhyolites	Bimodal	Gibbs (1976)
Skellefte, Sweden	Mid-Proterozoic	Zn, Cu	Leptites	Bimodal	Rickard and Zweifel (1975)
Pyhasalmi-Pielavesi, Finland	Mid-Proterozoic	Zn, Cu	Rhyolitic metatuff	Bimodal	Huhtala (1979)

[a] Metals listed in order of decreasing abundance. Most deposits contain significant precious melat values. Modified somewhat from Sillitoe (1982b)

8.4.1 Massive Sulfide Deposits
of the Bathurst-Newcastle District, New Brunswick, Canada

The Bathurst-Newcastle district embraces over twenty Zn-Pb-Cu-Ag massive sulfide deposits (Fig. 8.9), one of which, the Brunswick No. 12 deposit, contains over 100 million tons of ore grading 13 percent of combined zinc and lead (Luff, 1977). All the deposits occur within rocks of the Tetagouche Group, a sequence of felsic and mafic volcanics and clastic metasedimentary rocks (Harley, 1979). A good deal of uncertainty surrounds the precise age and regional structural setting of the Tetagouche Group due to paucity of fossils, poor exposure, and polyphase deformation. It appears, however, that a sedimentary unit consisting

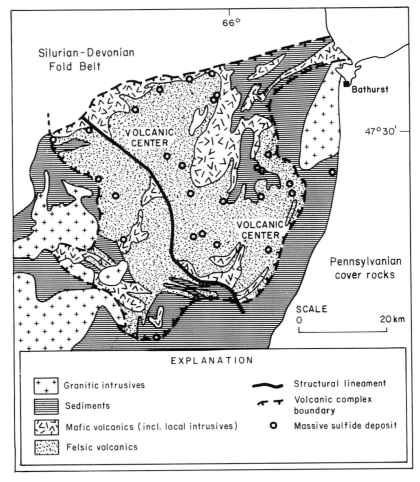

Fig. 8.9. Geology of the Bathurst-Newcastle mining district, northern New Brunswick (modified from Harley 1979)

mainly of arenaceous sandstones and feldspathic wackes of early Ordivician age is succeeded upward by felsic volcanics, then basaltic volcanics, and finally dark slates and lithic wackes of mid-Ordivician age (see Harley, 1979 and references therein). Whitehead and Goodfellow (1978) have studied the geochemistry of the Tetagouche volcanics and demonstrate that they are strongly bimodal in character. In addition, the basalts have both tholeiitic and alkaline affinities, and rocks of calc-alkaline andesitic composition are conspicuously absent. There is thus little to indicate the former presence of a subduction-related arc system in this sequence.

Harley (1979) notes that, although all the massive sulfide deposits in the district exhibit a broad relationship to felsic volcanic rocks, two sub-types can be recognized. The largest deposits, such as Brunswick No. 12, Brunswick No. 6, and Orvan Brook, are regionally associated with sheet-like bodies of rhyolite porphyry, but occur in intravolcanic sedimentary horizons (Davies et al., 1973). They also exhibit an association with oxide, silicate, and carbonate facies iron formation (Helmstaedt, 1973) and tend to be laterally extensive. The other type of massive sulfide deposit occurs as smaller lenses and exhibits a close association with siliceous tuff breccias, and these deposits thus appear to be related to the presence of brecciated lava domes, a characteristic of Kuroko deposits.

The Orvan Brook deposit (Tupper, 1969) is of some interest because it occurs as a steeply dipping thin sulfide lens (max. 5 m) almost 2,000 m long, lying either within a quartz sericite schist or at its contact with an overlying graphitic schist. Below the sericite schist is an iron-formation unit consisting of quartz-chlorite schist containing scattered bands of quartz-hematite and jasper-hematite-magnetite iron formation. The immediate setting of the deposit is thus one of sedimentary rocks, though metarhyolites are present a short distance down section. The sulfide minerals consist of predominant pyrite with lesser sphalerite and galena, and minor amounts of chalcopyrite, arsenopyrite and tetrahedrite. The sulfide ore is massive, fine-grained, banded and locally contorted. Zinc to lead ratios in the ores are approximately 2:1 and the combined $Zn + Pb$ grade averages about 9 percent (Tupper, 1969).

The New Brunsick No. 12 deposit is easily the largest massive sulfide orebody in the Newcastle-Bathurst district, and contains almost 100 million tons of lead-zinc ore grading 9.2 percent zinc, 3.8 percent lead, 0.3 percent copper and 0.79 gm/ton silver. In addition, another 14 million tons of copper ore grading 1.1 percent copper, 1.3 percent zinc, 0.4 percent lead, and 0.30 gm/ton silver are known (Luff, 1977). The ores occur within a sequence of argillites and metasediments, including iron formation, that appear to have accumulated during a break in felsic volcanic activity (Fig. 8.10). These felsic volcanics are mainly crystal and siliceous metatuffs and are overlain by mafic volcanics, and thus the stratigraphic sequence exhibits strong similarities to that enclosing the Orvan Brook deposit discussed above.

Isoclinal folding and faulting have affected both the ores and their enclosing rocks, but both conformable massive sulfide lenses and subjacent stockwork

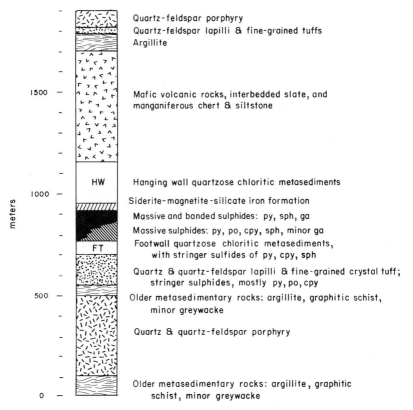

Fig. 8.10. Stratigraphic section of the Brunswick No. 12 area, New Brunswick. Note that although the volcanic rocks occur both downsection and upsection, the massive sulfide ores are sediment-hosted (from Franklin et al. 1981)

zones can be distinguished (Luff, 1977). In addition, a pyrrhotite-pyrite pipe-like feature is present in the footwall and is thought to be the original site where venting of the orefluids occurred. Four sulfide zones are recognized in the deposit, the largest of which is the main zone, a massive sulfide lens up to 1000 m long and 100 m thick. A number of zonal features are apparent in this lens. It is sandwiched between upper and lower pyrite units, and within it both pyrrhotite and chalcopyrite, and sphalerite and galena decrease upward. The quartz content, however, increases upward, from about 5 percent to as high as 20 percent, but the iron content of the sphalerite decreases upward through the lens.

Sulfur isotope studies of various ores in the district (Lusk and Crocket, 1969; Lusk, 1972) indicate that the sulfides in the southeastern portion are isotopically heavy (median $\delta^{34}S = 16‰$), whereas the ores in the central and northern areas are isotopically lighter (median $\delta^{34}S = 7‰$) (Franklin et al., 1981). The isotopic

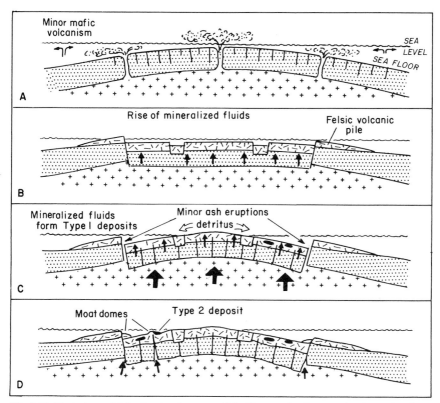

Fig. 8.11. Harley's model for the development of the Tetagouche Group volcanics and sediments in a caldera environment (from Harley 1979)

fractionation between individual sulfide minerals indicates temperatures ranging from 317–357 °C. Lusk and Crocket (1969) have suggested that these values represent metamorphic re-equilibration temperatures, but, given the fine-grained nature of most of the ores in the district, these temperatures may approximate original depositional temperatures.

Harley (1979) has suggested that the distribution of Tetagouche felsic volcanic rocks can be interpreted in terms of a resurgent caldera complex developed within a continental setting characterized by extensional tectonics (Fig. 8.11). This concept is certainly supported by the stratigraphic relationships of the Tetagouche Group and the clear bimodal character of the volcanics, but seems unduly bold considering the structural complexity of the area.

8.4.2 Discussion

This class of massive sulfide deposits, that are broadly volcanic-hosted, but apparently unrelated to subduction environments, may well represent an endmember type of rift-related massive sulfide deposits, the other endmembers being sediment-hosted massive sulfide deposits. This idea is not totally implausible when one recalls the evidence for volcanism represented by the tuffaceous bands at Mt. Isa and MacArthur River, two typical sediment-hosted deposits.

It is noteworthy that in many districts where these volcanic-hosted, but rift related, massive sulfides occur, the felsic volcanics are succeeded by mafic volcanics. This relationship has been noted for the New Brunswick ores, but is also stressed by Sillitoe (1982b, Table 1), and can be seen also in relation to many of the Proterozoic massive sulfide ores of central and southern Finland (Huhtala, 1979; Latvalahti, 1979). The precise role of tectonics in the petrogenesis of voluminous felsic volcanics that are then succeeded by basalts is not clear at this point, but it certainly merits further investigation.

A major uncertainty regarding rift environments and massive sulfide generation in continental settings relates to the differentiation between true intracontinental rifting and extensional environments behind arc systems (Hutchinson, 1980). Criteria for the recognition of one versus the other of these settings are not well established. This uncertainty is perhaps well illustrated by the question – would the felsic volcanism that characterizes the Great Basin of the western U.S. during late Cenozoic time have given rise to massive sulfide depsoits if that area had developed in a submarine setting? Another point relevant to this problem is the observation that the starved basin settings in which the mid-Paleozoic massive sulfides of Europe developed (Fig. 8.12) were subsequently overwhelmed by major flysch deposits (see Sawkins and Burke, 1980). Similar relationships also hold for the Paleozoic massive sulfide settings of the Selwyn Basin (Walker, 1970). This tendency of starved marine basin environments to be subsequently filled with strong influxes of flyschoid sediments is also seen in the case of the Ouchita Basin (Graham et al., 1975) and the Hazen Trough in Northern Ellesmere Island, Arctic Canada (Trettin, 1979). Essentially similar relationships are exhibited by the Proterozoic Piling Group on Baffin Island (Sangster, 1981). Massive sulfide deposits have not been discovered in these three latter terrains, but the Ouchita region does contain massive barite lenses. The point at issue is that these major influxes of flysch sediments that follow starved basin conditions are more suggestive of collisional or back-arc, rather than continental, rifting environments.

Clarification of the uncertainties regarding various types of extensional tectonic settings and their petrochemical and lithologic signatures will at best be a difficult matter, but new insights are continually being developed. For example, Tapponnier et al. (1982) have demonstrated from modelling studies that continental collision, such as that of south Asia, can spawn large strike-slip faults that tend to develop rifts near their distal extremities, and that such rifts can evolve into fully grown marginal basins. Furthermore, Badham (1982) has introduced the concept of strike-slip orogens, and shown that many of the puzzling complexities of the Hercynides can be interpreted in terms of a series of local rifting and compressional events, associated with the major west-northwest-trending strike-slip faulting and subsequent microplate collisions.

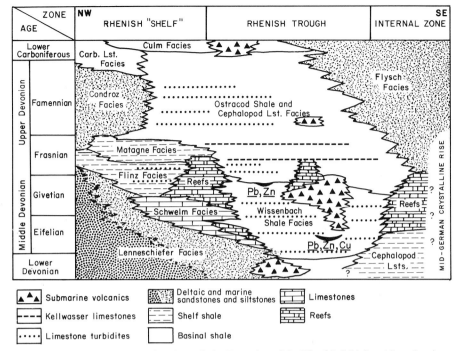

Fig. 8.12. Highly schematic section through the Devonian of the Rhenish Schiefergebirge showing facies relationships, and position of submarine volcanics and massive sulfide ores (modified from Krebs 1971)

8.5 Massive Sulfide Deposits in High-Grade Metamorphic Terrains

The huge lead-zinc sulfide lodes of Broken Hill, New South Wales (Johnson and Klingner, 1975) occur within strongly metamorphosed and deformed gneisses of the Willyama Complex. Other significant conformable massive sulfide deposits within high-grade metamorphic terrains were essentially unknown until the discovery of major tonnages of massive sulfide ores in the Proterozoic Namaqua Metamorphic Complex in South Africa (Tankard et al., 1982). Another possible example of conformable ores in high-grade metamorphic rocks is the mineralization found along the Singhbum Shear Zone in India (Banerji, 1981).

Clearly the reconstruction of the original lithologic and tectonic environments pertaining at the time of original deposition of these ores and their enclosing rocks is a hazardous matter, but the available information on these deposits suggests that they represent highly metamorphosed equivalents of rift-related massive sulfide deposits. Recognition of this fact, if correct, is important, for

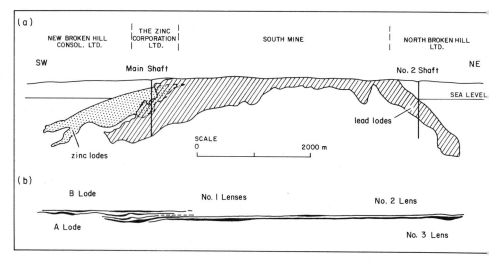

Fig. 8.13. Longitudinal projection of the Broken Hill ore deposit (a) and longitudinal projection through unfolded orebodies (b) (from Johnson and Klinger 1975)

exploration geologists have tended to shun high-grade metamorphic terrains in their search for sulfide ores.

The orebodies at Broken Hill, New South Wales contained 180 million tons of ore grading 0.2 percent Cu, 11.3 percent Pb, and 9.8 percent Zn and 175 gm/ ton Ag (Gustafson and Williams, 1981). The metamorphic rocks that host the lead-zinc orebodies consist of a series of felsic gneisses overlain by banded iron formation and amphibolite. Detailed investigations of the structural complexities in the area led Laing et al. (1978) to recognize three major episodes of folding, and to conclude that the orebodies lie close to the boundary between a lower sequence that is probably in part volcanogenic, and an upper purely sedimentary sequence. The lithounits most closely associated with the ore lenses are subjacent Potosi Gneiss (meta-rhyolite?), amphibolite, and banded iron formation, together with psammopelitic gneisses.

The six ore lenses at Broken Hill are stacked one approximately above another and form a mineralized zone 7.3 km long, 850 m wide and 250 m thick. The syngenetic concept of ore deposition is reinforced by the fact that each lens is of a distinctive metal composition, with the zinc-rich lenses lying below the lead-rich lenses (Fig. 8.13). The ores are characterized by relatively high manganese contents (3.8 percent Mn), but contain relatively small amounts of iron sulfides.

Several authors (e.g., Johnson and Klingner, 1975; Laing et al., 1978) envisage the sulfides as having been deposited in an elongate seafloor depression, based on the shape of the ore zone and apparent primary thickness variations of the Potosi Gneiss. These observations, taken in conjunction with the evidence

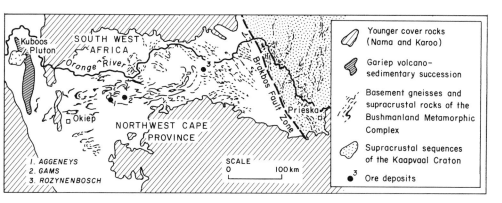

Fig. 8.14. Generalized map of Namaqualand and Bushmanland metamorphic complexes showing localities of major massive sulfide deposits and the O'Kiep copper district (from Anhauesser and Button 1974)

for mafic volcanism (amphibolite), and possible bimodalism (Potosi gneiss = metarhyolite?), are suggestive of an intracratonic rift environment. It is also noteworthy that it is in precisely such environments that other very large conformable lead-zinc massive sulfide deposits appear to have formed.

Almost 300 million tons of massive sulfide ore have been discovered in recent years in the Namaqualand Metamorphic Complex, South Africa. Previously, the only significant known sulfide ores known from this terrain were the disseminated copper ores present in noritoid lenses in the O'Kiep district at the western extremity of this high-grade metamorphic belt (Fig. 8.14). At the eastern end of the belt is the Copperton deposit containing 47 million tons of ore grading 1.7 percent Cu and 3.8 percent Zn with only minor lead (Wagener, 1980). Lead isotope systematics indicate an age of 1.35 million years for this deposit (Koeppel, 1980), which occurs in a quartz-rich envelope that is probably metachert. Carbonates and calc-silicates are also closely associated with the sulfides, as are mica-rich zones. Although Middleton (1976) concluded on the basis of textural evidence that the surrounding rocks were largely metavolcanics, Wagener (1980) demonstrates that the lithosetting prior to metamorphism was more likely one of fine-grained clastic and chemical sedimentary rocks. At Aggenys, further west, 200 million tons of Cu-Pb-Zn-Ag massive sulfide ore, distributed through three orebodies, have been discovered. Unfortunately further details on this important district have yet to be published.

The Gamsberg deposit (see Fig. 8.15) contains 143 millions tons of zinc ore grading 7.41 percent zinc and 0.55 percent lead (Rozendaal, 1980). Here, as elsewhere in the Namaqualand terrain, the host rocks and ores have been subjected to polyphase deformation and medium to high-grade metamorphism. The sulfides are associated with the Gams Iron Formation which exhibits lateral oxide to carbonate to sulfide transitions. In addition graphite, manganese, and barite

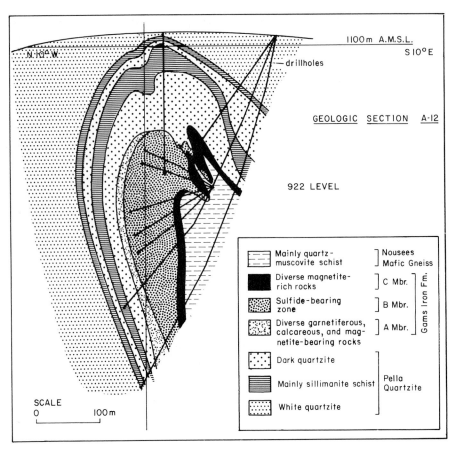

Fig. 8.15. Cross-section of the Gamsberg orebody, northern Cape, South Africa. Note association of sulfide zone with iron formation and calcareous metasediments (from Rozendaal 1980)

are present in the ore, which occurs as a steeply dipping lens (Fig. 8.15) within an overturned syncline. Rozendal (1980) interprets the various felsic gneisses in the footwall as having originally been an upward-fining sequence of arkose, quartzite, and shale deposited in a restricted basin without significant volcanic components. These units were succeeded by chemical sediments that mark the time of ore deposition (Moore, 1980). If this reconstruction is correct, then the environment was not atypical of those in which less metamorphosed sediment-hosted massive sulfide deposits formed.

Another interesting but puzzling aspect of the metallogeny of Namaqualand metamorphic terrain are the copper deposits of the O'Kiep district. Here, past production and reserves of copper sulfides contained in mafic rocks scattered through the high-grade gneisses of the area total 84 million tons of 2.1 percent

Cu (Lombaard and Schreuder, 1978). The noritoid bodies that host the disseminated copper sulfides exhibit a strong association with steep structures and megabreccias that transect the generally rather flat-lying structure of the various gneissic and granitic lithounits. Both the steep structures and the associated mafic units exhibit a strong east-west linear orientation.

Of the approximately 700 noritoid bodies that have been found scattered through the O'Kiep copper district, only about 27 contain economic copper concentrations (Stumpfl et al., 1976). The latter consist of three petrographic types, hypersthenite, hypersthene diorite, and mica diorite, and the copper sulfides they contain are mainly chalcopyrite and bornite. A deep-seated magmatic origin for these mafic bodies is indicated by their composition and setting, but rubidium-strontium isotopic studies indicate high initial strontium ratios (0.719, Stumpfl et al., 1976), and an age of metamorphism of close to 1.2 b.y.

Within the last decade over 150 million tons of copper ore (1.04 percent Cu) have been discovered in a similar lithologic and high-grade metamorphic setting at Caraiba, State of Bahia, Brazil (Townend et al., 1980). The norites and hypersthenites that contain the copper sulfides (mainly chalcopyrite and bornite) are steeply dipping and are interlayered with a series of gneisses, migmatites, and charnockites of probable early Proterozoic age. Some copper also occurs in calc-silicate rocks that contain significant amounts of anhydrite (Leake et al., 1979). The original depositional setting of these rocks is unclear, but the combination of copper-rich mafic rocks and lithologies suggestive of evaporites (see Leake et al., 1979) is certainly compatible with a rift environment.

8.6. Additional Facets of Rift-Related Metallogeny

In cases where continental rifting leads to successful ocean-opening events, the newly-created spreading ridge system gradually retreats from the adjacent young continental margins. Over time periods of about 50 million years these young continental margins tend to subside gradually and be covered by transgressive shallow marine sedimentary sequences (Sleep and Snell, 1976). In addition, old flaws inherited from the time of continental fragmentation, especially along the continuation of transform faults in the new ocean, tend to be a locus of earthquake activity and alkaline magmatism (Sykes, 1978). Many of the kimberlites of Africa, Brazil, and Australia exhibit a relationship to such structures (Mitchell and Garson, 1981).

A number of small stratiform copper and lead deposits occur along the western edge of Africa (Fig. 8.16). These deposits occur mainly in lower Cretaceous sandstones that discordantly overlie older rocks (Caia, 1976; Van Eden, 1978). The paleogeographic setting of the clastics is interpreted as deltaic and lagoonal, and clearly relates to a marine transgression over the subsiding continental edge some tens of millions of years after continental break-up. Whether the mineral-

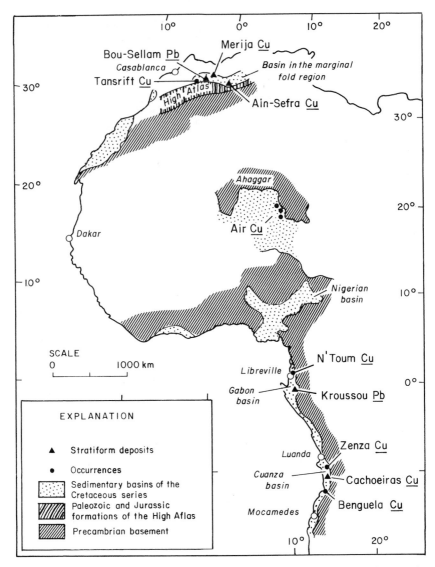

Fig. 8.16. Locations of the principal occurrences of stratiform copper and lead mineralization associated with the Lower Cretaceous unconformity in western Africa (from Caia 1976)

ization is truly syngenetic, or was introduced into the sediments along the unconformity is not clear, but in many respects the copper deposits exhibit similarities to the stratiform copper deposits discussed in the previous chapter, and may be a variant of them (Bjørlykke and Sangster, 1981). Similarly, the lead and zinc deposits exhibit a relationship to either limestones or the presence of cal-

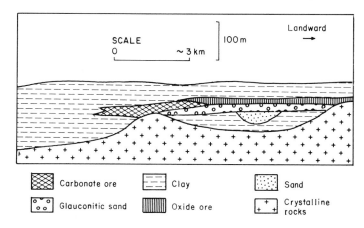

Fig. 8.17. Generalized cross-section of the Nikopol manganese district, Black Sea region, U.S.S.R. (from Cannon et al. 1983)

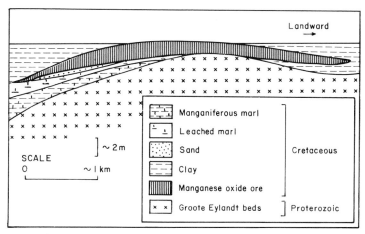

Fig. 8.18. Generalized cross-section of the Groote Eylandt manganese deposit, Gulf of Carpentaria, Australia (from Cannon et al. 1983)

careous cement in the sandstones, and may thus be a variant of Mississippi Valley-type deposits. Bjørlykke and Sangster (1981) intimate that this general setting of transgression can be applied to some of the older sandstone-hosted lead deposits of Europe, although distances from paleo-continental margins in some instances were considerable. This problem, however, does not apply to the important sandstone-hosted lead deposits of the Baltic Shield which are hosted by Eocambrian sandstones mainly overlying weathered Proterozoic granites (Bjørlykke and Sangster, 1981). The sandstones were apparently deposited dur-

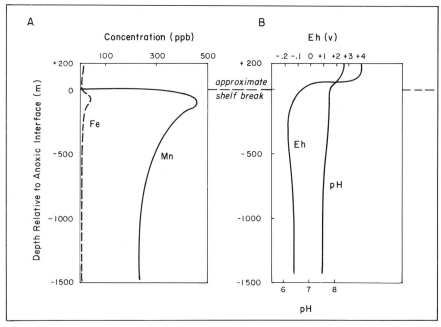

Fig. 8.19. Concentration-depth and Eh/pH-depth plots for the Black Sea showing sharp increase in manganese solubility at anoxic interface (from Cannon et al. 1983)

ing a marine transgression which followed a continental rifting event further west (Bjørlykke, 1978). By far the most important deposit in this environment is that at Laisvall (Rickard et al., 1979) where 80 million tons of ore grading 3.5% Pb and 0.44% Zn were formed. On balance, these Baltic Shield deposits appear to have been generated in a tectonic setting similar to that of the Cretaceous deposits of western Africa described above.

Some of the major high-grade manganese deposits of the world occur in sedimentary rocks above a basal unconformity (Cannon et al., 1983). The Oligocene age Nikopol and Chiatura deposits north of the Black Sea, USSR (Varentsov, 1964) (Fig. 8.17) and the Cretaceous Groote Eylandt deposits in northern Australia (McIntosh et al., 1975) (Fig. 8.18) are important examples. Analysis of the environments in which the hostrocks of these deposits formed indicates littoral and shallow marine conditions along irregular coastlines during a marine transgression. Such conditions may also apply to some of the carbonate-hosted manganese deposits of Morrocco (Varentsov, 1964) and eastern Mexico, and an unequivocal rift setting of similar lithologic characteristics is manifest for the manganese ores of the Boleo district, Baja California, Mexico (Wilson, 1955).

It is now generally accepted that many of the well-documented marine transgressive episodes of later Phanerozoic time relate to displacement of seawater by increased activity at spreading ridge systems (Valentine and Moores, 1972; Turcotte and Burke, 1978). Furthermore, these transgressive episodes have been correlated with anaerobic events in world oceans, conditions that are recognized as an important factor in the creation of organic rich source rocks for petroleum. The chemistry of manganese is such that its solubility relative to iron increases substantially under low Eh conditions (Fig. 8.19), and Cannon and Force (1983) suggest a correlation between the presence of such conditions in the world oceans and periods of major manganese ore accumulation. Whether the manganese was originally derived from hydrothermal activity at not too distant spreading ridge systems, or from continental hinterlands, or both, is not clear at present. What does emerge, however, is a relationship, albeit indirect, between plate tectonics in the form of increased spreading ridge activity and conditions conducive to the formation of an important class of manganese deposit.

8.6.1 Early Proterozoic Uraniferous Conglomerates and Rifting

The important uranium deposits of the Elliot Lake area, Ontario, Canada lie within the lower portion of the Huronian Supergroup (Frarey and Roscoe,

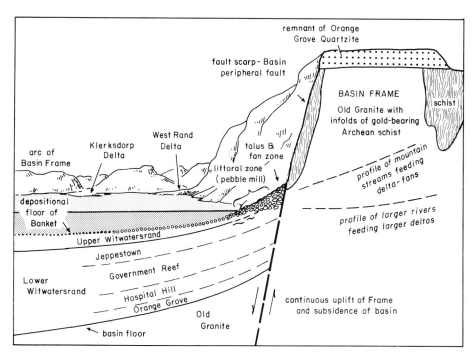

Fig. 8.20. Sketch to show conceptual model of the depositional environment of the gold-bearing paleoplacers of the Witwatersrand Supergroup (from Brock and Pretorius 1964)

1970; Young, 1973). This thick sequence of early Proterozoic clastic rocks exhibits clear evidence of having been deposited in an east-west trending rift basin. Not only is it initiated by basalt and rhyolite volcanics, but a series of east-west faults controlled the clastic sedimentation, which was clearly derived from the Archean Superior Province to the north. The bimodal volcanism, great thickness, and contemporaneous normal faulting all support the concept that sedimentation was controlled by rifting events.

Much the same setting may have pertained during the accumulation of the 16 km thickness of felsic and mafic volcanics, and clastic sediments present in the Witwatersrand Basin in South Africa. Pretorius (1975) has interpreted the Witwatersrand succession as having formed in a yoked basin that was faultscontrolled along its northern margin (Fig. 8.20), and van Biljon (1980) has presented a rather speculative tectonic model for the Witwatersrand Basin involving an embayment along a continental margin.

In addition to uranium, the conglomerates and carbon seams of the Witwatersrand system represent the source of most of the world's gold, and as Pretorius (1981b) has pointed out, if western world gold production is to be sustained, it is imperative that other major examples of Witwatersrand type gold deposits be discovered.

8.6.2 Major Occurrences of Banded Iron Formation in Relation to Rifting Events

It was formerly accepted that the great period of early Proterozoic development of banded iron formation was concentrated rather sharply at or close to 2.0 billion years ago. Recently, Gole and Klein (1981) have demonstrated that a continuum of deposition of banded iron formations existed from early Archean time until approximately 1.8 billion years ago, and that the major early Proterozoic development of banded iron formation should not be viewed as a more or less synchronous event. Despite this caveat, it is still probably correct to attribute the widespread early Proterozoic iron formations to the presence of increasing levels of oxygen in shallow marine environments. As detailed by Holland (1973), this factor of increasing oxygen availability caused the ferrous iron budget of the world's oceans to be essentially used up by about 1.8 billion years ago. It has also been suggested that local evaporation may have aided this process of iron deposition (Trendall, 1973; Button, 1976).

Condie (1982) has attempted to classify early and middle Proterozoic supracrustal successions into three basic lithologic assemblages: I. A quartzite-carbonate-shale, II. Bimodal volcanics-quartzite-arkose, and III. Continuous volcanic-graywacke. Group I assemblages, which include the Krivoy Rog Supergroup, U.S.S.R., the Transvaal Supergroup, South Africa, the Animikie Group, U.S.A and Canada, and the Minas Series of Brazil, all of which contain important iron formations, are considered to represent paleo-continental shelf environments. However, why these particular successions, all of which have aggregate thicknesses of 6 km or more, should have developed important iron formations and other basins of broadly similar age and lithology did not, is unclear. An important factor may have been ocean circulation patterns at the time and their control of the sites of upwelling of deep ocean water. This would be essentially analogous to the controls of marine phosphorite deposition during Phanerozoic time (Cook and McElhinny, 1979).

A relationship to plate tectonics in the above examples of iron formation may only be an indirect one, involving the control of continental geography, but it can be argued that the iron formations of the Hammersley Range, Australia, the Labrador Trough, and the Marquette Range, Michigan are more directly related to continental rift environments. The Hammersley Range contains the most extensive accumulation of sedimentary iron deposits known (Trendall and Blockley, 1970; Trendall, 1973), and the Mt. Bruce Supergroup, within which the Hammersley Group occupies a medial position, is about 10 km thick, and contains both basaltic and rhyolitic volcanics. In addition to this evidence for a rift environment, Horwitz and Smith (1976) have noted it coincides with a marked gravity high. They interpret this, together with similarities in the neighboring Yilgarn and Pilbara Archean terrains, as indicative of an early Proterozoic separation event that created the basin in which the Mt. Bruce Supergroup accumulated.

The initial accumulation of volcanics, sediments, and iron-formations in the Labrador Trough also appears to have taken place in a rift environment (Dimroth, 1981; Franklin and Thorpe, 1982), and Larue and Sloss (1980) have deduced that rifting accompanied deposition of the Marquette Supergroup, which contains the Menominee and Baraga Group iron-formations. A number of late Proterozoic iron-formations also occur within well-defined rift environments (Young, 1976). These include iron-formations in the Rapitan Group, northwestern Canada, and iron-formations in the upper part of the Adelaidian succession in Australia. The clearest example of iron ore accumulation in a rift setting, however, is provided by the Devonian Lahn-Dill deposits in Germany (Quade, 1976), that are associated with bimodal basalt-rhyolite volcanics (Lehmann, 1972; Sawkins and Burke, 1980).

8.7 Metallogenesis and Rifting – Some Final Thoughts

The interrelationship of rift tectonics and the generation of specific types of ore deposits has come into increasingly clearer focus within the last decade. Despite this many problems remain, especially in terms of our need to understand the variability inherent in rifting mechanisms, and their kinetics and geologic manifestations. Answers to these uncertainties will come only from more detailed geologic, geophysical, and geochemical studies of supracrustal successions and their relationship to continental basement. Hopefully patterns will finally emerge by which specific rifting mechanisms and kinetics can be related to the volume and petrochemistry of the associated igneous and sedimentary rocks, and the types of ore deposits present. In fact, it can be argued that some types of metallic ores are so characteristic of certain rift environments that their utilization as indicators of rifting is justifiable.

Unlike young Cordilleran terrains, most ancient rift sequences now occur within continental interiors where relief and consequent exposure tend to be limited. It follows that much remains to be learned about such sequences, and this will require careful collection and integration of surface, subsurface, and geophysical data. The recent discovery, below considerable cover, of the huge Olympic Dam copper and uranium deposits of Roxby Downs, Australia is perhaps a case in point (Roberts and Hudson, 1983). In the future, enlightened programs of basin analysis, not unlike those practiced by the petroleum industry, will be increasingly needed in the search for metal deposits formed in extensional tectonic paleo-environments.

Part III
Collisional Environments and Other Matters

Chapter 9 Metal Deposits in Relation to Collision Events

Although the Alpine-Himalayan belt provides a clear example of the consequences of Cenozoic collision tectonics, and the Caledonide-Appalachian belt an example of Paleozoic collision tectonics, the interpretation of the tectonic history of many Paleozoic and older orogenic belts is fraught with uncertainty. Wilson Cycle concepts provide a cogent explanation for the history of Iapetus, but there are many orogenic belts where the bulk of the evidence seems to militate against the former operation of a full Wilson Cycle. The problem is exacerbated by the fact that the large majority of orogenic belts provide reasonably clear evidence of an initial extensional phase followed eventually by a compressional phase. Even though this condition is similar to the early and final stages of a Wilson Cycle, it does not necessarily imply the creation of an oceanic tract during the interim period.

The formation and eventual subduction of an oceanic tract much wider than the present Red Sea can be expected to leave telltale evidence of its prior existence in the form of obducted ophiolites, provided erosion levels are not too deep. More significantly, irrespective of erosion levels, some evidence for the former presence of a calc-alkaline volcanoplutonic arc should be manifest along one side of the collision orogen. In some orogenic belts, such as the Damarides, not only is this evidence lacking, but paleomagnetic studies (McWilliams and Kroner, 1981) provide no evidence for signficant separation at any stage of the flanking, older cratonic blocks.

For reasons of exposure, access, and mineral potential the Damara Province has been the subject of considerable study (see Tankard et al., 1982 and references therein), and represents a key area in terms of understanding certain Proterozoic and perhaps Paleozoic orogenic belts that do not appear to fit the Wilson Cycle model. Tankard et al. (1982) provide an excellent summary of the sedimentation and tectonics of the Damara Province and the Gariep Province to the south, and also review the various models proposed for it.

The Damara Province represents a three-armed asymmetric orogenic system in which lithologic and structural continuity is observable between each arm (Fig. 9.1). Two of these arms parallel the Atlantic coast and may represent original depositional basins whose western flanks are now represented in part by lithosequences in the Ribera Province of Brazil (Porada, 1979). The three armed nature of this orogenic system is highly suggestive of the hotspot-associated rift geometries documented by Burke and Dewey (1973). In fact, initial sedimenta-

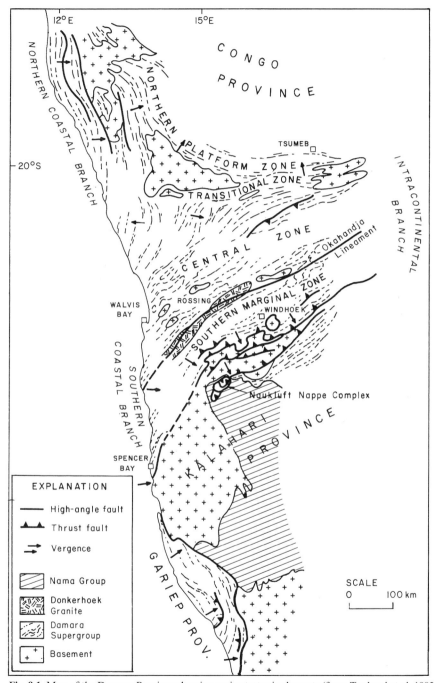

Fig. 9.1. Map of the Damara Province showing major tectonic elements (from Tankard et al. 1982)

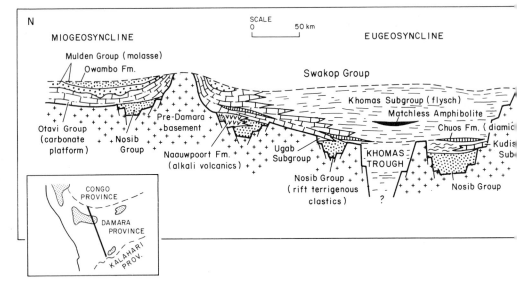

Fig. 9.2. North-south cross section of the Damara Province showing control of stratigraphic elements by extensional (rift) faulting (from Tankard et al. 1982)

tion of the Damara Supergroup, represented by arkosic arenites (Nosib Group) appears to have been on continental crust, and commenced about 1000 m.y. ago. Locally rhyolites were erupted and at one locality a considerable thickness of volcanic rocks of alkali-basaltic composition (Naauwpoort Formation, see Fig. 9.2) developed. Not only is this sequence of sediments and volcanics typical of the early stages of continental rifting, but stratiform copper deposits were formed at the interface between continental redbeds and marine sediments (Martin, 1978) (see Chap. 7). By about 830 m.y. ago a much broader trough developed and sedimentation across the entire width of the Damara Province commenced (see Fig. 9.2). Subsidence was more pronounced in the south, where a very thick flysch sequence accumulated, while on the northern foreland a substantial thickness of stromatolitic dolomitic limestones of platform type (Otavi Group) was deposited. Copper-zinc massive sulfide ores are associated with a brief, but extensive, pulse of basaltic volcanism (Matchless Amphibolite Belt) within the southern flysch belt, whereas Mississippi Valley-type lead-zinc mineralizaton is hosted by the carbonate rocks in the north. Uplift in the central zone of the province caused molasse sedimentation (Mulden Group) in adjacent areas, and by this stage major tectonism of the province was initiated. By 550 m.y. ago syntectonic granites were being intruded and metamorphism was at or close to its peak of intensity.

Approximately 50 m.y. later nappe tectonics were taking place in the Southern Marginal Zone and Nama Foreland, while farther north the Okahandja lineament became active and there was additional emplacement of granites. This was followed (510–480 m.y. ago) by the rise of mantled gneiss domes and emplacement of late granitoids. The Rossing uraniferous alaskites were formed 460m.y. ago, and by 400 m.y. ago sufficient uplift and cooling had occurred such that no further disruption of the Sr-Rb isotopic systems is evident.

Overall, the geology of the Damara Province has many of the features associated with Wilson Cycle collisional orogens – early rifting, major asymmetric thrusting, and basement reactivation – but lacks evidence of ocean opening and closing events. Despite this, Kasch (1979) and Barnes and Sawyer (1980) have suggested a continental collision model for it, in which they envisage northward subduction leading progressively from an Andean phase to a Zagros phase, followed by a Himalayan phase, and finally an Alpine phase of tectonism and magmatism. The two most telling arguments against this model come from the most recent, precision paleomagnetic data (McWilliams and Kroner, 1981), and the relative paucity of intermediate, low initial Sr ratio granitoid bodies that would be products of the subduction process.

Martin and Porada (1977) and Porada (1979) have championed a strictly ensialic model for the Damara Province, while acknowledging that the northern and southern coastal arms of the Province, with their strong eastward vergence of structures, probably resulted from a true Wilson Cycle collision event that closed a proto-South Atlantic Ocean. Evidence for an initial divergence includes early bimodal igneous activity along both the northern (e.g., Chela Group, Angola; Kroner and Correia, 1980) and southern (e.g., Stinkfonkein Formation; Tankard et al., 1982) arms of the system.

Porada (1979) notes that similar tectonic activity (graben formation) occurred within the Ribeira Province of Brazil, that was probably contiguous to the Damara Province approximately a billion years ago. The model suggested by Martin and Porada (1978) for the ensialic Damara Province arm involves foundering of dense eclogitic upper mantle to provide the compressional forces for orogenic shortening and thrust tectonics during the metamorphic culmination.

The concepts favored by Kroner (1980) to explain Pan-African tectonic belts in general, and the Damara Province in particular, represent an extension of those of Martin and Porada (Fig. 9.3). Kroner envisages prolonged early rifting culminating in crustal thinning and extrusion of primitive tholeiitic basalts into basins (e.g., Matchless Amphibolite Belt). Subsequently, delamination and sinking of dense subcrustal lithosphere occurs and the onset of compression leads to flat 'subduction' of continental crust along the zone of delamination. The thickened crust thus produced leads eventually to uplift and exposure of the deep portions of the orogen where considerable metamorphism and anatectic magmatism have occurred.

These models of ensialic orogeny certainly explain the geologic relationships and paleomagnetic data, but the source of the compressive forces involved remains obscure. It is, however, this very compression that generates the simi-

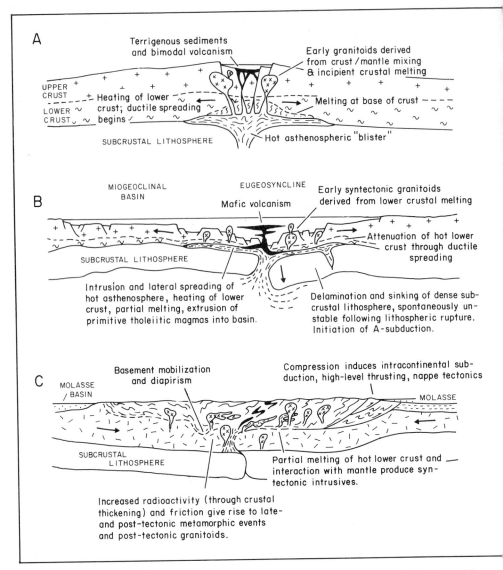

Fig. 9.3. Simplified schematic sections to show inferred evolution of Proterozoic ensialic mobile belts, as suggested by the geology of the Damara Province. Note initial phase of extension, followed by a compressional (collision) phase (from Tankard et al. 1982)

larities of these belts to collision orogens of Wilson Cycle type. Perhaps the softening of these zones due to attenuation and strong heating makes them susceptible to forces transmitted across plates from their far edges. Whatever the ultimate causes, it appears that both Wilson Cycle and ensialic orogens merit designation as collisional tectonic belts and I plan to consider both as such.

This rather extended discussion of the Damaride Province is considered warranted because resolution of the broad dichotomy between concepts of Wilson Cycle orogeny and those of ensialic orogeny, and the fundamental differences and similarities between the two, is central to a fuller understanding of ancient orogenic belts. A key issue here is that initial rifting stages and final collisional stages appear to be common to both, and this has significant implications in terms of the metal deposits we can expect to find in such belts.

The metal deposits in collisional orogenic belts can be divided into two types: those formed prior to the main pulse of tectonism, and those generated as a result of the tectonic and associated metamorphic activity. We have dealt with the former, mainly in the two previous chapters, but it is worth re-emphasizing that the tectonic events associated with collision are important in terms of regurgitating rift-related deposits that were formerly buried beneath miogeoclinal wedges or within deep rift troughs. This explains why sediment-hosted massive sulfide deposits younger than mid-Paleozoic are unknown, although possible contemporary examples of such ore deposits are represented by the Red Sea sulfide muds and sulfide mounds in the Guaymas Basin. In addition, the tendency of collision orogens produced by closure of an oceanic tract to contain a spectrum of juxtaposed ore deposit types, formed initially in a variety of tectonic settings has been well documented by Sillitoe (1978) in Pakistan.

9.1 Ophiolite-Hosted Metal Deposits

True Wilson Cycle collisions, and arc-arc or arc-continent collisions tend to result in the obduction of ophiolite complexes and thus are critical to the preservation of slices of oceanic crust and mantle. However, because strong uplift and subsequent deep erosion are typically attendant on collision events, these ophiolite complexes tend to have a limited preservation potential. Thus, the Cenozoic Alpine-collision belt has numerous ophiolite complexes scattered along its length, and contains many of the most significant examples of ophiolite-hosted metal deposits (see Chap. 5). Paleozoic age collision belts of Wilson Cycle-type such as the Urals and Caledonide/Appalachian orogeny also contain a number of mineralized ophiolite complexes, but relative to the Alpine-Himalayan belt, they are less numerous. Proterozoic ophiolite complexes are rare, probably because the level of erosion in Proterozoic orogens tends to be deep, and any such complexes they may have harboured have been largely lost to the forces of erosion.

9.2 Tin-Tungsten Deposits Associated
with Collisional Granites

One of the hallmarks of collisional orogenic belts, both those of Wilson Cycle-type and intracratonic-type, is the generation of considerable volumes of anatectic (S-type) granites. These intrusives are in many instances two-mica granites and, as opposed to the I-type granitic intrusives of arc systems, tend to exhibit diffuse contact zones characterized by migmatites. Such granites are particularly prevalent along the Hercynian belt of western Europe (Fig. 9.4), and Pitcher (1979) characterizes such granitic complexes as Hercynotype as opposed to those of Andinotype, which are subduction related (Fig. 9.5). He further points out that relative amounts of gabbro-diorite/tonalite-granodiorite/granite are quite distinctive for each type. In Hercynotype settings the relative proportions of these rock types are judged to be 2:18:80, whereas in Andinotype settings the ratios are closer to 15:50:35. Interestingly, the controversy that raged in petrologic circles several decades ago (Read, 1957) regarding the origin and emplacement of granite was largely between those workers whose field ex-

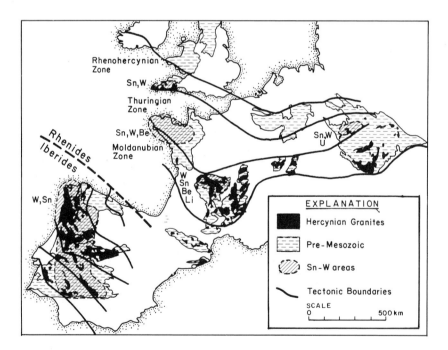

Fig. 9.4. Map of pre-Mesozoic and Hercynian granitoids in western and central Europe beyond the Alpine orogen. Granitoids shown in *black* (modified from Stemprok 1980)

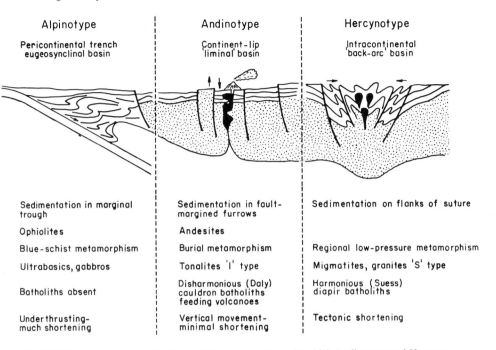

Fig. 9.5. Pitcher's conceptual depiction of the tectonic settings in which Andinotype and Hercynotype granitic intrusives are generated (from Pitcher 1979)

perience was limited to Hercynotype granites, and those whose experience was limited to Andinotype granitic rocks.

Important tin and tungsten deposits are associated with Hercynian granites in southwest England (Dines, 1956), the Erzegebirge-Krusne Hory area, Germany and Czechoslovakia (Tischendorf et al., 1978), and the western Iberian Penninsula (Cotelo Neiva, 1972), and lesser deposits are associated with Hercynian granites in Brittany and the Massif Central in France (Stemprok, 1981) (see Fig. 9.4). Numerous attempts have been made to interpret the Hercynides in terms of a collisional event preceded by closing of the Rheic Ocean (e.g., Bromley, 1976; Dewey and Burke, 1973; Mitchell, 1974). However, the lack of a well-defined Andinotype arc on either flank of the Hercynian belt, and the evidence of a rifting event only about 70 million years prior to collision (Sawkins and Burke, 1980) support the concept that the Hercynian belt is more appropriately viewed as a predominantly ensialic-type collision belt, of the type detailed in the opening section of this chapter. Transcurrent faulting may also have been important in the evolution of this belt (Badham, 1982), as noted in the preceding chapter. If the Lizard Complex is in fact a true ophiolite, however, (Kirby, 1979), then some oceanic crust must have been generated during the antecedent rifting events. S-type granites of Hercynian age (Middle Devonian to Carboni-

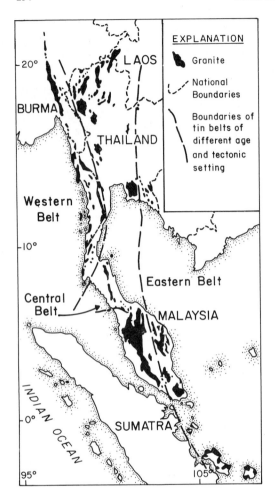

EXPLANATION

Granite

National
Boundaries

Boundaries of
tin belts of
different age
and tectonic
setting

Fig. 9.6. Map of granitoid bodies associated with the tin belts of Southeast Asia (from Beckinsale 1979)

ferous) that have tin-tungsten-molybdenum greisen and skarn deposits associated with them are also known in Nova Scotia and New Brunswick (Ruitenberg and Fyffe, 1982). The best known deposit in this area is that at Mt. Pleasant (Petruk, 1973), a subvolcanic porphyry deposit containing 9 million tons of close to 0.4 percent WO_3 and 0.2 percent MoS_2, and having considerable potential for additional ore. Sillitoe (pers. comm.) suggests, however, that the intrusive which spawned this deposit is related to a major post-collisional transform.

The Central Tin Belt in Southeast Asia (Mitchell, 1977) is a less controversial example of a collisional orogen, and contains major tin deposits associated with S-type granites. As depicted in Figure 9.6, it is flanked to the west by the younger back-arc magmatic tin belt (see Chap. 3), and to the east by a pre-collision magmatic arc of Permo-Triassic age (Mitchell and Garson, 1981). This eastern belt is puzzling, however, because lead and strontium data indicate that the tin granites of Indonesia, that lie within this belt, are of crustal origin (Jones et al., 1977). Nevertheless, it also contains a porphyry copper deposit at Loci in Thailand, a typical product of subduction-related magmatism (Hutchinson and Taylor, 1978) that appears to belong to an arc system sandwiched between the Central and Eastern Tin Belts (Sillitoe, pers. comm.).

The Central Tin Belt accounts for about half the tin production of the western world, although most of this comes from placer deposits (Mitchell and Garson, 1981). The tin-bearing granites are primarily peraluminous two-mica granites and adamellites of late Triassic age, and exhibit high initial $^{87}Sr/^{86}Sr$ ratios (Beckinsale et al., 1979). They are thus of characteristic S-type.

9.2.1 Mineralization

The tin and tungsten mineralization of the Hercynian belt is closely associated with the younger group of granitic intrusives (260–300 m.y.), which are predominantly alumina-rich alaskites and lithium albite granites. The most important deposits are closely associated in space with intrusive contacts and occur as stockworks, vein complexes, or single veins characterized by greisen-type alteration and the presence of tourmaline (Stemprok, 1981). Where limestones occur adjacent to igneous contacts, skarn-type deposits are formed locally. Vein deposits only loosely related to igneous contacts exhibit a control by regional structural directions and fissure systems. These veins are less important economically, but tend to be more extensive vertically.

Vein fillings consist predominantly of quartz with lower amounts of micas, topaz, tourmaline, K-feldspar, fluorite, and siderite. The metallic minerals are cassiterite and wolframite, accompanied by variable amounts of the sulfides arsenopyrite, pyrite, pyrrhotite, sphalerite, galena, chalcopyrite, bismuthinite and stannite. The sulfosalt association that characterizes the inner-arc tin deposits of Boliva is essentially absent in Hercynian tin deposits (Stemprok, 1981). However, zoning, a feature of most arc-related hydrothermal deposits, is also developed in these collision-related ores, and is manifest as a change from tin-dominated veins in the central portions of districts to base metal sulfidedominated veins on their peripheries. Such zoning is particularly well developed around the tin-centers in Devon and Cornwall (Fig. 9.7). In greisen and skarn deposits the tungsten-bearing mineral is typically scheelite rather than wolframite.

9.2.2 The Panasqueira Tin-Tungsten Deposits, Northern Portugal

The Panasqueira district is of interest on two counts: it is the largest producer of tungsten in western Europe, and is almost certainly the most thoroughly studied collision-related hydrothermal deposit in the world. The ores in the Panasqueira district average 0.3 percent W, and in 1978 mine production repre-

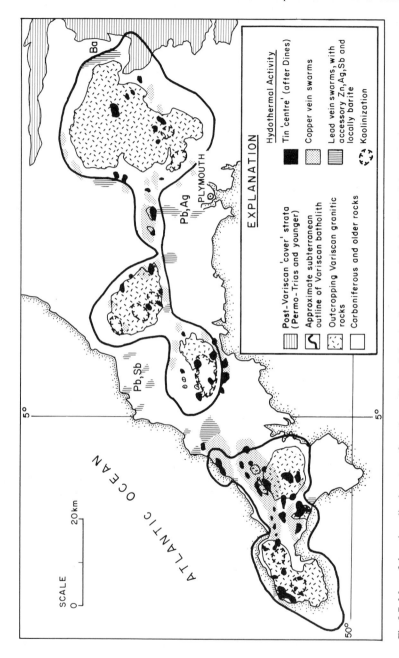

Fig. 9.7. Map of the mineralized centers of southwest England showing broad zonal relationships of tin, copper, and lead mineralization. Note clear indication of a spatial association of mineralization with the roof zones of the Variscan (Hercynian) granites (from Moore 1982)

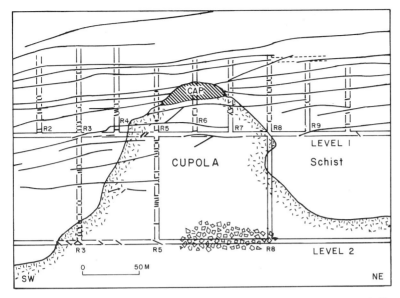

Fig. 9.8. Cross section of the Panasqueira cupola showing flat vein structures and silica cap (from Kelly and Rye 1979)

sented 1,450 tons of tungsten concentrate (75% WO_3), 62 tons of cassiterite concentrate (75% SnO_2), and 1,101 tons of chalcopyrite concentrate (22%Cu). The geology, mineralogy, and fluid inclusions of the deposit have been extensively studied by Kelly over a period of several years (Kelly and Rye, 1979), and the following descriptions and data are taken from that work.

The Panasqueira veins overlie a hidden cupola of strongly altered and greisenized two-mica granite. The granite was intruded about 290 m.y. ago into a sequence of dark schists which exhibit a rather broad aureole of contact metamorphism (mainly spotting), indicative of a more extensive intrusive at depth. The area is also intruded by post-granite dolerite and aplite dikes.

The Panasqueira vein system is unusual in that the veins occupy horizontal dilation structures, thought to have formed by the reduction of overburden pressure. The mineralization consequently is restricted to a narrow vertical interval (100–300 m) in the schists above the cupola, but is laterally extensive (Fig. 9.8). Kelly and Rye (1979) note that the veins, which formed by openspace filling, are clearly later than emplacement of the Panasqueira Granite, which they view as a structural conduit for ore fluids of deeper provenance.

Four stages of mineralization are identified (Fig. 9.9), each of which appears to be contemporaneous throughout most of the vein system. The silica cap immediately above the apex of the granite cupola is thought to have been formed by early precipitation of quartz in a void created by slight withdrawal of mag-

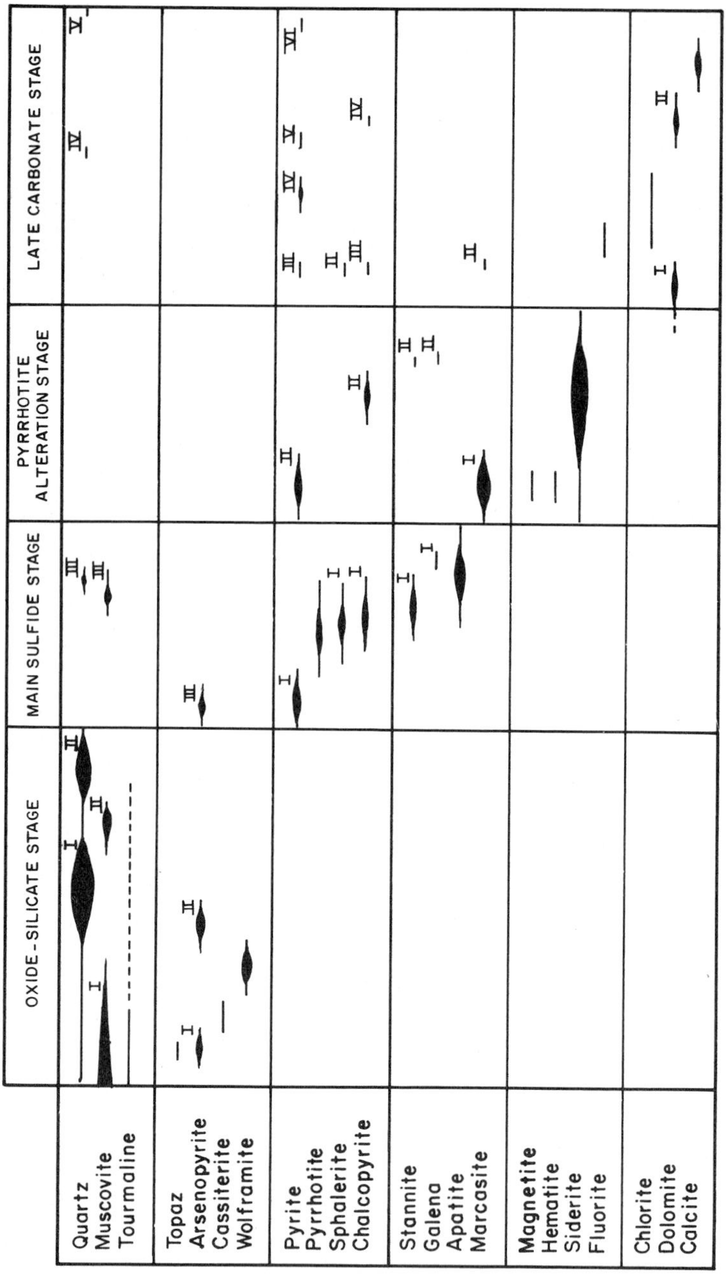

Fig. 9.9. General paragenesis of the tin-tungsten veins of the Panasqueira deposit. Roman numerals identify multiple generations of a given mineral (from Kelly and Rye 1979)

ma, and is weakly mineralized. The vein apatites are fluorapatite, and all the white micas are fluormuscovites of rather uniform composition.

Fluid inclusion studies indicate that the ore solutions were sodium chloride brines (5–10 wt%), that ranged in temperature from 230° to 360 °C during mineralization stages I, II and III (see Fig. 9.9). During the final stage of vein deposition the temperatures dropped to below 120 °C and the salinity of the fluids was less than 5 wt%. The carbon dioxide contents of the ore solutions declined with time, but were as high as 9 mole percent during formation of the silica cap, though through most of the mineralization CO_2 contents were less than 2 mole percent. Calculations based on the fluid inclusion data indicate that fluid pressure must have attained 1000 bars at times, and depth estimates for the vein system during mineralization provide a range of 600–1300 m below the water table.

$\delta^{18}O_{H_2O}$ data from the deposit indicate a high degree of ore fluid exchange with the schist country rocks and/or the underlying granite, and Kelly and Rye (1979) conclude the earlier stage fluids could have been either magmatic in origin or highly exchanged meteoric water. Based on their $\delta^{18}O_{H_2O}$ values, the late-stage fluids appear to have contained a dominant meteoric component. The available δD data are puzzling in that they indicate two isotopically distinct waters during stage I mineralization, one with values in the range -41 to -63 δD_{H_2O}, another with values in the range -67 to -124. $\delta^{34}S$ data derived from sulfide minerals indicate a narrow range of 0.1 to -0.9, and are interpreted to indicate H_2S dominated solutions and sulfur of possible magmatic provenance. $\delta^{13}C$ values of carbonates in the veins imply a graphitic or organic carbon component for the carbon contained in the hydrothermal solutions. Overall, the stable isotope data appear to indicate a strong country rock signature in the mineralizing fluids, but inasmuch as the underlying granite is of S-type (i.e., formed by anatexis of crustal materials) a magmatic origin of the earlier stage ore fluids and the metals seems probable.

The Hercynian tin-tungsten veins are cut by steep, later faults that contain weak base metal mineralization of uncertain age and provenance, but in general the ores have not suffered tectonic or significant thermal disturbance since their formation. In view of the indicated shallow depth at which they formed, it is somewhat surprising that they have not been eroded away, but it can be surmised that they were protected by post-ore cover rocks that have since been removed.

9.2.3 Discussion and Suggestions for Exploration

The tin and tungsten deposits associated with S-type granitoid intrusives in collision belts resemble the magmatic hydrothermal vein-type deposits associated with I-type granitoid intrusives in subduction-related terrains in many respects (e.g., morphology and zoning). This is not surprising for both are almost certainly formed in large measure by hydrothermal fluids emanating from shallow-seated magmatic systems. The main difference between the two groups lies in the predominance of tin and tungsten in the former, and base and precious metals in the latter. As noted earlier, where tin and tungsten metallization does occur in arc systems, the deposits tend to be confined to the innermost zones of continental margin arcs where the intrusives manifest a distinct S-type character.

The tin-tungsten deposits in question exhibit a close spatial association with the roof zones of collision-related granites, especially those that are emplaced during the late stages of orogenesis. Granitic bodies of this class, that exhibit high degrees of differentiation and some postmagmatic alteration, are obvious broad exploration targets. Also, because of the zoning characteristics of such systems, diffuse base metal vein mineralization in collision orogens deserves attention, for it may represent the distal manifestation of subsurface tin-tungsten mineralization. Unfortunately, neither geochemical nor geophysical techniques have much utility in such situations, although Yeates et al. (1982) have reported encouraging results from the application of gamma-ray spectrometry to prospecting for tin and tungsten granites in the Lachlan Fold Belt. Apparently in this area mineralized granites contain, on average, significantly higher U (5 ppm) than non-mineralized granites. Also, careful gravity surveys could help to locate shallow subsurface granitic intrusives, and their uppermost portions could be subsequently tested by diamond drilling. Attention should also be focussed on broad areas of greisenization, in the event that they host low grade tin-tungsten ores amenable to bulk mining techniques. The East Kempville deposit in southwest Nova Scotia is an example of this, and contains 38 million tons of 0.2% Sn in a greisen zone developed along the contact of a monzogranite of late Devonian age (Richardson et al., 1982).

9.3 Uranium Deposits Associated with Collision Granites

The S-type granites that are generated in collision orogens are also in some instances associated with uranium deposits. The major examples of such uranium mineralization occur in the Massif Central of France (Cuney, 1978), the Bohemian Massif in Czechoslovakia (Ruzicka, 1971) (Fig. 9.10) and at Rossing in Namibia (Berning et al., 1976). Although the hydrothermal uranium deposits of the Hercynian terrains of Europe exhibit a strong spatial association with granites, their age of formation is in some instances distinctly younger than the granitic masses exposed at the surface (Leroy, 1978). As with the Hercynian tin-tungsten deposits, mineralization ages tend to be in the 280–295 m.y. range, coincidental with the very last phase of Hercynian magmatism.

Uranium deposits in collision settings are predominantly of vein type, but in some cases also occur in breccia zones. In the Margnac-Fanay district of the Central Massif, the vein deposits occur within an area of older two-mica granite (Saint Sylvestre granite) that is laced with faults, microgranite dikes, lampro-

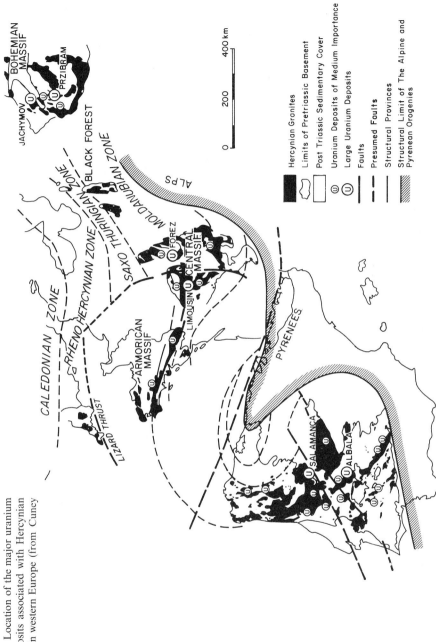

Fig. 9.10. Location of the major uranium vein deposits associated with Hercynian granites in western Europe (from Cuney 1978)

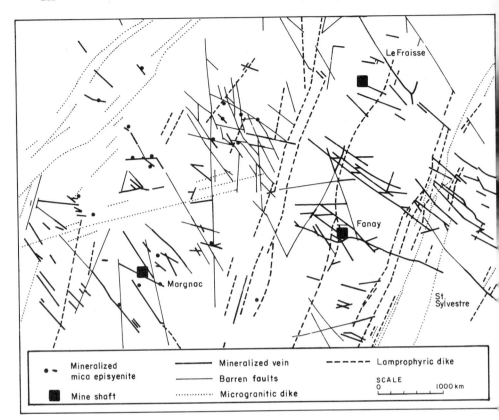

Fig. 9.11. Distribution of veins, faults, and dikes in the Margnac and Fanay uranium districts, developed within the Bois Noirs granite, central France (from Leroy 1978)

phyre dikes, and mineralized veins (Fig. 9.11) (Leroy, 1978). Here, and also in the Boise Noirs-Limouzat vein system (Cuney, 1978), detailed studies indicate multistage mineralization of the vein structures with quartz, pitchblende, sulfides, hematite, and carbonates arrayed in complex paragenetic sequences. In the case of the Bohemian Massif ores, uranium mineralization tends to represent a distinct stage that postdates an earlier quartz-carbonate-sulfide stage of mineralization (Ruzicka, 1971). Here too, detailed paragenetic relationships are complex, and short uranium ore shoots occur within larger vein systems.

Fluid inclusion studies on the French deposits cited above provide data that seem to mirror the paragenetic complexity of the veins. Ore fluid temperatures varied from over 300 °C to less than 100 °C, and variations also occur in salt and CO_2 contents of the fluids. The genetic model that has evolved from these studies suggests a mixing of meteoric water with deepseated (magmatic) CO_2,

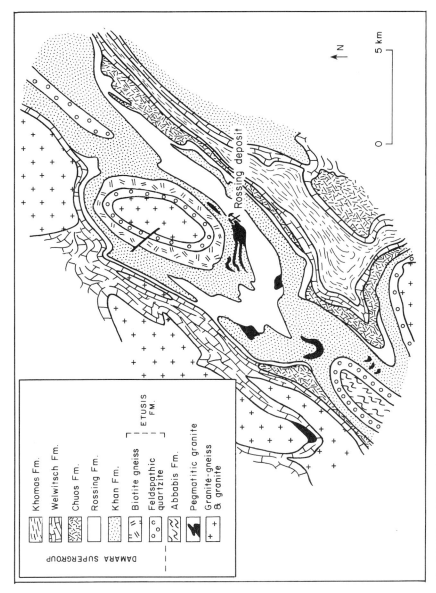

Fig. 9.12. Map of the Rossing uranium district, Damara Province, Namibia (modified from Smith 1965)

Legend (Damara Supergroup):
Khomas Fm.
Welwitsch Fm.
Chuos Fm.
Rossing Fm.
Khan Fm.
Biotite gneiss — ETUSIS FM.
Feldspathic quartzite — ETUSIS FM.
Abbabis Fm.
Pegmatitic granite
Granite-gneiss & granite

Rossing deposit

N

0   5 km

and the leaching and concentration of uranium from the host granites. However, the manifestations of late Hercynian magmatism in these areas (mainly microgranite and lamprophyre dikes) conceivably provided a proportion of the aqueous fluids and metals involved in mineralization, in addition to the CO_2 and heat.

9.3.1 The Rossing Uranium Deposit, Namibia

Although grade and tonnage figures for the Rossing orebody are not known to the author, this deposit is generally conceded to be the largest uranium producer in the free world. It lies in the central, high-grade metamorphic zone of the Damaride orogenic belt, where granitized sedimentary rocks, and possibly volcanics, of the Etusis and Khan Formations, and remobilized early Precambrian basement (Abbabis Formation) have been intruded by anatectic granites. The Abbabis Formation includes a variety of gneisses, phyllites, marbles, and biotite schist, and is exposed in the cores of anticlines and domal structures (Smith, 1965) (Fig. 9.12). The overlying rocks of the Damara Supergroup consist of clastic and calcareous sediments now metamorphosed to gneisses, schists and marbles, and all strongly deformed.

The uranium mineralization occurs within a migmatite zone characterized by largely concordant relationships between uraniferous pegmatitic granites and the gneisses, schists, and marbles of the Khan and Rossing Formations (Fig. 9.13). The granitic rocks that contain the uranium mineralization are termed alaskites by the mine geologists, and they display a spectrum of textures ranging from aplitic to granitic and pegmatitic. The alaskite intrusions vary from thin conformable dikes, typically in closely spaced arrays, to more robust intrusions of discordant character. Relationships of the alaskite with country rocks detailed by Berning et al. (1976), lead these authors to deduce a passive, metasomatic emplacement of the alaskite. However, contact metamorphic effects between alaskite and adjacent country rock are clearly evident, and the local presence of a melt phase cannot be totally discounted.

Most of the alaskite in the area is unmineralized or only weakly mineralized. Economic grade uranium mineralization is concentrated where the alaskite was emplaced in a garnet gneiss/amphibole unit (northern ore zone) or into the amphibole-biotite schist/lower marble/low cordierite gneiss sequence of the central ore zone. The controls of ore localization in this manner are not understood. Uraninite is the main primary ore mineral, and is confined to alaskite as very small grains (several microns to 0.3 mm), occurring either occluded within quartz, feldspar and biotite, or within cracks, or interstitially to these minerals. It also exhibits a preferential association with biotite and zircon. Associated with the uraninite are much lesser amounts of betafite, whereas fluorite, sulfides (pyrite, chalcopyrite, bornite, molybdenite, and arsenopyrite), and oxides (magnetite, hematite and ilmenite) occur somewhat sporadically in the ore. Secondary uranium minerals, mainly beta-uranophane, represent 40 percent of the uranium present in the orebody (Berning et al., 1976).

A precise genetic model for the Rossing deposit is not at hand, but clearly the formation of the alaskite must have involved a concentration of uranium, probably abetted by enhanced uranium levels in the basement rocks, where the alaskite or the metasomatizing fluids that produced it were generated.

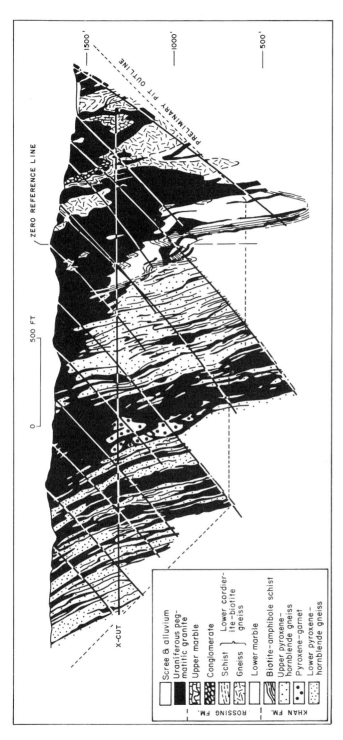

Fig. 9.13. Cross section of the Rossing uranium deposit (from Berning et al. 1976)

9.3.2 Discussion and Suggestions for Exploration

The fact that the collision-related S-type granites generate uranium deposits in some areas, tin-tungsten deposits in others, and neither in still others, presumably reflects the geochemical characteristics of the protolith from which they themselves originated, and their subsequent crystallization history. It follows that uranium deposits of this general type are best sought within terrains of demonstrably enhanced uranium content.

Clearly, deposits of Rossing-type that contain large tonnages of bulk-minable uranium ore are attractive exploration targets, but their recognition in non-arid climatic environments would be extremely difficult. Not only are the uranium minerals very fine-grained, but in areas of higher rainfall they would be leached downward from the surface. Notwithstanding these difficulties, the fact that no other deposits comparable to Rossing have been found in the rest of the Damaride belt, or elsewhere, would indicate that deposits of this type are not common.

9.4 Additional Examples of Collision-Related Terrains and Metallogenic Implications

The nature of major ocean-closing collision events (Dewey, 1977) is such that a considerable array of geologic environments can be generated. Thus, in addition to the deformation and metamorphism that occur in the core of the collision belt, sedimentation will occur in collision-related basins. These include remanent basins, foreland and hinterland basins, and intermountane troughs. Apart from small sandstone-type uranium, vanadium, or copper deposits which tend to form in sequences of subaerial clastics, such as those in the Siwaliks of the Sulaiman Range of Pakistan (Moghal, 1974), major metal deposits are not apparently generated in such environments. Furthermore, such sedimentary sequences are largely restricted to young collision belts (Mitchell and Garson, 1981) and, unlike the pre-collision rift sequences, tend to be missing from older collision-related terrains where erosion has cut deeper.

Of somewhat different character are the collisional terrains that result from the accretion of oceanic arcs and microcontinents to active continental margins. It is now generally recognized, for example, that a significant fraction of the North American Cordillera from southern Mexico to Alaska could be composed of terrains accreted to the craton by plate tectonic rafting (Coney, 1981). Interpretation of the accretion history of these terrains is obscured by later transform faulting, but Coney estimates that the North American continent has grown by as much as 30% through accretionary additions since the mid-Jurassic. The probability of a significant number of suspect (allochthonous) terrains in the Appalachian orogen has also been proposed (Williams and Hatcher,

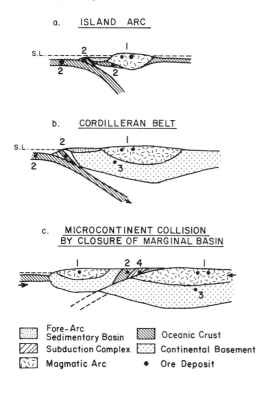

a. ISLAND ARC

b. CORDILLERAN BELT

c. MICROCONTINENT COLLISION
BY CLOSURE OF MARGINAL BASIN

	Fore-Arc Sedimentary Basin		Oceanic Crust
	Subduction Complex		Continental Basement
	Magmatic Arc	●	Ore Deposit

Fig. 9.14. Schematic metallogenic consequences of superposition of: a. principal-arc deposits (I) on ophiolitic deposits (2), and b. pre-arc rift-related deposits (3); juxtaposition of: a. and b. principal-arc deposits with accreted ophiolitic deposits in subduction complex (2), and c. with obducted ophiolitic deposits during collision, and c. of two belts of principal-arc deposits during collision; and c. generation of metamorphic-hydrothermal deposits (4) as a consequence of collision (from Sillitoe 1981a)

1982). The metallogenic implications of such events are not fully understood, but it is patently obvious that coherent metallogenic relationships cannot be expected to extend beyond the margins of a single terrain unless they were developed after accretion, and the search for broad metallogenic patterns in such areas would be futile in many cases. From the exploration viewpoint each separate terrain must obviously be considered on its own merits (Fig. 9.14).

The now mined-out Kennecott deposits of Alaska represent an important example of world class orebodies in an accreted terrain. Jones et al. (1977) define a Wrangellia terrain, named after the Wrangell Mountains in Alaska, that occurs in a number of discreet areas from Alaska to Oregon (Fig. 9.15). Each of these areas contains a distinctive sequence of middle to upper Triassic rocks consisting predominantly of thick tholeiitic flows and pillow lavas, overlain by platform carbonates. Paleomagnetic data from the Alaska segment volcanics (Hillhouse, 1977) indicate that this terrain has been translated at least 3000 km northward and rotated by about 90°. The Wrangellia terrains thus appear to represent an enormous, presumably rift-related, outpouring of continental basalts, that was disrupted and translated northward between late Triassic and early Cretaceous time.

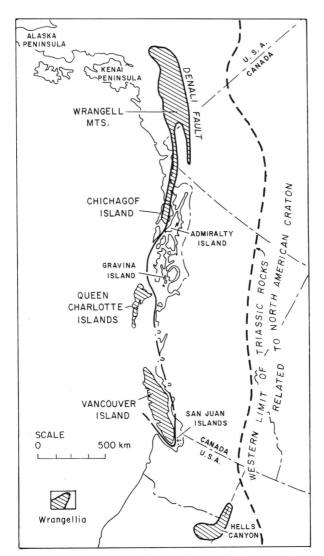

Fig. 9.15. Map showing distribution of terrains of Triassic age that are considered to represent fragments of Wrangellia (from Jones et al. 1977)

The Nikolai Greenstones of the Alaska Wrangellia fragment have an intrinsic copper content of 155 ppm (MacKevett et al., 1981), a value indicative of rift-related basalts (Sawkins, 1976b). The rich Kennecott ores occur in the lower 130 m of the Chitistone Limestone, that immediately overlies the Nikolai Greenstones (Bateman and McLaughlin, 1920) (Fig. 9.16). They are localized along a fault-truncated limb of a syncline as massive wedges of chalcocite and

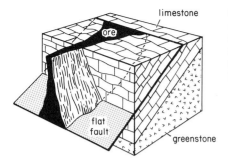

Fig. 9.16. Schematic block diagram to show typical occurrence of replacement ores of the Kennecott Mine, Alaska. Note position of ores just above copper-rich Nikolai greenstones and their structural control (from Bateman and McLaughlin 1920)

limestone

ore

flat
fault

greenstone

lesser copper oxides that probably reflect the filling of voids and caverns produced during an earlier karstification event (MacKevett et al., 1981).

Silberman et al. (1981) present stable isotope data for the Nikolai Greenstones near the Kennecott deposits that indicate a metamorphic-segregation origin for vein and flow top copper mineralization within these volcanics. They also report potassium-argon results indicative of a thermal-metamorphic episode at approximately 112 m.y. This age pertains to the mineralization, and thus redistribution of copper both within this unit and into the overlying Chitistone Limestone, and agrees with the age of accretionary collision deduced from stratigraphic and structural evidence. If this scenario is correct, then the Kennecott ores represent an important, if unusual, example of collision-related metallogeny.

9.5 Metallogenesis and Collision Events – Some Final Thoughts

Collision tectonic events are important in terms of the generation of lithophile element deposits such as tin and uranium. Certain amounts of base metals may also be involved in these systems, but their economic significance is at best minor. However, because collision events involve the metamorphism and deformation of earlier rocks, especially those deposited in prior rifting events, and ophiolite complexes are caught up in collision events, collision terrains can contain all of the deposit types discussed in Chaps. 5, 7, and 8 and are thus important but challenging areas to the exploration geologist (Sillitoe, 1978, 1980d).

One cannot but wonder what metal deposits will be found when the extensive collisional terrains present on all the continents are subjected to more careful scrutiny by exploration geologists conversant with the concepts set forth in this and previous chapters. Some of the details may prove to be erroneous, but the broad picture seems to be emerging in reasonably clear focus.

Chapter 10   Metal Deposits and Plate Tectonics –
an Attempt at Perspective

The rush to interpret all manner of geologic phenomena in terms of plate interactions has certainly led to some rather facile pronouncements, but, if a bare
majority of the relationships between metal deposits and plate environments described in the foregoing chapters are essentially correct, then plate tectonics
must be viewed as a concept of major significance in terms of the space-time distribution of many metal deposits. Despite this, Sangster (1979) attempts to re-
fute the utility of plate tectonic concepts in understanding metallogenesis. Sangster's difficulties stem mainly from his excessively narrow view of plate tectonic
theory and his unwillingness to accept the idea that plate tectonics operated during the Precambrian. Nevertheless, it is appropriate to review some of the other
concepts that have been suggested as important in terms of controlling the time-
space distribution of metal deposits.

10.1 Lineaments and Metal Deposits

A number of authors have maintained that lineaments, representing fundamental flaws in the continental crust, are major factors in the control of metallogenesis (e.g., Noble, 1980; Favorskaya, 1977; Kutina, 1980). The availability of
high quality earth imagery has also provided an impetus to the recognition and
interpretation of continental lineaments (e.g., Norman, 1980). Although many
of these efforts do not stand up well to scrutiny (Gilluly, 1976), the whole question of the possible significance of deep crustal flaws to certain groups of metal
deposits cannot be summarily dismissed.

Sykes (1978, 1980) has demonstrated that the reactivation of zones of weakness in continental crust can be related to the development of transform faults
in nascent ocean basins, and that these zones tend to control sites of intracontinental alkaline magmatism in west Africa and elsewhere (see also Marsh, 1973;
Culver and Williams, 1979). Such structures do not appear to be overly important in terms of metallogenesis, although associated kimberlites may be dia-
mond-bearing, and carbonatites may have potential for niobium or fluorite deposits (Mitchell and Garson, 1981, p. 311). Also, Heyl (1972) has documented
the structures, alkaline rocks and Mississippi Valley-type deposits that lie along
the 38th parallel lineament (see Fig. 7.17). Whether certain of the Mississippi

Valley deposits that lie close to this structure are genetically related to it is somewhat contentious, but it is noteworthy that major amounts of fluorite are present in some of the deposits that lie along this structure, and fluorine enrichment is characteristic of many alkaline rocks.

The Colorado Lineament represents a major crustal flow of considerable antiquity (Warner, 1978), and it is clear that it exerted a control on the magmatism that is associated with the ores of the Colorado Mineral Belt (see Fig. 3.1). Furthermore, the Walker Lane (see Fig. 1.17) is a lineament that in some manner controlled the sites of major Miocene precious metal deposits in the western Great Basin. Recently Hoy (1982b) has noted that all significant stratabound lead-zinc deposits in southeastern British Columbia, regardless of age and host-rock type, seem to be regionally controlled by a northeast-trending tectonic zone. Thus, middle Precambrian sediment-hosted massive sulfide deposits (e.g., Sullivan), late Proterozoic mineralization in marbles and calc-silicate rocks of the Shuswap Metamorphic Complex, and deposits in carbonate rocks of the Kootenay Arc (Lower Cambrian) in the Salmo and Duncan areas all fall within this zone. Hoy suggests that the zone is underlain by northeast-trending basement fractures that were the loci for recurrent faulting that controlled the discharge of metal-bearing fluids. Furthermore, O'Driscoll (1981) has noted the relationship between major west-northwesterly zones of crustal disturbance in the Yilgarn Block, western Australia and the sites of major nickel deposits in more northerly trending greenstone belts.

The Russian ore deposits literature is replete with references to the importance of deep crustal flaws as important controls of metallogeny (e.g., Smirnov, 1977), but in most cases these concepts result from an unwillingness of Soviet geologists (at least until recently) to accept plate tectonic interpretations of many geologic features. Much the same applies to the concepts of metallogeny in relation to geosynclinal theory (Bilibin, 1968; Smirnov, 1977) that prevail(ed) in that country.

10.2 Transform Faults and Metal Deposits

Considering their status as a major type of plate boundary, transform faults appear to have limited import in terms of metallogenesis. This is primarily because, except where 'leaky', transform faults have no magmatism associated with them. Thus, major structures such as the Sagaing-Namyin Fault, Burma (Curray et al., 1980), and the Central Range Fault, Taiwan (Biq, 1971) have no known mineralization directly associated with them. However, Sillitoe (1978) has noted a possible genetic relationship between the Cenozoic Chaman transform fault in Pakistan and stibnite vein deposits, and compared this setting with that of late Cenozoic mercury deposits in the Coast Ranges of California. Albers (1981), however, suggests a relationship of these mercury deposits to the Coast Range Thrust, a subduction-related feature.

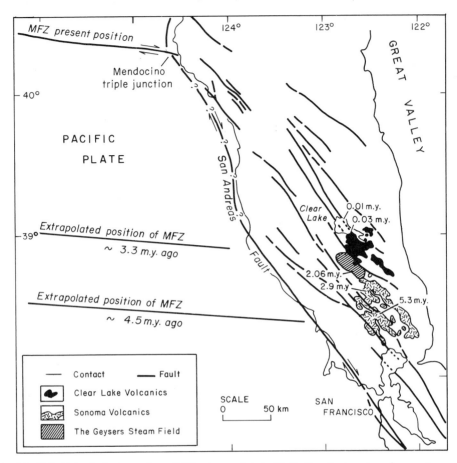

Fig. 10.1. Major faults in northern California associated with the San Andreas transform system. Also shown are the northward-younging series of lava fields associated with the system (from McLaughlin 1981)

The precise setting of northern California mercury deposits is of some importance because of the world-class McLaughlin gold deposit discovered in this area recently (Albers, 1981; D. Giles, pers. comm.). The late Cenozoic geologic history of this area is dominated by transform faulting and volcanism. The Clear Lake volcanics (Hearn et al., 1982) represent the northernmost and youngest (0.01 to 2.1 m.y.) group of a series of late Cenozoic volcanics that are strung out along the central Coast Ranges of California. All of these volcanics exhibit a spatial association with the San Andreas transform and associated faults to the east, and a general northward younging (23.5 to 0.01 m.y.) of volcanism is apparent (Fig. 10.1) (see Hearn et al., 1981 and references therein). Although these volcanics range in composition from basalt to rhyolite

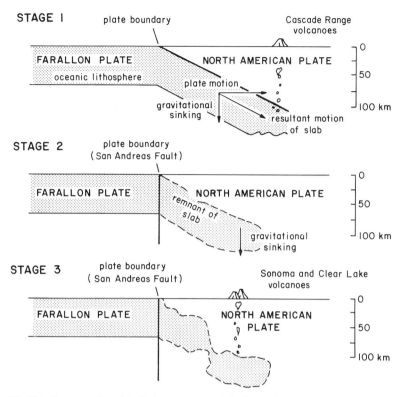

Fig. 10.2. Conceptual model of Isherwood to explain the origin of the Clear Lake volcanics, northern California (from Isherwood 1981)

and are essentially of calc-alkaline type, they exhibit complex strontium isotope variations suggestive of multiple magma sources in the upper mantle and lower crust (Futa et al., 1982).

The northward migration of volcanism referred to above has led to the suggestion of a hotspot control of igneous activity (Hearn et al., 1982), but Isherwood (1981) sees the main control of magmatism as downward settling of a subducted slab after its detachment from the Farallon Plate by the San Andreas transform (Fig. 10.2). Whatever the ultimate triggering mechanism for the magmatism, its association with transform faulting is clear, as is the relation of the mercury and gold deposits to this magmatism. The gold mineralization that forms the important McLaughlin deposit appears to be of typical hotspring type, and additional examples of disseminated gold mineralization may well occur along leaky transforms elsewhere. Geophysical studies (Isherwood, 1982) indicate that magma bodies are still present under the Clear Lake volcanic field and heat from these is responsible for the Geysers system, a major geothermal energy resource.

Another 'leaky' portion of the San Andreas transform occurs in the Salton Sea area, in the Imperial Valley. Here offsets of the transform system appear to be connected by short, and thus magmatically active, segments of spreading ridge (see Chap. 5). Little of this igneous activity completely penetrates the thick Miocene clastic section, but considerable geothermal activity indicates magma bodies at depth. Although the hot mineralized brines do not appear to be creating ore deposits, the exhalation of these brines into an anoxic marine environment could well result in a massive sulfide deposit.

The intersections of a spreading axis and transform faults also appear to be important in terms of localizing the metalliferous brine pools in the Red Sea (see Fig. 8.2). There is reason to suppose that similar situations accompanied the development of nascent ocean basins at other times in the geologic past, even though the lack of documented examples is puzzling (Shanks, 1977).

10.3 Plate Tectonics and Metal Deposits of Surficial Origin

Metal deposits in which the prime cause of metal concentration is due to surficial (weathering) processes are obviously dependent primarily on climatic factors for their origin, but plate tectonics can play a critical role in the emplacement or elevation of the protolith of certain of these deposits. Laterite-type nickel deposits provide a case in point, for all are formed in areas where tropical weathering processes act on the mantle portions of ophiolite complexes (Coleman, 1977; Golightly, 1981). Major examples include the laterite nickel deposits

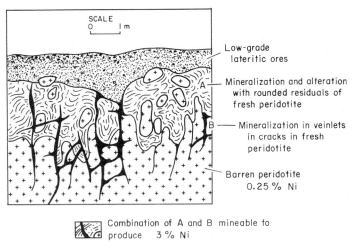

Fig. 10.3. Schematic section of laterite-type nickel deposits such as those developed in New Caledonia and other tropical areas where ophiolites are exposed (modified from Boldt 1967)

in New Caledonia, Cuba, the Dominican Republic, Columbia, Indonesia, and the Philippines (Boldt, 1967).

In deposits of this type the ultramafic protolith typically contains about 0.2% nickel but weathering results in the development of a mantle of low-grade lateritic nickel ore that in many instances is separated from unweathered peridotite by a zone of garnierite-bearing, semi-decomposed rock containing up to 3% Ni (Fig. 10.3). Clearly the initial crucial step in the history of formation of these deposits is the emplacement of ophiolite complexes resulting from plate interactions.

Henley and Adams (1979) have noted that the formation of giant gold placer deposits around the Pacific basin can be related to erosion and sequential hydraulic concentration, and point out that the tectonic uplifts that initiated the erosion can be related to Mesozoic and Tertiary plate motions. These include changes in spreading rate (Pitman and Hayes, 1973) that influence global sea-levels, and thus impact on the sequential erosion-deposition stages that are important to the evolution of giant placer deposits. Thus, here again we are confronted with the far-reaching effects of plate tectonics on ore formation.

10.4 An Enigmatic Class of Uranium Deposits

Within the last two decades a major new type of uranium deposit, the so-called unconformity-type, has come to be recognized, and additional discoveries of such deposits have had a major impact on the uranium resources of the Western World. The known deposits of this type occur almost exclusively in two terrains of Proterozoic age, the Pine Creek Geosyncline in northermost Australia, and the Athabasca Basin in west-central Canada. Although there are perhaps some fundamental, but hitherto unrecognized, differences between the uranium deposits in each of these areas, the two districts exhibit similarities in geologic setting and age, host rock alteration, mineralogy, geochemistry, and spatial association with graphitic or carbonaceous rocks (Hoeve et al., 1980; Needham et al., 1980).

In both areas metamorphosed lower Proterozoic sedimentary sequences overlie Archean rocks, and are themselves unconformably overlain by essentially undeformed middle Proterozoic sandstone-dominated sequences. In both areas tholeiitic mafic magmatism is broadly synchronous with the major period of uranium emplacement, and background uranium levels are high in the metamorphosed units below the unconformity. Within the Athabasca Basin (Fig. 10.4) the deposits occur both within carbon-rich metamorphics just below the unconformity and within the lowermost units of the overlying Athabasca Formation (Fig. 10.5), especially where east-northeast trending faults are present. The deposits thus exhibit a very strong relationship (control?) with respect to the unconformity. In the Pine Creek Geosyncline (Fig. 10.6) the deposits oc-

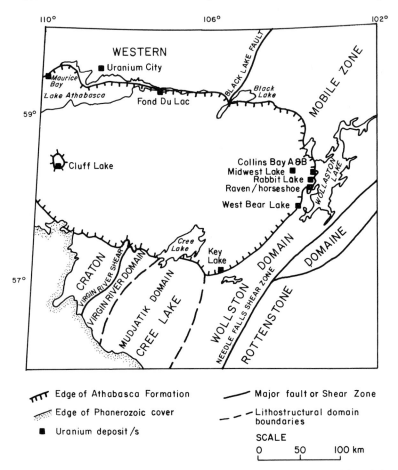

Fig. 10.4. Map showing the major unconformity-type uranium deposits of the Athabasca Basin, Canada (modified from Sibbald et al. 1977)

cur within carbonaceous metapelites (Cahill Fm) below the unconformity (Fig. 10.7) (Hegge et al., 1980), and most Australian workers have tended to minimize the significance of the unconformity at the base of the mid-Proterozoic sandstones (Kombolgie Fm) as a factor in ore genesis.

Mineralogic and geochemical research on these unconformity-type uranium deposits has produced a considerable data base and certain constraints regarding genetic models (e.g., Ypma and Fuzikawa, 1980), but little concensus regarding the source of the uranium. What does seem to be clear is that the fluids involved were of connate or meteoric rather than magmatic origin, that redox reactions were important in the transportation and eventual deposition of the uranium, and that chlorite was an important alteration product associated with

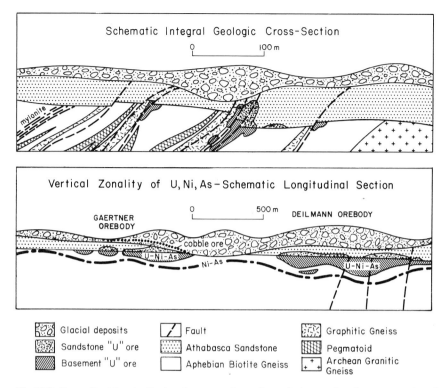

Fig. 10.5. Generalized longitudinal and cross sections of a typical unconformity-type uranium deposit in the Athabasca Basin (from Kirchner et al. 1980)

ore deposition. Furthermore, paragenesis and element associations in these deposits are complex (Ferguson and Winer, 1980; Hoeve et al., 1980).

Genetic models that have been put forward for these deposits run the gamut from leaching of uranium and associated elements from the rocks above the unconformity (Hoeve et al., 1980), to derivation of the uranium from the adjacent sub-unconformity metamorphics (Ferguson et al., 1980), to a deeper seated origin related to convective geothermal systems (Binns et al., 1980). Whatever the precise mechanisms for collection, transport, and deposition of the uranium may be however, it is noteworthy that both areas exhibit high uranium background levels and that the deposits themselves represent only the final stage of uranium concentration.

Rossiter and Ferguson (1980) have attempted a geotectonic synthesis of the Proterozoic metal deposits of northern Australia, and, with respect to the Pine Creek Geosyncline and its uranium ores, suggest that during the Proterozoic rifting of the Pine Creek region away from a paleo-continental margin occurred, with resultant emplacement of uraniferous granitic rocks due to mantle plume

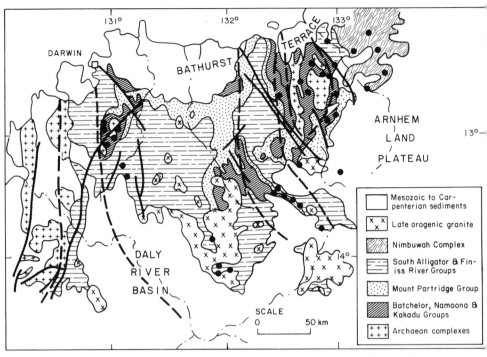

Fig. 10.6. Generalized geology and location of major uranium deposits (*solid circles*), Pine Creek Geosyncline, northern Australia (modified from Needham et al. 1980)

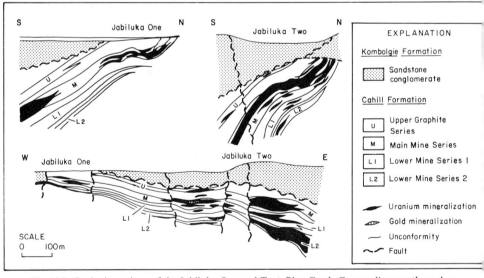

Fig. 10.7. Geologic sections of the Jabiluka One and Two, Pine Creek Geosyncline, northern Australia. Note that ores extend for a considerable distance below the Kombolgie uncomformity (from Hegge et al. 1980)

activity. In support of their model they note that the petrochemistry of the Proterozoic mafic igneous rocks in the region is supportive of this rifting plus hotspot scenario.

10.5 Metal Deposits and Plate Tectonics: Time-Space Perspectives

The relationships of metal deposits to various types of plate activity explored in the preceding chapters, if essentially correct, are impressive. In view of the thermal requirements of virtually all ore-generating systems, such a relationship is hardly surprising if one accepts that plate activity is primarily the result of the continuing requirement of the mantle to dissipate heat. The convective transfer of this heat to the surface and upper crust via magmatism sets in motion a variety of potential ore-generating mechanisms, and it is thus predictable that most major metal concentrations will exhibit time-space relationships to active or nascent (e.g., continental rifting) plate boundaries.

Some workers (e.g., Pereira and Dixon, 1963; Laznicka, 1973) have attempted to demonstrate that the fundamental nature of ore genesis has changed with the passage of geologic time. Although I reject this concept in favor of a more uniformitarian approach to ore genesis, it is clear that certain types of metal deposits are unevenly distributed with respect to the geologic time scale (Meyer, 1981), and such irregularities require explication. Many of these time patterns, such as the strong concentration of porphyry-type deposits to the latter third of the Phanerozoic can be logically viewed as the result of erosion of the upper portions of arc systems. However, in explaining other age anomalies one has to take cognizance of both crustal and atmospheric evolution. Thus, metal deposits that tend to form in continental rifting environments are absent from Archean terrains, because stable continental blocks of any consequence had not developed until the time of the Archean-Proterozoic transition. The one exception to this is represented by southern Africa where essentially stable Proterozoic regimes appear to have been ushered in by 2.8 b.y. ago (e.g., Witwatersrand Supergroup).

Another non-uniformitarian aspect of earth history is the evolutionary change of the earth's atmosphere (Schidlowski, 1976 and references therein). These changes had important effects on those deposits whose formation was critically dependent on redox reactions in near-surface environments. Thus, low partial pressures of oxygen were a factor in the detrital concentration of uraninite in paleoplacers, whereas higher oxygen pressures were almost certainly a factor in the formation of stratiform copper deposits, early Proterozoic banded iron formations, and unconformity-type uranium deposits. Also sandstone-type uranium deposits related to concentrations of plant material in permeable sandstones could not form until the evolution of land plants in

Devonian time. It is noteworthy that these are the deposit types that exhibit the strongest degree of time dependency.

Finally, as noted in Chapter 8, the paucity of sediment-hosted massive sulfide deposits in post-Paleozoic terrains is best explained by the deep burial of any such deposits within untectonized failed rifts or continental margins.

10.6 Metal Deposits and Plate Tectonics – Exploration Perspectives

There are two contrasting statements that can be made regarding the implications of plate tectonics to mineral exploration that are both inherently correct: (i) utilization of plate tectonics has never resulted in the discovery of a metal deposit, and (ii) the use of plate tectonic principles has enormous significance to the exploration for metal deposits. The contradictory nature of these two statements is apparent rather than real. Metal deposits are found by the investigation of mineralized or altered outcrops, and more and more in recent years by the follow-up of geochemical and/or geophysical anomalies. The primary conceptual tool that is used in exploration planning is that of the lithologic association. For example, it has long been recognized that certain massive sulfide deposits are associated with felsic pyroclastics erupted in sub-marine environments, and that stratiform copper deposits are associated with clastic sedimentary rocks deposited in continental settings. Similarly, the association of porphyry copper and base metal skarn deposits with shallow-seated, felsic calc-alkaline stocks is well documented.

The main impact of plate tectonics on all this has been to broaden and deepen our understanding of the tectonic environments in which many of these lithologic associations develop (Dickinson, 1980), and to provide insights into their relative spatial positions. Thus, once a particular tectonic setting, perhaps blurred by metamorphism and deformation, is recognized, the exploration geologist can have a much clearer idea of the various potential ore-generating environments that could have existed within that setting. Metallogenesis can now be understood within the fundamental context of continental evolution, and this in turn permits the conception of exploration programs aimed at specific types of deposits.

Not only are metal deposits becoming increasingly difficult to find, but rising exploration costs have far outstripped increases in the prices of most metals in the past two decades. This is particularly true with respect to deep exploration targets, and it is this third dimension (downward) that will increasingly represent the frontier of future mineral exploration. As noted by Boldy (1981) the range of the diamond drill and the depth at which mining can be carried out (given economic viability) considerably exceeds the penetration range of relevant geophysical techniques.

The utilization of plate tectonic concepts in exploration is obviously no panacea, but does provide a meaningful framework within which the geologic and geochemical processes that lead to economic metal concentrations can be more fully understood. On a more specific level, plate tectonics have formed the backdrop to progress in our understanding of paleogeography, metallogenic zoning in arc systems, arc segmentation, intraplate magmatism, and the nature and products of rifting. All of this can be translated into the currency of fresh ideas by the imaginative mineral explorationist, much as has been done by those involved in the search of oil. Undoubtedly the future will see refinements, and perhaps some significant corrections, in the theory of plate tectonics, but each step along the way will have implications in terms of mineral exploration strategy.

Afterword

The writing of a book such as this one is a humbling experience, for one is constantly confronted with the gaps that exist in one's knowledge, and the awesome amount of information, even outside of the field of economic geology, that is pertinent to a full understanding of metallogenesis. Although certain of my interpretations will probably not stand the test of time, I am convinced that the study of metallogenesis must be approached within the context of plate tectonic theory. This approach has leant a tangible sense of excitement and enrichment to my efforts in this field, and if this book achieves the same for the bulk of those students, teachers and explorationists who use it, it will have succeeded in its primary purpose.

References

Adamides NG (1980) The form and environment of formation of the Kalavasos ore deposits, Cyprus. In: Panayiotou A (ed) Ophiolites: Internat Ophiolite Symp Cyprus 1979 117–178

Agar RA (1981) Copper mineralization and magmatic hydrothermal brines in the Rio Pisco section of the Peruvian Coastal Batholith. Econ Geol 76: 677–693

Aguirre L, Charrier R, Davidson J, Mpodozis A, Rivano S, Thiele R, Tidy E, Vergara M, Vicente JC (1974) Andean magmatism: its paleogeographic and structural setting in the central part (30 °-35 °S) of the Southern Andes. Pac Geol 8: 1–35

Alabaster T, Pearce JA, Mallick DIJ, Elboushi IM (1980) The volcanic stratigraphy and location of massive sulfide deposits in the Oman ophiolite. In: Panayiotou A (ed) Ophiolites: Int Ophiolite Symp Cyprus 1979 751–757

Albers JP (1981) A lithologic-tectonic framework for the metallogenic provinces of California. Econ Geol 76: 765–790

Albers JP, Robertson JF (1961) Geology and ore deposits of East Shasta copper-zinc district, Shasta County, California. US Geol Surv Prof Pap 338: 1–107

Anderson DL (1975) Chemical plumes in the mantle. Geol Soc Am Bull 86: 1593–1600

Anderson JA (1982) Characteristics of leached capping and techniques of appraisal. In: Titley SR (ed) Advances in Geology of the Porphyry Copper Deposits. Univ Arizona Press, Tucson 12: 274–295

Anderson P, Guilbert JM (1979) Precambrian massive sulfide deposits of Arizona – a distinct metallogenic epoch and province. Nev Bur Mines Geol Rep 33: 39–48

Anderson RN, Delong SE, Schwarz, WM (1978) Thermal model for subduction with dehydration in the downgoing slab. J Geol 86: 731–739

Anhaeusser CR (1976) The nature and distribution of Archean gold mineralization in southern Africa. Miner Sci Eng 8: 46–84

Anhaeusser CR, Button A (1974) A review of southern African stratiform ore deposits – their position in time and space. Econ Geol Res Unit Univ of the Witwatersrand, Inform Circ 85: 1–48

Annels AE (1974) Some aspects of the stratiform ore deposits of the Zambian copper belt and their genetic significance. In: Bartholome P (ed) Gisements stratiformes et provinces cupriferes ed P. Bartholome. Liege 235–254

Archibald DA, Clark AH, Farrar E, Zaw UK (1978) Potassium-argon ages of intrusion and scheelite mineralization, Cantung, Tungsten, Northwest Territories. Can J Earth Sci 15: 1205–1207

Armstrong RL (1982) Metamorphic core complexes – from Arizona to southern Canada. Ann Rev Earth Planet Sci 10: 129–154

Atkinson WW Jr, Einaudi MT (1978) Skarn formation and mineralization in the contact aureole at Carr Fork, Bingham, Utah. Econ Geol 73: 1326–1365

Backer H, Richter H (1973) Die rezente hydrothermal-sedimentäre Lagerstätte Atlantis-II-Tief in Roten Meer. Geol Rundschau 62: 697–741

Badham JPN (1981) Shale-hosted Pb-Zn deposits: products of exhalation of formation waters? Trans Inst Min Metall 90: B70–B76

Badham JPN (1982) Strike slip orogens – an explanation for the Hercynides. J Geol Soc 139: 495–506

Bahnemann KP (1972) A review of the stratigraphy and the metamorphism of the basement rocks in the Messina district, Northern Transvaal. Unpubl DSc thesis, Univ of Pretoria

Bailey DK (1980) Volatile flux, geotherms, and the generation of the kimberlite-carbonatite-alkaline magma spectrum. Min Mag 43: 695–700

Balce GR, Crispin OA, Samaniego CM, Miranda CR (1981) Metallogenesis in the Philippines: Explanatory text for the CGMW metallogenic map of the Philippines. In: Metallogeny of Asia, 1981 Geol Soc Jpn Rep 261: 125–148

Baldock JW (1969) Geochemical dispersion of copper and other elements at the Bukusu carbonatite complex, Uganda. Trans Min Metall Inst 78: B12–B28

Ballard RD, Francheteau J, Juteau T, Rangan C, Normark W (1981) East Pacific Rise at 21° N: the volcanic, tectonic and hydrothermal processes of the central axis. Earth Planet Sci Lett 55: 1–10

Banerji AK (1981) Ore genesis and its relationship to volcanism, tectonism, granitic activity, and metasomatism along the Singhbum Shear Zone, Eastern India. Econ Geol 76: 905–912

Baragar WRA (1969) The geochemistry of Coppermine River basalts. Geol Surv Can Pap 69–44: 1–43

Barker F, Millard HT Jr, Knight RJ (1979) Reconnaissance geochemistry of Devonian island-arc and intrusive rocks, West Shasta district, California. In: Barker F (ed) Trondhjemites, Dacites, and Related Rocks. Elsevier Amsterdam, 531–545

Barnes HL (ed) 1979 Geochemistry of hydrothermal ore deposits. 2nd ed. Wiley, New York, 798 p 789 p

Barnes SJ, Sawyer EW (1980) An alternative model for the Damara Mobile Belt: Ocean crust subduction and continental convergence. Precambrian Res 13: 297–336

Barnes SJ, Coats CJA, Naldrett AJ (1982) Petrogenesis of a Proterozoic nickel sulfide-komatiite association: the Katiniq Sill, Ungava, Quebec. Econ Geol 77: 413–429

Barnett ES, Hutchinson RW, Adamcik A, Barnett R (1982) Geology of the Agnico Eagle gold deposit, Quebec. Geol Assoc Can Spec Pap 25: 403–426

Barr DA, Fox PE, Northcote KE, Preto VA (1976) The alkaline suite porphyry copper deposits – a summary. In: Sutherland Brown A (ed) Porphyry deposits of the Canadian Cordillera. Can Inst Min Metall Spec Vol 15: 359–367

Barrero LD (1976) Mapa metalogenico de Colombia 1:5,000,000. Bogata Colombia, Inst Nacional Invest Geol-Mineras

Bateman AM, McLaughlin DH (1920) Geology of the ore deposits of Kennecott, Alaska. Econ Geol 15: 1–80

Baum W, Gobel VM (1980) Investigations on metallogeny, calc-alkaline magmatism, and related tectonism in a continental margin province, western Cordillera of Colombia, S.A. Proc Fifth Quad IAGOD Symp 591–605

Beane RE, Titley SR (1981) Porphyry copper deposits. Econ Geol 75th Anniv Vol. 214–269

Bear LM (1963) The geology and mineral resources of the Akaki-Lythrodondha area. Cyprus Geol Surv Dep Mem 3 122 p

Beaty DW, Taylor HP Jr (1982) Some petrologic and oxygen isotopic relationships in the Amulet Mine, Noranda, Quebec, and their bearing on the origin of Archean massive sulfide deposits. Econ Geol 77: 95–108

Beaty DW, Taylor HP Jr (1983) High-^{18}O altered volcanic rocks at the Kidd Creek massive suflide deposit. Econ Geol 78: in press

Beckinsale RD (1979) Granite magmatism in the tin belt of Southeast Asia. In: Atherton MP, Tarney J (eds) Origin of Granite Batholiths: Geochemical Evidence. Shiva, Orpington, England, 34–44

Beckinsale RD, Suensilpong S, Nakapaduncrat S, Walsh JN (1979) Geochronology and geochemistry of granite magmatism in Thailand in relation to a plate tectonic model. J Geol Soc (Lond) 136: 529–537

Bell K, Blenkinsop J (1981) A geochronological study of the Buchans area, Newfoundland. Geol Assoc Can Spec Pap 22: 91–112

Bellido BE, de Montreuil DL (1972) Aspectos generales de la metalogenia del Peru. Peru Servicio de Geologia y Mineria. Geologia Economica 1: 1–149

Benes K, Hanus V (1967) Structural control and history of origin of hydrothermal metallogeny in western Cuba. Min Deposita 2: 318–338

Berger BR, Eimon PI (1982) Comparative models of epithermal silver-gold deposits. AIME Preprint 82-13 SME-AIME Mtg Dallas Texas

Berggren WA (1969) Micropaleontologic investigations of Red Sea cores - summation and synthesis of results. In: Degens, Ross (eds) Hot brines and recent heavy metal deposits in the Red Sea, Springer, Berlin Heidelberg New York 329–335

Berning J, Cooke R, Hiemstra SA, Hoffman U (1976) The Rossing uranium deposit, South West Africa. Econ Geol 71: 351–368

Bichan R. (1969) Chromite seams in the Hartley Complex of the Great Dyke of Rhodesia. In: Magmatic Ore Deposits. Econ Geol Monogr 4: 95–113

Bickel MJ (1978) Heat loss from the earth: a constraint on Archean tectonics from the relation between geothermal gradients and the rate of plate production. Earth Planet Sci Lett 40: 301–315

Bignell RD (1975) Timing, distribution and origin of submarine mineralization in the Red Sea. Inst Min Metall Trans 84: B1–B6

Bignell RD, Cronan DS, Tooms JS (1976) Red Sea metalliferous brine precipitates. Geol Assoc Can Spec Pap 14: 147–179

Bilibin YA (1968) Metallogenic Provinces and Metallogenic Epochs. Queens College Press, Flushing, New York, 1–35

Billings GK, Kesler, SE, Jackson SA (1969) Relation of zinc-rich formation waters, northern Alberta, to the Pine Point ore deposit. Econ Geol 64: 385–391

Binns RA, McAndrew J, Sun S–S (1980) Origin of uranium mineralization at Jabiluka. In: Uranium in the Pine Creek Geosyncline. Int Atomic Energy Agency Vienna 543–562

Biq Chingchang (1971) Dual-trench structure in the Taiwan-Luzon region. Proc Geol Soc China 15: 65–75

Bird JM, Dewey JF, Kidd WSF (1971) Proto-Atlantic Ocean crust and mantle: Appalachian/Caledonian ophiolites. Nat Phys Sci 231: 28–31

Bjorlykke A, Sangster DF (1981) An overview of sandstone lead deposits and their relation to red-bed copper and carbonate-hosted lead-zinc deposits. Econ Geol 75th Anniv Vol: 179–213

Bjorlykke K (1978) The eastern marginal zone of the Caledonide orogen, Norway. Nor Geol Unders no 305: 1–81

Blake DW, Kretschmer EL, Theodore TG (1978) Geology and mineralization of the Copper Canyon deposits, Lander County, Neveda. Nev Bur Mines Geol Rep 32: 45–48

Blecha M (1965) Geology of the Tribag Mine. Can Min Metall Bull 58: 1077–1082

Boast MA, Coleman ML, Halls C (1981) Textural and stable isotopic evidence for the genesis of the Tynagh base metal deposit, Ireland. Econ Geol 76: 27–55

Bogodanov B, Dachev H, Vulchanov A (1974) Metallogeny of Bulgaria in the context of plate tectonics. In: Problems of Ore Deposition, vol 2, 4th IAGOD Symp. 435–443

Boldt JR Jr (1967) The Winning of Nickel. D van Nostrand Princeton NJ, 487 p

Boldy J (1981) Prospecting for volcanogenic ore. Can Inst Min Bull 74, No 834: 55–65

Bollingberg H, Brooks CK, Noe-Nygaard A (1975) Trace element variations in Faeroes basalts and their possible relationships to oceanfloor spreading history. Bull Geol Soc Den 24: 55–60

Bonham HF Jr, Garside LJ (1979) Geology of the Tonapah, Lone Mountain, Klondike, and northern Mud Lake quadrangles, Nevada. Nev Bur Mines Geology Bull 82: 1–142

Bonin B, Bowden P, Vialette Y (1979) Le comportement des elements Rb et Sr en cours des phases de mineralisation, l'example de Ririwai (Liruei) Nigeria. C R Acad Sci Paris, Ser D 289: 707–710

Bookstrom AA (1977) The magnetite deposits of El Romeral, Chile. Econ Geol 72: 1101–1130

Bookstrom AA (1981) Tectonic setting and generation of Rocky Mountain porphyry molybdenum deposits. In: Dickinson WR, Payne WD (eds) Relations of Tectonics to Ore Deposits in the Southern Cordillera. Ariz Geol Soc Dig Vol XIV: 215–226

Bor-Ming Jahn, Chen PY, Yen TP (1976) Rb-Sr ages of granitic rocks in southeastern China and their tectonic significance. Geol Soc Am Bull 86: 763–776

Bortolotti V, Lapierre H, Piccardo GB (1976) Tectonics of the Troodos Massif (Cyprus): preliminary results. Tectonophysics 35: T1–T6

Bowden P (1982) Magmatic evolution and mineralization in the Nigerian Younger Granite Province. In: Evans AM (ed) Metallization Associated with Acid Magmatism. Wiley, New York 51–62

Bowden P, Kinnaird JA (1978) Younger granites of Nigeria – a zinc-rich tin province. Trans Inst Min Metall 87: B66–B69

Boyle RW (1979) The geochemistry of gold and its deposits. Geol Surv Can Bull 280: 584 p

Bridgwater D, Sutton J, Watterson J (1974) Crustal downfolding associated with igneous activity. Tectonophysics 21: 57–77

Brimhall GH, Jr (1979) Lithologic determination of mass transfer mechanisms of multiple-stage porphyry copper mineralization at Butte, Montana: Vein formation by hypogene leaching and enrichment of potassium-silicate protore: Econ Geol 74: 556–589

Brock BB, Pretorius DA (1964) Rand basin sedimentation and tectonics. In: Haughton SH (ed) The Geology of Some Ore Deposits in Southern Africa. Geol Soc S Afr 1: 549–599

Bromley AV (1976) Granites in mobile belts - the tectonic setting of the Cornubia batholith. J Camborne School Mines 76: 40–47

Brooks C, Theyer P (1981) Rb/Sr geochronology in the Thompson belt, Manitoba: implications for Aphebian crustal development and metallogenesis. Can J Earth Sci 18: 932–943

Brown AC (1971) Zoning in the White Pine copper deposit, Ontonagon County, Michigan. Econ Geol 66: 543–573

Brown AC (1980) The diagenetic origin of stratiform copper deposits. Proc Fifth IAGOD Symp 1: 81–90

Brown GC (1980) Calc-alkaline magma genesis: the Pan-African contribution to crustal growth? In: Al-Shanti (ed) Evolution and Mineralization of the Arabian-Nubian Shield. Pergamon, Oxford 3: 19–30

Brown M (1980) Textural and geochemical evidence for the origin of chromite deposits in the Oman ophiolite. In: Panayiotou A (ed) Ophiolites. Proc Int Ophiolite Symp Cyprus, 714–721

Bryner L (1969) Ore deposits of the Philippines – an introduction to their geology. Econ Geol 64: 644–666

Buchanan L (1981) Precious metal deposits associated with volcanic environments in the Southwest. Ariz Geol Soc Dig XIV: 237–262

Bugge JAW (1978) Norway. In: Bowie SHU, Kualheim A, Haslam HW (eds) Mineral Deposits of Europe Vol 1. Northwest Europe. Inst Min Metall, 199–249

Burchfield BC (1979) Geologic history of the central western United States. Nev Bur Mines Geol Rep 33: 1–12

Burgath K, Weiser TH (1980) Primary textures and genesis of Greek podiform chromite deposits. In: A Panayiotou (ed) Ophiolites. Proc Int Ophiolite Symp Cyprus, 675–690

Burke K (1976) The Chad Basin: an active intra-continental basin. Tectonophysics 36: 197–206

Burke K (1977) Aulacogens and continental breakup. Ann Rev Earth Planet Sci 5: 371–396

Burke K, Dewey JF (1973) Plume-generated triple junctions: key indicators in applying plate tectonics to old rocks. J Geol 81: 406–433

Burke K, Kidd WSF (1980) Volcanism on earth through time. In: Strangway DW (ed) The Continental Crust and its Mineral Deposits. Geol Assoc Can Spec Pap 20: 503–522

Burke K, Whiteman AJ (1973) Uplift, rifting and breakup of Africa. In: Tarling DH, Runcorn SK (eds) Implications of Continental Drift to the Earth Sciences. Academic Press, London 2: 735–755

Burke K, Dewey JF, Kidd WSF (1976) Dominance of horizontal movements, arc and microcontinental collisions during the later permobile regime. In: Windley BF (ed) The Early History of the Earth. Wiley, London, 113–129

Burke K, Dewey JF, Kidd WSF (1977) World distribution of sutures – the sites of former oceans. Tectonophysics 40: 69–99

Burke KC, Kidd WSF, Turcotte DL, Dewey JF, Mouginis-Mark PJ, Parmentier EM, Sengor AM, Tapponier PE (1981) Tectonics of basaltic volcanism. In: Basaltic Volcanism on the Terrestrial Planets. Pergamon, New York, 803–898

Burnham CW (1981) Physicochemical constraints on porphyry mineralization. In: Dickinson WR, Payne WD (eds) Relations of Tectonics to Ore Deposits in the Southern Cordillera. Ariz Geol Soc Dig XIV: 71–77

Burt DM (1974) Metasomatic zoning in Ca-Fe-Si exoskarns. In: Hoffman AW and others (eds) Geochemical Transport and Kinetics. Carnegie Inst Wash 634: 287–293

Burton B (1975) Paragenetic study of the San Martin mine, Durango, Mexico. Unpubl MS thesis Univ of Minnesota

Buseck PR (1966) Contact metasomatism and ore deposition. Concepcion del Oro, Mexico. Econ Geol 61: 97–136

Button A (1976) Iron-formation as an end-member in carbonate sedimentary cycles in the Transvaal Supergroup, South Africa. Econ Geol 71: 193–201

Cahen L (1970) Igneous activity and mineralization episodes in the evolution of the Kibaride and Katangide orogenic belts of Central Africa. In: Clifford TN, Gass IG (eds) African Magmatism and Tectonics. Oliver and Boyd, Edinburgh, 97–118

Cahen L, Francois A, Ledent D (1971) Sur l'age des uraninites de Kambove ouest et de Kamato principal et revision des reconnaissances relatives aux mineralisations uranfieres du Katanga et du Copperbelt de Zambia. Ann Soc Geol Belg 94: 185–198

Caia J (1976) Paleogeographical and sedimentological controls of copper, lead, and zinc mineralizations in the Lower Cretaceous sandstones of Africa. Econ Geol 71: 409–422

Callahan WH (1967) Some spatial and temporal aspects on the localization of Mississippi Valley-Appalachian type ore deposits. Econ Geol Monogr 3: 14–19

Callow KJ, Worley HW Jr (1965) The occurrence of telluride minerals at the Acupan gold mine, Mountain Province, Philippines. Econ Geol 60: 251–268

Cameron EN (1980) Evolution of the lower critical zone, eastern Bushveld Complex, and its chromite deposits. Econ Geol 75: 845–871

Cameron EN, Desborough GA (1969) Occurrence and characteristics of chromite deposits – Eastern Bushveld Complex. Econ Geol Monogr No 4: 23–40

Campbell FA, Ethier VG, Krouse HR, Both RA (1978) Isotopic composition of sulfur in the Sullivan orebody, British Columbia. Econ Geol 73: 246–268

Campbell FA, Ethier VG, Krouse HR (1980) The massive sulfide zone: Sullivan orebody. Econ Geol 75: 916–926

Cannon WF, Force ER (1983) Potential for high-grade shallow-marine manganese deposits in North America. Symp Soc Econ Geol Cameron (in press)

Carlson SR, Sawkins FJ (1980) Mineralogic and fluid inclusion studies of the Turmalina Cu-Mo-bearing breccia pipe, Northern Peru. Econ Geol 75: 1233–1238

Carne RC (1979) Geological setting and stratiform mineralization Tom Claims, Yukon Territory. Dep of Indian and Northern Affairs EGS 1979-4: 1–30

Carne RC, Cathro RJ (1982) Sedimentary exhalative (Sedex) zinc-lead-silver deposits, northern Canadian Cordillera. Can Inst Min bull 75, no 840: 66–78

Carpenter AB, Trout ML, Pickett EE (1974) Preliminary report on the origin and chemical evolution of lead- and zinc-rich oilfield brines in central Mississippi. Econ Geol 69: 1191–1206

Casadevall T, Ohmoto H (1977) Sunnyside Mine, Eureka mining district, San Juan County, Colorado: Geochemistry of gold and base metal ore deposition in a volcanic environment. Econ Geol 72: 1285–1320

Cassard D, Rabinovitch M, Nicolas A, Moutte J, Leblanc M, Prinzhofer A (1981) Structural classification of chromite pods in southern New Caledonia. Econ Geol 76: 805–831

Chafee MA (1982) Geochemical prospecting techniques for porphyry copper deposits. In: Advances in the Geology of the Porphyry Copper Deposits. Univ Arizona Press Tucson 13: 297–307

Chapman HJ, Spooner ETC (1977) [87]Sr enrichment of ophiolitic sulfide deposits in Cyprus confirms ore formation by circulating seawater. Earth Planet Sci Lett 35: 71–78

Chappell BW, White AJR (1974) Two contrasting granite types. Pac Geol 8: 173–174

Chase CG, Gilmer TH (1973) Precambrian plate tectonics: the Midcontinent Gravity High. Earth Planet Sci Lett 21: 70–78

Chivas AR, Wilkins, RWT (1977) Fluid inclusion studies in relation to hydrothermal alteration and mineralization at the Koloula porphyry copper prospect, Guadacanal. Econ Geol 72: 153–169

Churchill RK (1980) Meteoric water leaching and ore genesis at the Tayoltita silver-gold mine, Durango, Mexico. Unpubl Ph D thesis Univ Minnesota 162 p

Clark KF, Foster CT, Damon PE (1982) Cenozoic mineral deposits and subduction-related mag-

Clayton RH, Thorpe L (1982) Geology of the Nanisivik zinc-lead deposit. Geol Assoc Can Spec Pap 25: 739–760

Clemmey H (1974) Sedimentary geology of a late Precambrian copper deposit at Kitwe, Zambia. In: Gisements Stratiformes et Provinces Cypriferes, Liege 255–266

Coleman RG (1977) Ophiolites: Ancient Oceanic Lithosphere. Springer, New York Berlin Heidelberg, 229 p

Coleman RG (1981) Tectonic setting of ophiolite obduction in Oman. J Geophys Res 86: 2497–2508

Clark KF, Foster CT, Damon PE (1982) Cenozoic mineral deposits and subductionrelated magmatic arcs in Mexico. Geol Soc Am Bull 93: 533–544

Clarke AH, Caelles JC, Farrar E, Haynes SJ, Lortie RB, McBride SL, Quirt SG, Robertson RCR, Zentilli M (1976) Longitudinal variations in the metallogenic evolution of the Central Andes. Geol Soc Can Spec Pap 14: 23–58

Coleman RG, Huston C, El-Boushi IM, Al-Hinai KM, Bailey EH (1978) Occurrence of copper-bearing massive sulfides in the Semail ophiolite, Sultanate of Oman. Precambrian Res 6:A11–A12

Colley H, Greenbaum D (1980) The mineral deposits and metallogenesis of the Fiji Platform. Econ Geol 75: 807–829

Colvine AC (ed) (1983) The geology of gold in Ontario. Ont Geol Surv Misc Pap 110: 1–278

Condie KC (1982) Early and middle Proterozoic supracrustal successions and their tectonic settings. Am J Sci 282: 341–357

Coney PJ (1972) Cordilleran tectonics and North American plate motion. Am J Sci 272: 603–628

Coney PJ (1981) Accretionary tectonics in western North America. In: Dickinson WR, Payne WD (eds) Relations of Tectonics to Ore Deposits in the Southern Cordillera. Ariz Geol Soc Dig XIV: 23–38

Coney PJ, Reynolds SJ (1977) Cordilleran Benioff zones. Nature 270: 403–406

Conn HK (1979) The Johns-Manville platinum-palladium prospect, Stillwater Complex, Montana, USA. Can Min 17: 463–468

Constantinou G (1980) Metallogenesis associated with the Troodos ophiolite. In: Panayioutou A (ed) Ophiolites. Int Ophiolite Symp Cyprus, 663–674

Constantinou G (1976) Genesis of the conglomerate structure, porosity and collomorphic textures of the massive sulfide ores of Cyprus. In: Strong DF (ed) Metallogeny and Plate Tectonics. Geol Assoc Can Spec Pap 14: 187–210

Constantinou G, Govett GJS (1972) Genesis of sulfide deposits, ochre and umber of Cyprus. Inst Min Metall Trans 8: B36–B46

Cook PJ, McElhinny MW (1979) A re-evaluation of the spatial and temporal distribution of sedimentary phosphate deposits in the light of plate tectonics. Econ Geol 74: 315–330

Corbett KD (1981) Stratigraphy and mineralization in the Mt. Read Volcanics, western Tasmania. Econ Geol 76: 209–230

Corliss JG, Dymond J, Gordon LI, Edmond JM, von Herzen RP, Ballard RD, Green K, Williams D, Bainbridge A, Crane K, van Andel, TjH (1979) Submarine thermal springs on the Galapagos rift. Science 203: 1073–1083

Cornwall HR, Rose HJ Jr (1957) Minor elements in Keweenawan lavas, Michigan. Geochim Cosmochim Acta 12: 209–224

Cotelo Neiva JM (1972) Tin-tungsten deposits and granites from Northern Portugal. 24th Int Geol Congr Sect 4: 282–288

Cotterill P (1969) The chromite deposits of Selukwe, Rhodesia. Econ Geol Mono 4: 154–186

Cousins CA (1969) The Merensky Reef of the Bushveld Igneous Complex. Econ Geol Monogr No 4: 239–251

Coveney RM Jr (1981) Gold quartz veins and auriferous granite at the Oriental Mine, Alleghany district, California. Econ Geol 76: 2146–2199

Cox KG, Johnson RL, Monkman LJ, Stillman CJ, Vail JR, Wood DN (1965) The geology of the Nuanetsi Igneous Province. Philos Trans R Soc 257A: 71–218

Craig H (1966) Isotopic composition and origin of the Red Sea and Salton Sea geothermal brines. Science 154: 1544–1547

Craig H (1969) Geochemistry and origin of the Red Sea brines. In: Degens ET, Ross DA (eds) Hot Brines and Recent Heavy Metals in the Red Sea. Springer New York Berlin Heidelberg, 208–242

Cross TA, Pilger RH Jr (1978) Constraints on absolute plate motion and plate interaction inferred from Cenozoic igneous activity in the western United States. Am J Sci 278: 865–902

Crough ST (1979) Hotspot epeirogeny. Tectonophysics 61: 321–333

Culver SJ, Williams HR (1979) Late Precambrian and Phanerozoic geology of Sierra Leone. J Geol Soc (Lond) 136: 604–618

Cuney M (1978) Geological environment, mineralogy, and fluid inclusions of the Bois Noirs-Limouzat uranium vein, Forez, France. Econ Geol 73: 1567–1610

Curray JR, Emmel FJ, Moore DG (1980) Structure, tectonics and geological history of the northeastern Indian Ocean. In: Nairn AEM, Stehli FG (eds) The Ocean Basins and Continental Margins 6 The Indian Ocean. Plenum, New York

Dadet P, Marchesseau J, Millon R, Motti E (1970) Mineral occurrences related to stratigraphy and tectonics in Tertiary sediments near Umm Lajj, eastern Red Sea area, Saudi Arabia. Philos Trans R Soc Lond A 267: 99–106

D'Argenio B, Alvarez W (1980) Stratigraphic evidence for crustal thickness changes on the southern Tethyan margin during the Alpine cycle. Geol Soc Am Bull 91: 681–689

Dalziel IWD (1981) Back-arc extension in the southern Andes - a review and critical discussion. Philos Trans R Soc Lond A 300: 319–336

Darnley AG (1960) Petrology of some Rhodesian Copperbelt orebodies and associated rocks. Inst Min Metall Trans Lond 69: 137–173, 371–398, 540–569

Date J, Tanimura S (1974) Dacite and rhyolite associated with the Kuroko mineralization. Min Geol Spec Issue No 6. Soc Min Geol of Jpn 261–265

Davies JL, Fyffe LR, Irrinki RR (1973) The geology of the Miramachi zone (north) northeastern New Brunswick. Can Inst Min Metall Ann Conf Preprint 1–26

Davis GR (1969) Aspects of the metamorphosed sulfide ores at Kilembe, Uganda. Sedimentary Ores, Proc 15th Inter-University Geol Cong Spec Publ No 1 Univ of Leicester, 273–296

Dawson KM (1977) Regional metallogeny of the Northern Cordillera. Geol Surv Can Pap 77 1A: 1–4

Degens ET, Ross DA (eds) (1969) Hot brines and Recent Heavy Metal deposits in the Red Sea: A geophysical and geochemical account. Springer, New York Berlin Heidelberg

Delong SE, Schwarz WM (1979) Thermal effects of ridge subduction. Earth Planet Sci Lett 44: 239–246

DePaolo DJ, Wasserberg GJ (1979) Sm-Nd age of the Stillwater Complex and the mantle evolution curve for neodymium. Geochim Cosmochim Acta 43: 999–1008

Dewey JF (1977) Suture zone complexities: a review. Tectonophysics 40: 53–68

Dewey JF (1980) Episodicity, sequence and style at convergent plate boundaries. In: Strangway DW (ed) The Continental Crust and its Mineral Deposits. Geol Assoc Can Spec Pap 20: 553–573

Dewey JF, Burke KC (1973) Tibetan, Variscan and Precambrian basement reactivation: products of continental collision. J Geol 81: 683–692

Dewey JF, Burke KC (1974) Hotspots and continental breakup: implications for continental orogeny. Geology 2: 57–60
deWit MJ, Stern CR (1981) Variations in the degree of crustal extension during formation of a back
  arc basin. Tectonophysics 72: 229–260
deWit MJ, Hart R, Martin A, Abbott P (1982) Archean abiogenic and probable biogenic structures
  associated with mineralized hydrothermal vent systems and regional metasomatism, with implications for greenstone belt studies. Econ Geol 77: 1783–1802
Dick HLB (1982) The petrology of two back-arc basins of the northern Philippine Sea. Am J Sci
  282: 644–700
Dick LA (1976) Metamorphism and metasomatism at the MacMillan Pass tungsten deposit, Yukon
  and District of MacKenzie, Canada. Unpub MS thesis Queens Univ Kingston Ont 226 p
Dick LA (1979) Tungsten and base metal skarns in the Norther Cordillera. Geol Surv Can Pap 79-
  1A: 259–266
Dick LA, Hodgson CJ (1982) The MacTung W-Cu(Zn) contact metasomatic and related deposits
  of the northeastern Canadian Cordillera. Econ Geol 77: 845–867
Dickey JS (1975) A hypothesis of origin for podiform chromite deposits. Geochim Cosmochim Acta
  39: 1061–1074
Dickinson WR (1980) Plate tectonics and key petrologic associations. In: Strangway DW (ed) The
  Continental Crust and its Mineral Deposits. Geol Assoc Can Spec Pap 20: 341–360
Dickinson WR, Seely DR (1979) Structure and stratigraphy of fore-arc regions. Am Assoc Petrol
  Geol Bull 63: 2–31
Dickinson WR, Snyder WS (1979) Geometry of triple junctions related to San Andreas transform.
  J Geophys Res 84: 604–628
Dietz RS (1964) Sudbury structure as a astrobleme. J Geol 72: 412–434
Dimroth E (1981) Labrador Geosyncline: Type example of early Proterozoic cratonic reactivation.
  In: Kroner A (ed) Precambrian Plate Tectonics. Elsevier, Amsterdam, 331–352
Dines HG (1956) The metalliferous mining region of southwest England. Mem Geol Surv UK 2
  vols HMSO, London
Djumhani (1981) Metallic mineral deposits of Indonesia: A metallogenic approach. Geol Surv Jpn
  Rep 261, Metallogeny of Asia, 107–124
Donnelly ME, Hahn GA (1981) A review of the Precambrian massive sulfide deposits in central
  Arizona, and the relationship to their depositional environment. In Dickinson WR, Payne WD
  (eds) Relations of Tectonics to Ore Deposits in the Southern Cordillera. Ariz Geol Soc Dig
  XIV: 11–21
Dubois RL, Brummett RW (1968) Geology of the Eagle Mountain mine area. In: Ridge JD (ed)
  Ore Deposits of the United States 1933-1967 (Graton-Sales vol) New York. Am Inst Min
  Metall Petroleum Engineers, 1592–1606
Duke NA, Hutchinson RW (1974) Geological relationships between massive sulfide bodies and
  ophiolitic volcanic rocks near York Harbour, Newfoundland. Can J Earth Sci 11: 53–69
Duncan RA, Green DH (1980) Role of multistage melting in the formation of oceanic crust. Ge-
  ology 8: 22–26
Dunham KC (1948) Geology of the North Pennine orefield: V.1 Tyne to Stainmore. Mem Geol
  Surv UK 1–357
Dunnet D (1976) Some aspects of the Panantarctic cratonic margin in Australia. Philos Trans R Soc
  Lond A280: 641–654
East Pacific Rise Study Group (1981) Crustal processes of the mid-ocean ridge. Science 13: 31–40
Eastoe CJ (1978) A fluid inclusion study of the Panguna porphyry copper deposit, Bougainville,
  Papua New Guinea. Econ Geol 73: 721–742
Eaton GP (1979) A plate tectonic model for late Cenozoic crustal spreading in the western United
  States. In: Riecker RE (ed) Rio Grande Rift: Tectonics and Magmatism. Am Geophys Union,
  7–32
Eaton GP (1982) The Basin and Range Province: Origin and tectonic significance. Ann Rev Earth
  Planet Sci 10: 409–440

Edmond JM, Measures C, Mangum B, Grant B, Selater R, Collier R, Hudson A, Gordon LI, Corliss JB (1979) On the formation of metal-rich deposits at ridge crests. Earth Planet Sci Lett 46: 19–30

Edmond JM, Von Damm KL, McDuff RE, Measures CI (1982) Chemistry of hot springs on the East Pacific Rise and their effluent dispersal. Nature 297: 187–191

Edmunds FR (1973) Stratigraphy and lithology of the Lower Belt Series in the southern Purcell Mountains, British Columbia. In: Belt Symposium 1973, vol 1, Moscow, Idaho. Bur Mines Geol 230–234

Egin D, Hirst DM, Phillips R (1979) The petrology and geochemistry of volcanic rocks from the north Harsit River area, Pontid volcanic province, northeast Turkey. J Volc Geotherm Res 6: 105–123

Einaudi MT (1977a) Petrogenesis of the copper-bearing skarn at the Mason Valley Mine, Yerington district, Nevada. Econ Geol 72: 769–795

Einaudi MT (1977b) Environment of ore deposition at Cerro de Pasco, Peru. Econ Geol 72: 893–924

Einaudi MT, Meinert LD, Newberry RJ (1981) Skarn deposits. Econ Geol 75th Anniv Vol, 317–391

Eisbacher GH (1977) Tectono-stratigraphic framework of the Redstone Copper Belt, District of Mackenzie. Geol Surv Can Pap 77-35: 1–21

Ellis AJ (1979) Explored geothermal systems. In: Barnes HL (ed) Geochemistry of Hydrothermal Ore Deposits, 2nd ed. Wiley, New York, 623–683

Ellis MW and MacGregor JA (1967) The Kalengwa copper deposit in northwestern Zambia. Econ Geol 62: 781–797

Emslie RF (1978a) Elsonian magmatism in Labrador: age, characteristics and tectonic setting. Can J Earth Sci 15: 438–453

Emslie RF (1978b) Anorthosite massifs, Rapakivi granites, and late Proterozoic rifting of North America. Precambrian Res 7: 61–98

Ethier VG, Campbell FA, Both RA, Krouse HR (1976) Geological setting of the Sullivan orebody and estimates of temperature and pressure of metamorphism. Econ Geol 71: 1570–1588

Evernden JF, Kriz SJ, Chervoni C (1977) Potassium-argon ages of some Bolivan rocks. Econ Geol 72: 1042–1061

Fahley MP (1981) Fluid inclusion study of the Tonapah district, Nevada. Unpub MS thesis Colorado School of Mines

Fahrig WF, Wanless RK (1963) Age and significance of diabase dyke-swarms of the Canadian shield. Nature 200: 934–937

Farr JE, Scott SD (1981) Geochemistry of the Uwamuki #2 stockwork, Hokuroko district, Japan (abs). Geol Soc Am Abstr Progr 13: 449

Farrington JL (1952) A preliminary description of the Nigerian lead-zinc field. Econ Geol 47: 583–608

Favorskaya MA (1977) Metallogeny of deep lineaments and new global tectonics. Min Deposita 12: 163–169

Feiss PG, Hauck SA (1980) Tectonic setting of massive-sulfide deposits in the southern Appalachians, USA. Prof Fifth IAGOD Symp 567–580

Ferencic A (1971) Metallogenic provinces and epochs in southern Central America. Min Deposita 6: 77–88

Ferguson J, Winer P (1980) Pine Creek Geosyncline: Statistical treatment of whole rock chemical data. In: Uranium in the Pine Creek Geosyncline. Int Atomic Energy Agency Vienna, 191–208

Ferguson J, Ewers GR, Donnelly TH (1980) Model for the development of economic uranium mineralization in the Alligator Rivers uranium field. In: Uranium in the Pine Creek Geosyncline. Int Atomic Energy Agency Vienna, 563–574

Fernandez HE, Damasco FV (1979) Gold deposition in the Baguio gold district and its relationship to regional geology. Econ Geol 74: 1852–1868

Field CW, Gustafson LB (1976) Sulfur isotopes in the porphyry copper deposit at El Salvador, Chile. Econ Geol 71: 1533–1548

Finlow-Bates T, Large DE (1978) Water depth as a major control on the formation of submarine exhalative ore deposits. Geol Jahrb D30: 27–39

Fleischer VD, Garlick WG, Haldane R (1976) Geology of the Zambian Copper Belt. In: Handbook of Stratabound and Stratiform Ore Deposits. Elsevier, New York 6: 223–352

Fletcher CJN (1977) The geology, mineralization and alteration of Ilkwang mine, Republic of Korea: a Cu-W-bearing tourmaline breccia pipe. Econ Geol 72: 753–768

Floyd PA (1982) Chemical variation in Hercynian basalts relative to plate tectonics. J Geol Soc Lond 139: 507–522

Floyd PA, Winchester JA (1975) Magma type and tectonic setting discrimination using immobile elements. Earth Planet Sci Lett 27: 211–218

Ford AB (1975) Stratigraphy and whole-rock chemical variation in the stratiform Dufek intrusion, Pensacola Mountains, Antarctica (abs). Geol Soc Am Ann Mtg Salt Lake City, 1077–1078

Forrest K, Rye RO, Sawkins FJ (1983) Sulfur and oxygen systematics of sedimentary exhalative Zn-Pb-Ag deposition in a fault-bounded basin, Lik deposit, western Brooks Range, Alaska (abs). Geol Assoc Can – Min Assoc Can Mtg Victoria BC

Fox JS (1979) Host rock geochemistry and massive volcanogenic sulfide ores. Can Inst Min Bull 72: 127–134

Fox PJ, Detrick RS, Purdy GM (1980) Evidence of crustal thinning near fracture zones: Implications for ophiolites. In: Panayiotou A ed) Ophiolites: Int Ophiolite Symp Cyprus, 1979, 161–168

Francis EH (1968) Review of Carboniferous-Permian volcanicity in Scotland. Geol Rundsch 57: 219–246

Francois A (1974) Stratigraphie, tectonique et mineralisations dans l'arc cuprifere du Shaba (Republique du Zaire). In: Bartholome P (ed) Gisments stratiformes et provinces cupriferes. Liége 79–101

Franklin JM, Thorpe RI (1982) Comparative metallogeny of the Superior, Slave and Churchill Provinces. Geol Assoc Can Spec Pap 25: 3–90

Franklin JM, Lydon JW, Sangster DF (1981) Volcanic-associated massive sulfide deposits. Econ Geol 75th Anniv Vol: 485–627

Frarey MJ, Roscoe SM (1970) The Huronian Supergroup north of Lake Huron. Geol Surv Can Pap 70-40: 143–158

French BM (1970) Possible relationship between meteorite impact and igneous petrogenesis as indicated by the Sudbury structure, Ontario, Canada. Bull Volc 34: 466–517

Frietsch R, Papunen H, Vokes FM (1979) The ore deposits in Finland, Norway and Sweden – a review. Econ Geol 74: 975–1001

Fripp REP (1976) Stratabound gold deposits in Archean banded iron formation, Rhodesia. Econ Geol 71: 58–75

Frost JE (1965) Controls of ore deposition for the Larap mineral deposits, Camarines Norte, Philippines. Unpubl PhD Diss Stanford Univ, 173 p

Fujii K (1974) Tectonics of the Green Tuff region, northern Honshu, Japan. Min Geol Spec Issue No 6 Soc Min Geol Jpn 251–260

Futa K, Hedge CE, Hearn BC, Donnelly-Nodan JM (1982) Strontium isotopes in the Clear Lake Volcanics. US Geol Surv Prof Pap 1141: 61–66

Fyfe WS (1980) Crust formation and destruction. In: Strangway DW (ed) The Continental Crust and its Mineral Deposits. Geol Assoc Can Spec Pap 20: 77–88

Fyon JA, Crocket JH, Schwarcz HP (1983) The Carshaw and Malga Iron-formation hosted gold deposits of the Timmins area. In: Colvine AC (ed) The geology of gold in Ontario. Ont Geol Surv Misc Pap 110: 98–110

Gabrielse H, Reesor JE (1974) The nature and setting of granitic plutons in the central and eastern parts of the Canadian Cordillera. Pac Geol 8: 109–138

Gale GH, Pearce JA (1982) Geochemical patterns in Norwegian greenstones. Can J Earth Sci 19: 386–397

Gale GH, Roberts A (1974) Trace element geochemistry of Norwegian Lower Paleozoic basic volcanics and its tectonic implications. Earth Planet Sci Lett 22: 380–390

Gandhi SS, Brown AC (1975) Cupriferous shales of the Adeline Island Formation, Seal Lake Group, Labrador. Econ Geol 70: 145–163

Garlick WG (1981) Sabkhas, slumping and compaction at Mufulira, Zambia. Econ Geol 76: 1817–1847

Garlick WG, Fleischer VD (1972) Sedimentary environment of Zambian copper deposition. Geol Mijnbouw 51: 277–298

Gass IG (1980) The Troodos massif: its role in the unravelling of the ophiolite problem and its significance in the understanding of constructive plate margin processes. In: Panayiotou A (ed) Ophiolites. Int Ophiolite Symp Cyprus, 1979, 23–35

Gaut A (1981) Field relations and the petrography of the biotite granites of the Oslo region. Nor Geol Unters 367: 39–64

Gealy WK (1980) Ophiolite obduction mechanism. In: Panayiotou A (ed) Ophiolites. Int Ophiolite Symp Cyprus, 1979, 228–243

Gervasio FS (1971) Ore deposits of the Philippines mobile belt. J Geol Soc Philippines 25: 1–24

Geyti A, Schonwandt HK (1979) Bordvika – A possible porphyry molybdenum occurrence within the Oslo Rift, Norway. Econ Geol 74: 1211–1230

Gibbs A (1976) Geology and genesis of the Baqf lead-zinc deposits, Iran. Inst Min Metall Trans 85: B205–B220

Giles DL, Nelson CE (1983) Principal features of epithermal lode gold deposits of the circum-Pacific Rim. Circum-Pacific Energy and Minerals Resource Conf Proc Honolulu, 1982

Gill JB (1981) Orogenic andesites and plate tectonics. Springer, Minerals and Rocks 16, 390 p

Gilligan LB (1978) Mineral deposits in the New South Wales part of the Lachlan fold belt. A review. Geol Surv N S W Rep No GS 1978/320: 1–7

Gilligan LB, Felton EA, Olgers F (1979) The regional setting of the Woodlawn deposit. Geol Soc Austr J 26: 135–140

Gilluly J (1976) Lineaments - ineffective guides to ore deposits. Econ Geol 71: 1507–1514

Girdler RW (1969) The Red Sea – a geophysical background. In: Degens and Ross (ed) Hot Brines and Recent Heavy Metal Deposits in the Red Sea. Springer, Berlin Heidelberg New York, 38–58

Glaskovsky AA, Gorbunov GI, SysoevFA (1977) Deposits of nickel. In: Smirnov VI (ed) Ore Deposits of the USSR, Vol, II, 3–79

Godlevskii MN, Grinenko LN (1963) Some data on the isotopic composition of sulfur in sulfides of the Noril'sk deposit. Geochemistry 1: 35–41

Goldie RJ (1979) Metamorphism of the Flavrian and Powell plutons, Noranda area, Quebec. J Petrol 20: 227–238

Goldie RJ, Kotila B, Seward D (1979) The Don Rouyn mine; an Archean porphyry copper deposit near Noranda, Quebec. Econ Geol 74: 1680–1684

Gole MJ, Klein C (1981) Banded-iron-formations through much of Precambrian time. J Geol 89: 169–184

Golightly JP (1981) Nickeliferous laterite deposits. Econ Geol 75th Anniv Vol, 710–734

Goodell PC, Petersen U (1974) Julcani mining district, Peru: A study of metal ratios. Econ Geol 69: 347–361

Goodwin AM, Riddler RH (1970) The Abitibi orogenic belt. Geol Surv Can Pap 70-40: 1–28

Goosens PJ (1972) Metallogeny in Ecuadorian Andes. Econ Geol 67: 458–468

Goossens PJ (1976) Lithologic, geochemical, and metallogenic belts in the Northern Andes, and their structural relationships. Soc Min Eng AIME Trans 260: 60–67

Gordon PSL (1973) The Selebi-Kitwe nickel-copper deposits, Botswana. Geol Soc S Afr Spec Publ 3: 167–187

Graham SA, Dickinson WR, Ingersoll RV (1975) Himalayan-Bengal model for flysch dispersal in the Appalachian-Ouchita System. Geol Soc Am Bull 86: 273–286

Grainger DJ, Grainger RL (1974) Explanatory notes on the 1:2,500,000 mineral deposits map of Papua New Guinea. Bur Min Geol Geophys Bull 148: 1–171

Grammelvedt G (1979) The geology of the Lokken-Holdal area IGCP Project 60. Caledonian-Appalachian stratabound sulfides. Trondheim Nor Geol Unders Presymp Excursion Guidebook, 106–120

Grant JN, Halls C, Avila W, Avila G (1977) Igneous geology and the evolution of hydrothermal systems in some sub-volcanic tin deposits of Bolivia. Spec Publ 7, Geol Soc Lond 117–126

Grant JN, Halls C, Sheppard SMF, Avila W (1980) Evolution of the porphyry tin deposits of Bolivia. In: Granitic Magmatism and Related Mineralization, Min Geol Spec Issue No 8, 151–174

Grant NK (1971) South Atlantic, Benue Trough, and the Gulf of Guinea Cretaceous triple junction. Bull Geol Soc Am 82: 2295–2298

Gray RF, Hoffmann VJ, Bagan RJ, McKinley HL (1968) Bishop tungsten district, California. In: Ridge JD (ed) Ore Deposits of the United States, 1933–1967 (Graton-Sales vol) NY Am Inst Min Metall Petr Engineers, 1531–1554

Green AH, Naldrett AJ (1981) The Langmuir volcanic peridotite-associated nickel deposits: Canadian equivalents of the Western Australian occurrences. Econ Geol 76: 1503–1523

Green JC (1983) Geologic and geochemical evidence for the nature and development of the Precambrian Midcontinent Rift of North America. Tectonophysics 94:413–438

Grenne T, Grammeltvedt G, Vokes FM (1980) Cyprus-type sulfide deposits in the western Trondheim district, central Norwegian Caledonides. In: Panayiotou A (ed) Ophiolites. International Ophiolite Symp Cyprus, 1979, 727–743

Gross GA (1967) Geology of the iron deposits of Canada. Vol 2. Geol Surv Can Econ Geol Rep 22: 1–11

Groves DI, Barrett FM, McQueen KG (1979) The relative roles of magmatic segregation, volcanic exhalation and regional metamorphism in the generation of volcanic-associated nickel ores of Western Australia. Can Mineralogist 17: 319–336

Gruenewaldt G. von (1977) The mineral resources of the Bushveld Complex. Min Sci Engng 9: 83–95

Guilbert JM (1981) A plate tectonic-lithotectonic classification of ore deposits. In: Dickinson WR, Payne WD (eds) Relations of Tectonics to Ore Deposits in the Southern Cordillera. Ariz Geol Soc Dig XIV: 1–10

Guild PW (1974) Distribution of metallogenic provinces in relation to major earth structures. In: Petrascheck WE (ed) Metallogenetische und Geochemische Provinzen. Springer, Vienna New York, 10–24

Guild PW (1978) Metallogenesis in the western United States. J Geol Soc Lond 135: 355–376

Gustafson LB, Hunt JP (1975) The porphyry copper deposit at El Salvador, Chile. Econ Geol 70: 857–912

Gustafson LB, Williams N (1981) Sediment-hosted stratiform deposits of copper, lead and zinc. Econ Geol 75th Anniv Vol: 139–178

Haapala I (1977) The controls of tin and related mineralization in the rapakivi-granite areas of south-eastern Fennoscandia. Geol Foren Stock Forth 99: 130–142

Hackett JP, Bischoff JL (1973) New data on the stratigraphy, extent and geologic history of the Red Sea geothermal deposits. Econ Geol 68: 533–564

Hall WE, Mackevett EM Jr (1962) Geology and ore deposits of the Darwin quadrangle, Inyo County, California. US Geol Surv Prof Paper 368: 1–87

Hamilton JM (1977) Sr isotope and trace element studies of the Great Dyke and Bushveld mafic phase and their relation to early Proterozoic magma genesis in Southern Africa. J Petrol 18: 24–52

Hamilton JM, Delaney GD, Hauser RL, Ransom PW (1983) Geology of the Sullivan deposit, Kimberley, B.C., Canada. In: Sangster DF (ed) Sediment-hosted stratiform lead-zinc deposits. Min Assoc Can, Short Course Handb 8: 31–84

Hamilton JM, Bishop DT, Morris HC, Owens OE (1982) Geology of the Sullivan orebody, Kimberley, B.C., Canada. Geol Assoc Can Spec Pap 25: 597–665

Hamilton W (1970) The Uralides and the motion of the Russian and Siberian platforms. Geol Soc Am Bull 81: 2553–2576

Hammond P (1952) Allard Lake ilmenite deposits. Econ Geol 47: 634–649

Hannak WW (1981) Genesis of the Rammelsberg ore deposit near Goslar/Upper Harz, Federal Republic of Germany. Handbook of Strata-bound and Stratiform Ore Deposits. Elsevier Amsterdam 9: 551–642

Hanor JS (1979) The sedimentary genesis of hydrothermal fluids. In: Barnes HL (ed) Geochemistry of Hydrothermal Ore Deposits. 2nd ed, Wiley, New York, 137–172

Hargraves RB (1962) Petrology of the Allard Lake anorthosite suite. Petrologic Studies – Buddington Volume Geol Soc Am, 163–190

Hargraves RB (1978) Punctuated evolution of tectonic style. Nature 276: 459–461

Harley DN (1979) A mineralized Ordivician resurgent caldera complex in the Bathurst-Newcastle mining district, New Brunswick, Canada. Econ Geol 74: 786–796

Harper GD (1980) The Josephine Ophiolite – Remains of a late Jurassic marginal basin in northwestern California. Geology 8: 333–337

Harris JF (1961) Summary of the geology of Tanganyika. Part IV Economic Geology. Geol Surv Tanganyika Mem 1: 1–143

Harrison JE (1972) Precambrian Belt basin of northwestern United States. Geol Soc Am Bull 83: 1215–1240

Harrison JE (1974) Copper mineralization in miogeosynclinal clastics of the Belt Supergroup, northwestern United States. In: Bartholome P (ed) Gisements stratiformes et provinces cupriferes. Liége, Soc Geol Belgique, 353–366

Harrover RD, Norman DI, Savin SM, Sawkins FJ (1982) Stable oxygen isotope and crystallite size analysis of the De Long Mountain, Alaska cherts: An exploration tool for submarine exhalative deposits. Econ Geol 77: 1761–1766

Hassan MA, Al-Sulaimi JS (1979) Copper mineralization in the northern part of Oman Mountains near Al Furaijah, United Arab Emirates. Econ Geol 74: 919–924

Hattori K, Muehlenbachs K (1980) Marine hydrothermal alteration at a Kuroko ore deposit, Kosaka, Japan. Contrib Min Petrol 74: 285–292

Hattori K, Sakai H (1979) D/H ratios, origins, and evolution of the ore-forming fluids for the Neogene veins and Kuroko deposits of Japan. Econ Geol 74: 535–555

Haug JL (1976) Geology of the Merry Widow and Kingfisher contact metasomatic skarn-magnetite deposits, Northern Vancouver Island, British Columbia. Unpubl MS thesis Calgary, 174 p

Hawkins JW (1980) Petrology of back-arc basins and island arcs: their possible role in the origin of ophiolites. In: Panayiotou A (ed) Ophiolites. Inter Ophiolite Symp Cyprus, 1979, 224–254

Hearn BC, Donnelly-Nolan JM, Goff FE (1982) The Clear Lake Volcanics: Tectonic setting and magma sources. US Geol Surv Prof Pap 1141: 25–46

Heaton THE, Sheppard SMF (1977) Hydrogen and oxygen isotope evidence for seawater-hydrothermal alteration and ore deposits, Troodos complex, Cyprus. In: Volcanic Processes in Ore Genesis. Geol Soc Lond Spec Publ 7: 42–57

Hegge MR, Mosher DV, Eupene GS, Anthony PJ (1980) Geologic setting of the East Alligator uranium deposits and prospects. In: Uranium in the Pine Creek Geosyncline. Int Atomic Energy Agency Vienna, 259–272

Helmstaedt H (1973) Structural geology of the Bathurst-Newcastle district. In: Rast N (ed) Field Guide to Excursions: N Engl Intercollegiate Geol Conf 1973, 34–43

Henley RW, Adams J (1979) On the evolution of giant gold placers. Inst Min Metall Trans 88: B41–B50

Henley RW, McNabb A (1978) Magmatic vapor plumes and groundwater interaction in porphyry copper emplacement. Econ Geol 73: 1–20

Henley RW, Thornley P (1979) Some geothermal aspects of polymetallic massive sulfide formation. Econ Geol 74: 1600–1612

Henley RW, Thornley P (1981) Low grade metamorphism and the geothermal environment of massive sulfide ore formation, Buchans, Newfoundland. Geol Assoc Can Spec Pap 22: 205–228

Hernon RM, Jones WR (1968) Ore deposits of the Central Mining district, New Mexico. In: Ridge JD (ed) (Graton-Sales Vol) NY Am Inst Min Metall Petr Engineers, 1211–1238

Herz N (1969) Anorthosite belts, continental drift, and the anorthosite event. Science 164: 944–947

Herz N (1977) Timing of spreading in the South Atlantic: information from Brazilian alkalic rocks. Geol Soc Am Bull 88: 101–112

Hess HH (1960) Stillwater igneous complex – a quantiative mineralogical study, Montana. Geol Soc Am Mem 80: 1–230

Hewton RS (1982) Gayna River: A Proterozoic Mississippi Valley-type zinc-lead deposit. Geol Assoc Can Spec Pap 25: 667–700

Heyl AV (1972) The 38th parallel lineament and its relationship to ore deposits. Econ Geol 67: 879–894

Hillhouse JW (1977) Paleomagnetism of the Triassic Nikolai Greenstone, McCarthy Quadrangle, Alaska. Can J Earth Sci 14: 2578–2592

Hodgson CJ, Lydon JW (1977) Geological setting of volcanogenic massive sulfide deposits and active hydrothermal systems: some implications for exploration. Can Min Metall Bull 70: 360–366

Hoeve J, Sibbad TII, Ramaekers P, Lewry JF (1980) Athabasca Basin unconformitys-type uranium deposits: A special class of sandstone-type deposits: In: Uranium in the Pine Creek Geosyncline. Int Atomic Energy Agency Vienna 575–594

Hoffman PF (1980) Wopmay Orogen: a Wilson cycle of early Proterozoic age in the northwest of the Canadian Shield. Geol Assoc Can Spec Pap 20: 523–552

Hohmann GW, Ward SH (1981) Electrical methods in mining geophysics. Econ Geol 75th Anniv Vol, 806–828

Holland HD (1973) The oceans: a possible source of iron in iron-formations. Econ Geol 68: 1169–1172

Hollister VF (1978) Geology of the Porphyry Copper Deposits of the Western Hemisphere. NY, AIME, 219 p

Hollister VF, Potter RR, Barker AL (1974) Porphyry-type deposits of the Appalachian orogen. Econ Geol 69: 618–630

Hoagland AD (1976) Appalachian zinc-lead deposits. In: Wolf K H (ed) Handbook of Strata-bound and Stratiform Ore Deposits, Elsevier, New York 6: 495–534

Horn DR, Horn BM, Delach MN (1973) Ocean magnanese nodules, metal values and mining sites. Tech Rep No 4 GX 33616 Natl Sci Foundation, Washington, 1–57

Horton DJ (1978) Porphyry-type copper-molybdenum mineralization belts in eastern Queensland, Australia. Econ Geol 73: 904–921

Horwitz RC, Smith RE (1976) Bridging the Yilgarn and Pilbara Blocks, Western Australia Shield (abst) Int Geol Cong Abstr Vol Sydney: 12

Howard PF (1959) Structure and wallrock alteration at the Elizabeth Mine, Vermont. Econ Geol 54: 1214–1249, 1414–1443

Hoy T (1982a) The Purcell Supergroup in southeastern British Columia: Sedimentation, tectonics and stratiform lead-zinc deposits. Geol Assoc Can Spec Pap 25: 127–147

Hoy T (1982b) Stratigraphic and structural setting of stratabound lead-zinc deposits in southeastern B.C. Can Inst Min Bull 75 No 840: 114–134

Hudson T, Plafker G, Peterman ZE (1979) Paleogene anatexis along the Gulf of Alaska margin. Geology 7: 573–577

Huebschman RP (1973) Correlation of fine carbonaceous bands across a Precambrian stagnant basin. J Sediment Petrol 43: 688–699

Huhtala T (1979) The geology and zinc-copper deposits of the Pyhasalmi-Pielavesi district, Finland. Econ Geol 74: 1069–1083

Humphris SE, Thompson G (1978) Hydrothermal alteration of oceanic basalts by seawater. Geochim Cosmochim Acta 42: 107–125

Hunter DR (1973) Localization of tin mineralization with reference to Southern Africa. Min Sci Eng 5: 53–77

Hunter DR (1976) Some enigmas of the Bushveld Complex. Econ Geol 71: 229–248

Hutchinson RW (1980) Massive base metal sulfide deposits as guides to tectonic evolution. In: Strangway DW (ed) The Continental Crust and Its Mineral Deposits. Geol Assoc Can Spec Pap 20: 659–684

Hutchinson CS, Taylor D (1978) Metallogenesis in SE Asia. J Geol Soc Lond 135: 407–428

Hynes A, Francis DM (1982) A transect of the early Proterozoic Cape Smith foldbelt, New Quebec. Tectonophysics 88: 23–60

Ihlen PM, Vokes FM (1977) Metallogeny associated with the Oslo Rifting: the Oslo Paleorift. Part 2 Guide to excursions NATO adv study inst Oslo, 147–174

Iijima A (1974) Clay and zeoloitic alteration zones surrounding Kuroko deposits in the Hokuroku District, Northern Atika, as submarine hydrothermal-diagenetic alteration products. Min Geol Spec Issue 6: 267–289

Ingersoll RV (1982) Triple-junction instability as cause for late Cenozoic extension and fragmentation of the western United States. Geology 10: 621–624

Isherwood WF (1982) Geophysical overview of the Geysers. US Geol Surv Prof Pap 1141: 83–95

Ishihara S (1977) The magnetite-series and ilmenite-series granitic rocks: Min Geol (Tokyo) 27: 293–305

Ishihara S (1978) Metallogenesis in the Japanese island-arc system. J Geol Soc 135: 389–406

Ishihara S (1981) The granitoid series and mineralization. Econ Geol 75th Anniv Vol, 458–484

Ishihara S, Sasaki A (1978) Sulfur in Kuroko deposits - a deep seated origin? Min Geol 28: 361–367

Ishihara S, Sawata H, Shibata K, Terashima S, Arrykul S, Sato K (1980) Granites and Sn-W deposits of Peninsular Thailand. In: Granitic Magmatism and Related Mineralization. Min Geol Spec Issue 8: 223–241

Jackson ED (1969) Chemical variation in coexisting chromite and olivine in chromitite zones of the Stillwater Complex. Econ Geol Monogr 4: 41–71

Jackson ED, Silver EA, Dalrymple GB (1972) Hawaiian-Emperor chain and its relation to Cenozoic circum-Pacific tectonics. Geol Soc Am Bull 38: 601–618

Jacobsen JBE, McCarthy TS (1976) An unusual hydrothermal copper deposit of Messina, South Africa. Econ Geol 71: 117–130

Jacobsen JBE, McCarthy TS, Laing CJ (1976) The copper-bearing breccia pipes of the Messina district, South Africa. Min Deposita 11: 33–45

Jacobson RRE, MacLeon WN, Black R (1958) Ring complexes in the younger Granite Province of northern Nigeria. Mem Geol Soc Lond 1: 1–72

Jankovic S (1980) Porphyry-copper and massive-sulfide ore deposits in the northeastern Mediterannean. In: Ridge JD (ed) Proc Fifth IAGOD Symp 431–444

Jardine DE (1966) An investigation of brecciation associated with the Sullivan mine orebody of Kimberly, B.C. Unpubl M Sc thesis Univ Manitoba, 121 p

John TU (1963) Geology and mineral deposits of east-central Balabac Island, Palawan Province, Philippines. Econ Geol 58: 107–130

John YW (1978) Sangdong mine, Korea. In: Imai H (ed) Geological Studies of the Mineral Deposits of Japan and East Asia. Tokyo, Univ Toyko Press, 196–200

Johnson IR, Klingner GD (1975) Broken Hill ore deposit and its environment. In: Knight CL (ed) Economic Geology of Australia and Papua New Guinea I Metals Australas Inst Min Metall Monogr 5: 476–491

Johnson WP, Lowell JD (1961) Geology and origin of mineralized breccia pipes in Copper Basin, Arizona. Econ Geol 56: 916–940

Jones DL, Silbering NJ, Hillhouse JW (1977) Wrangellia - a displaced terrane in northwestern North America. Can J Earth Sci 14: 2565–2577

Jones MT, Reed BL, Doe BR, Lanphere MA (1977) Age of tin mineralization and plumbotectonics, Belitung, Indonesia. Econ Geol 72: 745–752

Jones WR, Peoples JW, Howland AL (1960) Igneous and tectonic structures of the Stillwater Complex, Montana. US Geol Surv Bull 1071-H: 281–340

Kamilli RJ (1978) The genesis of stockwork molybdenite deposits: implications from studies at the Henderson Mine. (abst) Geol Soc Am Abstr Progr 10: 431

Kamilli RJ, Ohmoto H (1977) Paragenesis, zoning, fluid inclusion, and isotopic studies of the Finlandia Vein, Colqui District, Central Peru. Econ Geol 71: 950–982

Kanasewich ER (1968) Precambrian rift: genesis of stratabound ore deposits: Science 161: 1002–1005

Kanehira K, Tatsumi T (1970) Bedded cupriferous deposits in Japan, a review. In: Tatsumi T (ed) Volcanism and Ore Genesis. Tokyo, University of Tokyo Press, 51–76

Karig DE (1971) Origin and development of marginal basins in the western Pacific. J Geophys Res 76: 2542–2561

Karson J, Dewey JF (1978) Coastal Complex, western Newfoundland: an Early Ordivician oceanic fracture zone. Geol Soc Am Bull 89: 1037–1049

Karvinen WO (1981) Geology and evolution of gold deposits, Timmins area, Ontario. In: Pye EG, Roberts RG (eds) Genesis of Archean, Volcanic-Hosted Gold Deposits, Ont Geol Surv Misc Pap 97: 29–46

Kasch KW (1979) A continental collision model for the tectonothermal evolution of the (southern) Damara belt. Precambrian Res Unit Univ Cape Town, Ann Rep 16: 101–107

Keith SB (1978) Paleosubduction geometries inferred from Cretaceous and Tertiary magmatic patterns in southwestern North America. Geology 6: 516–521

Kelly WC, Rye RO (1979) Geologic, fluid inclusion and stable isotope studies of the tin-tungsten deposits of Panasquiera, Portugal. Econ Geol 74: 1721–1822

Kelly WC, Turneaure FS (1970) Mineralogy, paragenesis and geothermometry of the tin and tungsten deposits of the Eastern Andes, Bolivia. Econ Geol 65: 609–680

Kelsey GL, Glavinovich PS, Sheridan MF (1980) High-potassium metarhyolites associated with volcanogenic sulfides, Ambler district, northwest Alaska. Geol Soc Amer Abstr Progr 12: 114

Kerr JW (1977) Cornwallis lead-zinc district, Mississippi Valley-type deposits controlled by stratigraphy and tectonics. Can J Earth Sci 14: 1402–1426

Kerrich R (1981) Archean gold-bearing chemical sedimentary rocks and veins: A synthesis of stable isotope and geochemical relations. In: Pye EG, Roberts RG (eds) Genesis of Archean, Volcanic-Hosted Gold Deposits. Ont Geol Surv Misc Pap 97: 144–175

Kerrick DM (1970) Contact metamorphism in some areas of the Sierra Nevada. Geol Soc Am Bull 81: 2913–2938

Kesler SE (1973) Copper, molybdenum and gold abundances in porphyry-copper deposits. Econ Geol 68: 106–113

Kesler SE (1977) Geochemistry of manto fluorite deposits, northern Coahuila, Mexico. Econ Geol 72: 204–218

Kesler SE (1978) Metallogenesis of the Caribbean region. J Geol Soc Lond 135: 429–441

Kiltin DA, Pavlova TG (1974) Ophiolite complex of the Baikal fold zone: Dokl Akad Nauk SSSR 215: 413–416 (p 33–36 in translation)

Kimbach FW, Cruson MG, Brooks RA (1981) Geology of stockwork gold deposits as exemplified by the Cinola deposit. Colo Min Assoc, 1981, Min Yearbook, 122–129

Kindle ED (1972) Classification and description of copper deposits, Coppermine River area, District of Mackenzie. Geol Surv Can Bull 214: 1–109

Kinkel AR Jr, Hall WE, Albers JP (1956) Geology and base-metal deposits of West Shasta copper-zinc district, Shasta County, California. US Geol Surv Prof Pap 285: 1–156

Kirby GA (1979) The Lizard Complex as an ophiolite. Nature 282: 58–61

Kirchner G, Lehnert-Thiel K, Rich J, Strnad JG (1980) The Key Lake U-Ni deposit: A model for lower Proterozoic uranium deposition. Proc Int Uranium Symp on the Pine Creek Geosyncline. Int Atom Energy Agency Vienna, 617–629

Kirkham RV (1972) Geology of copper and molybdenum deposits. Can Geol Surv Pap 72-1A: 82–87

Kisvarsanyi G (1977) The role of Precambrian igneous basement in the formation of the stratabound lead-zinc-copper deposits in southeast Missouri. Econ Geol 72: 435–442

Kisvarsanyi EB (1980) Granitic ring complexes and Precambrian hot-spot activity in the St. Francois terrane, Midcontinent region, United States. Geology 8: 43–47

Kloosterman JB (1969) A two-fold analogy between the Nigerian and Amazonian tin provinces. In: Fox W (ed) A Second Conf on Tin, 2: 197–222

Knutson J, Ferguson J, Roberts WMB, Donnelly HT, Lambert IB (1979) Petrogenesis of the copper-bearing breccia pipes Redbank, Northern Territory, Australia. Econ Geol 74: 814–826

Koeppel V (1980) Lead isotope studies of stratiform ore deposits of the Namaqualand, NW Cape Province, South Africa, and their implications on the age of the Bushmanland sequence. Fifth IAGOD Symp Vol, 195–208

Konstantynowicz E (1973) Genesis of Permian copper deposits in Poland. Int Geol Rev 15: 1054–1066

Kovalenko VA, Glaskyshev GD, Nosik LP (1975) Isotopic composition of sulfide sulfur from deposits of Talnakh ore node in relation to their selenium content. Int Geol Rev 17: 725–736

Kovalev AA, Karyakin YuV (1980) Volcanism, subvolcanic processes and ore deposits of the Caucasian collision orogen. Fifth IAGOD Symp Vol, 313–324

Kowalik J, Rye RO, Sawkins FJ (1981) Stable isotope study of the Buchans polymetallic sulphide deposits. Geol Assoc Can Spec Pap 22: 229–254

Kratz K, Mitrofanov F (1980) Main type reference sequences of the early Precambrian in the USSR. Earth-Sci Rev 16: 295–301

Krebs W (1981) The geology of the Meggen ore deposit. Handbook of Strata-bound and Stratiform Ore Deposits. Elsevier, Amsterdam 9: 509–550

Krogh TE, Davis GL (1971) Zircon U-Pb ages of Archean metavolcanic rocks in the Canadian Shield. Carnegie Inst Wash Year Book 70: 241–242

Kroner A (1977a) Precambrian mobile belts of southern and eastern Africa – Ancient sutures or sites of ensialic mobility? A case for crustal evolution towards plate tectonics. Tectonophysics 40: 101–135

Kroner A (1977b) The Precambrian geotectonic evolution of Africa: Plate accretion versus plate destruction. Precambrian Res 4: 163–213

Kroner A (1980) Pan African crustal evolution. Episodes. Int Union Geol Sci 2: 3–8

Kroner A, Correia H (1980) Continuation of the Pan African Damara belt into Angola: A proposed correlation of the Chela Group in southern Angola with the Nosib Group in northern Namibia/S.W.A. Geol Soc S Afr Trans 83: 5–16

Kuhn TH (1941) Pipe deposits of the Copper Creek area, Arizona. Econ Geol 36: 512–538

Kuran VM, Godwin CI, Armstrong RL (1982) Geology and geochronometry of the Scheelite Dome tungsten-bearing skarn property, Yukon Territory. Can Inst Min Bull 75: 137–142

Kutina J (1980) Regularities in the distribution of ore deposits along the Mendocino Latitude, western United States. Global Tect Metall 1: 134–193

Kwak TAP (1978) The conditions of formation of the King Island scheelite contact skarn, King Island, Tasmania, Australia. Am J Sci 278: 969–999

Kwak TAP, Tan TH (1981) The geochemistry of zoning of skarn minerals at the King Island (Dolphin) mine. Econ Geol 76: 468–497

Kyle RJ (1976) Brecciation, alteration, and mineralization in the Central Tennessee Zinc District. Econ Geol 71: 892–903

Kyle RJ (1981) Geology of the Pine Point lead-zinc district. In: Wolfe KH (ed) Handbook of Stratabound and Stratiform Ore Deposits Vol 9. Elsevier, Amsterdam 643–741

Lago BL, Rabinowicz M, Nicolas A (1982) Podiform chromite ore bodies: A genetic model. J Petrol 23: 103–125

Laing WP, Marjoribanks RW, Rutland RWR (1978) Structure of the Broken Hill mine area and its significance for the genesis of the orebodies. Econ Geol 73: 1112–1136

Lambert IB, Sato T (1974) The Kuroko and associated ore deposits of Japan: A review of their features and metallogenesis. Econ Geol 69: 1215–1236

Lang B (1979) The base metals-gold hydrothermal ore deposits of Baia Mare, Romania. Econ Geol 74: 1336–1351

Large DE (1980) Geological parameters associated with sediment-hosted, submarine exhalative Pb-Zn deposits: an empirical model for mineral exploration. Geol Jahrb 40: 59–129

Large RR (1977) Chemical evolution and zonation of massive sulfide deposits in volcanic terrains. Econ Geol 72: 549–572

Larue DK, Sloss LL (1980) Early Proterozoic sedimentary basins of the Lake Superior region: Summary. Geol Soc Am Bull 91: 450–452

Latvalahti U (1979) Cu-Zn-Pb ores in the Aijala-Orijarvi area, southwest Finland. Econ Geol 74: 1035–1059

Laurent A (1980) Environment of formation, evolution and emplacement of the Appalachian ophiolites of Quebec. In: Panayiotou A (ed) Ophiolites. Int Ophiolite Symp Proc Cyprus, 1979, 628–636

Laznicka P (1973) Development of nonferrous metal deposits in geological time. Can J Earth Sci 10: 18–25

Laznicka P (1976) Porphyry copper and molybdenum deposits of the U.S.S.R. and their plate tectonic settings. Trans Inst Min and Metall 85: B14–32

Lea ER, Dill DB (1968) Zinc deposits of the Balmat-Edwards district, New York. AIME Graton-Sales Vol 1: 20–48

Leake BE, Farrow CM, Townend RA (1979) A pre-2000 M yr old granulite facies metamorphosed evaporite from Caraiba, Brazil? Nature 277: 49-50.

LeBas MJ (1977) Carbonatite-Nephelinite Volcanism. Wiley, London, 1–347

Lebedev LM (1972) Minerals of contemporary hydrotherms of Cheleken. Geochem J 9: 485–504

LeBlanc M (1976) Oceanic crust at Bou Azzer. Nature 261: 34–35

Lee WHK (1967) Thermal history of the earth. Unpubl PhD thesis, Univ of California, Los Angeles

Leeman WP (1982) Tectonic and magmatic significance of strontium isotopic variations in Cenozoic volcanic rocks from the western United States. Geol Soc Am Bull 93: 487–503

Lee-Moreno JL (1980) The metallogenic tin province of Mexico. In: Metallogensis in Latin America Prog with Abstracts. Mexico City Int Symp, p 8

Lehmann E (1972) On the source of the iron in the Lahn ore deposits. Min Deposita 7: 247–270

Leitch CHB (1981) Mineralogy and textures of the Lahanos and Kizilkaya massive sulfide deposits, northeastern Turkey, and their similarity to Kuroko ores. Min Deposita 16: 241–257

Lenthall DH (1974) Tin production from the Bushveld Complex. Inf Circ 93 Econ Geol Res Unit, Univ of the Witwatersrand, 1–15

Leroy J (1978) The Margnac and Fanay uranium deposits of the La Crouzille District (Western Massif Central, France): Geologic and fluid inclusion studies. Econ Geol 73: 1611–1634

Lindgren W (1933) Mineral Deposits. McGraw Hill, New York

Lindgren W, Ross CP (1916) The iron deposits of Daiquiri, Cuba. Am Inst Min Engineers Trans 53: 40–66

Lindsey DA (1977) Epithermal beryllium deposits in water-laid tuff, western Utah. Econ Geol 72: 219–232

Lipman PW (1980) Cenozoic volcanism in the western United States: implication for continental tectonics. In: Geophysics: continental tectonics. Natl Acad Sci, Wash, 161–174

Lipman PW, Steven TA, Mehnert HH (1970) Volcanic history of the San Juan Mountains, Colorado, as indicated by potassium-argon dating. Geol Soc Am Bull 81: 2329–2352

Lipman PW, Fisher FS, Mehnert HH, Naeser CW, Luedke RG, Steven TA (1976) Multiple ages of mid-Tertiary mineralization and alteration in the western San Juan Mountains, Colorado. Econ Geol 71: 571–588

Lister CRB (1972) On the thermal balance of an oceanic ridge. Geophys J R Astron Soc 26: 515–535

Lister CRB (1980) Heat flow and hydrothermal circulation. Ann Rev Earth Planet Sci 8: 95–117

Livaccari RF (1979) Reply on Late Cenozoic tectonic evolution of western United States. Geology 7: 371–373

Locke A (1926) The formation of certain orebodies by mineralization stoping. Econ Geol 21: 431–453

Lombaard AF, Schreuder FJG (1978) Distribution pattern and general geological features of steep structures, megabreccias and basic rocks in the Okiep copper district. In: Verwoerd WJ (ed) Mineralization in Metamorphic Terrains. Geol Soc S Afr Spec Publ 4: 269–296

Lonsdale PF, Bischoff JL, Burns VM, Kastner M, Sweeney RE (1980) A hightemperature hydrothermal deposit on the seabed at a Gulf of California spreading center. Earth Planet Sci Lett 49: 8–20

Lorenz V, Nicholls IA (1976) The Permocarboniferous Basin and Range Province of Europe. An application of plate tectonics. In: Falke H (ed) The Continental Permain in Central, West, and South Eruope. Riedel Publ, Co Dordrecht, Holland, 313–342

Lorinczi GI, Miranda JC (1978) Geology of the massive sulfide deposits of Campo Morado, Guerrero, Mexico. Econ Geol 73: 180–191

Loudon AG, Lee MK, Dowling JF, Bourn R (1975) Lady Loretta silver-lead-zinc deposit. In: Economic Geology of Australia and Papua New Guinea. Austalas Min Metall Monogr 5: 377–382

Lowell GR (1976) Tin mineralization and mantle hotspot activity in southeastern Missouri. Nature 261: 482–483

Lowell JD, Guilbert JM (1970) Lateral and vertical alteration-mineralization zoning in porphyry ore deposits. Econ Geol 65: 373–408

Luff WM (1977) Geology of Brunswick No. 12 Mine. Can Inst Min Bull 70–782: 109–119

Lupton JE, Weiss RF, Craig HC (1977) Mantle helium in the Red Sea brines. Nature 266: 244–246

Lusk J (1972) Examination of volcanic-exhalative and biogenic origins of sulfur in the stratiform massive sulfide deposits in New Brunswick. Econ Geol 67: 169–183

Lusk J, Crocket JH (1969) Sulfur isotope fractionation in coexisting sulfides from the Heath Steele B-1 orebody, New Brunswick, Canada. Econ Geol 64: 147–155

Lydon JW (1983) Chemical parameters controlling the origin and deposition of sediment-hosted stratiform lead-zinc deposits. In: Sangster DF (ed) Sediment-hosted stratiform lead-zinc deposits. Min Assoc Can, Short Course Handb 8: 175–250

McCallum IS, Raedeke LD, Mathez EA (1980) Investigations of the Stillwater Complex: Part I Stratigraphy and structure of the banded zone. Am J Sci 280A: 59–87

McConnell RB (1974) Evolution of taphrogenic lineaments in continental platforms. Geol Rundsch 63: 389–430

McDougall I (1976) Geochemistry and origin of basalt of the Columbia River Group, Oregon and Washington. Geol Soc Am Bull 87: 777–792

McDougall I, Lovering JF (1963) Fractionation of chronium, nickel, cobalt, and copper in a differentiated dolerite-granophyre sequence at Red Hill, Tasmania. J Geol Soc Austr 10: 325–338

McGetchin TR, Burke KC, Thompson GA, Young RA (1980) Mode and mechanism of plateau uplifts. Dynamics of Plate Interiors. Geodynamic Series vol 1, Am Geol Union, 99–110

McIlveen GR (1974) The Eden-Comerong-Yalwal rift zone and the contained gold mineralization. Rec Geol Surv N S W 16: 245–277

McIntosh JL, Farag JS, Slee KJ (1975) Groote Eylandt manganese deposits. In: Knight CL (ed) Economic Geology of Australia and Papua New Guinea. Metals, 815–821

McKenzie DP (1967) Some remarks on heat flow and gravity anomalies. J Geophys Res 72: 6261–6273

McKenzie D (1978) Some remarks on the development of sedimentary basins. Earth Planet Sci Lett 40: 25–32

McLaughlin RJ (1981) Tectonic setting of pre-Tertiary rocks and its relation to geothermal resources in the Geysers – Clear Lake area. US Geol Surv Prof Pap 1141: 3–24

McLeod WN, Turner DC, Wright EP (1971) The geology of the Jos Plateau. Geol Surv Nigeria Bull 32 2: 1–168

McWilliams MO, Kroner A (1981) Paleomagnetism and tectonic evolution of the Pan-African Damara Belt, Southern Africa. J Geophys Res 86: 5147–5162

MacDonald KC, Becker K, Spiess FN, Ballard RD (1980) Hydrothermal heat flux of the "black smoker" vents on the East Pacific Rise. Earth Planet Sci Lett 48: 1–7

MacGeehan PJ, Maclean WH (1980) Tholeiitic basalt-rhyolite magmatism and massive sulfide deposits at Matagami, Quebec. Nature 283: 153–157

MacGeehan PJ, Maclean WH, Bonenfaut AJ (1981) Exploration significance of the emplacement and genesis of massive sulfides in the Main Zone at the Norita Mine, Matagami, Quebec. Can Inst Min Metall Bull 74 no 828: 59–75

MacIntyre DG (1982) Geologic setting of recently discovered stratiform barite-sulfide deposits in northeast British Columbia. Can Inst Min Bull 75 no 840: 99–113

MacIntyre DG (1983) Geology and stratiform barite-sulfide deposits of the Gataga district, northeast British Columbia. In: Sangster DF (ed) Sediment-hosted stratiform lead-zinc deposits. Min Assoc Can, Short Course Handb 8: 85–120

MacKenzie WB (1970) Hydrothermal alteration associated with the Urad and Henderson molybdenite deposits, Clear Creek County, Colorado. Unpubl PhD thesis, Univ Michigan 208 p

MacKevett EM Jr, Armstrong AK, Potter RW, Silberman ML (1980) Kennecott-type copper deposits, Wrangell Mountains, Alaska – An update and summary (Abst) Mineral Deposits of the Pacific Northwest Symp Proc. US Geol Surv Open-File Rep 81-355: 50–51

Magee M (1968) Geology and ore deposits of the Ducktown district, Tennessee. Ore Deposits of the United States, 1933–1967. AIME Graton-Sales Vol 1: 207–241

Mainwaring PR, Naldrett AJ (1977) Country-rock assimilation and the genesis of Cu-Ni sulfides in the Waterhen intrusion, Duluth Complex, Minnesota. Econ Geol 72: 1269–1284

Maliotis G, Khan MA (1980) The applicability of the induced polarization method of geophysical exploration in the search for sulfide mineralization within the Troodos ophiolite complex of Cyprus. In: A Panayiotou (ed) Ophiolites. Proc Int Ophiolite Symp Cyprus, 1979, 129–138

Manton WI (1968) The origin of associated basic and acid rocks in the Lebombo-Nuanetsi igneous province, southern Africa, as implied by strontium isotopes. J Petrol 9: 23–39

Marcotte D, David M (1981) Target definition of Kuroko-type deposits in Abitibi by discriminant analysis of geochemical data. Can Inst Min Metall Bull 74 no 828: 102–108

Marsh JS (1973) Relationship between transform directions and alkaline igneous rock lineaments in Africa and South America. Earth Planet Sci Lett 18: 317–323

Marshak RS, Karig DE (1976) Triple junctions as a cause for anomously near-trench igneous activity between the trench and volcanic arc. Geology 5: 233–236

Mason JK, McConnell CD (1983) Gold mineralization in the Beardmore-Geraldton area. In: Colvine AC (ed) The geology of gold in Ontario. Ont Geol Surv Misc Pap 110: 84–97

Marston RJ, Groves DL, Hudson DR, Ross JR (1981) Nickel sulfide deposits in Western Australia: A review. Econ Geol 76: 1330–1363

Martin H (1978) The mineralization of the ensialic Damara orogenic belt. Geol Soc S Afr Spec Pub No 4: 405–415

Martin H, Porada H (1978) The intracratonic branch of the Damara Orogen in Southwest Africa. I Discussion of geodynamic models. Precambrian Res 5: 311–338

Martin RF, Piwinskii AJ (1972) Magmatism and tectonic setting. J Geophys Res 77: 4966–4975

Materikov MP (1977) Deposits of tin. In: Smirnov VI (ed) Ore Deposits of the USSR 3: 229–294

Mathias BV, Clark GJ (1975) Mount Isa copper and silver-lead-zinc orbodies – Isa and Hilton Mines. In: Knight CL (ed) Economic Geology of Australia and Papua New Guinea. Australas Inst Min Metall Monogr 5: 351–371

Mathias BV, Clark GJ, Morris D, Russell RE (1973) The Hilton deposit – stratiform silver-lead-zinc mineralization of the Mt. Isa type. In: Metallogenic Provinces and Mineral Deposits in the Southwest Pacific. Bur Min Resource Australas Bull 141: 33–58

Maucher A, Schneider HJ (1967) The Alpine lead-zinc ores. Econ Geol Monogr 3: 71–89

May ER, Schmidt PG (1982) The discovery, geology and mineralogy of the Crandon Precambrian massive sulfide deposit, Wisconsin. Geol Assoc Can Spec Pap 25: 447–480

Meinert LD, Newberry R, Einaudi MT (1980) An overview of tungsten, copper and zinc-bearing skarns in western North America. In: Silberman ML, Field CW, Berry AL (eds) Symp on Mineral Deposits of the Pacific Northwest. USGS Open-File Rep 81-355: 303–327

Melson WG, Vallier TL, Wright TL, Byerly G, Nelson J (1976) Chemical diversity of abyssal volcanic glass erupted along Pacific, Atlantic, and Indian Ocean sea-floor spreading centers. Am Geophys Union Monogr 19: 351–368

Menard HW (1967) Sea-floor spreading, topography and the second layer. Science 157: 923–924

Menard HW, Atwater T (1969) Origin of fracture zone topography. Nature 222: 1037–1040

Mendelsohn F (1961) The geology of the Northern Rhodesian Copper Belt. MacDonald, London 523 p

Meyer C (1981) Ore-forming processes in geologic history. Econ Geol 75th Anniv Vol, 6–41

Middleton RC (1976) The geology of Prieska Copper Mines Limited. Econ Geol 71: 328–350

Milanovsky EE (1981) Aulacogens of ancient platforms: Problems of their origin and tectonic development. Tectonophysics 73: 213–248

Miller CF, Bradfish LJ (1980) An inner Cordilleran belt of muscovite-bearing plutons. Geology 8: 412–416

Mitchell AHG (1974) Southwest England granites: magmatism and tin mineralization in a post-collision tectonic setting. Trans Inst Min Metall 83: B95–97

Mitchell AHG (1977) Tectonic settings for emplacement of Southeast Asian tin granites. Bull Geol Soc Malaysia 9: 123–140

Mitchell AHG, Garson MS (1981) Mineral Deposits and Global Tectonic Settings. Academic Press, London, 405

Moghal MY (1974) Uranium in Siwalik sandstones, Sulaiman Range, Pakistan. In: Formation of uranium ore deposits. IAEA Vienna, 383–403

Mohr P (1982) Musings on continental rifts. In: Palmason G (ed) Continental and Oceanic Rifts. Geodynamic Ser 8: 293–309

Montoya JW, Hemley JJ (1975) Activity relations and stabilities in alkali feldspar and mica alteration reactions. Econ Geol 70: 577–594

Moorbath S (1962) Lead isotope abundance studies on mineral occurrences in the British Isles and their geological significance. Philos Trans R Soc Lond 254: 295–360

Moorbath S (1980) Aspects of the chronology of ancient rocks related to continental evolution. In: Strangway DW (ed) The Continental Crust and its Mineral Deposits. Geol Assoc Can Spec Pap 20: 89–115

Moore JM (1980) A study of certain paragneiss associations and their metallogenic characteristics in Namaqualand and Bushmanland. Univ Cape Town Precamb Res Unit Ann Rep 1979: 65–73

Moore JMcM (1982) Mineral zonation near the granitic batholiths of south-west and northern England and some geothermal anologues. In: Evans AM (ed) Metallization Associated with Acid Magmatism. Wiley, New York, 229–241

Moores E (1969) Petrology and structure of the Vourinos ophiolite complex, northern Greece. Geol Soc Am Spec Pap 118: 1–74

Morgan BA (1975) Mineralogy and origin of skarns in the Mount Morrison roof pendant, Sierra Nevada, Californa. Am J Sci 275: 119–142

Morgan WJ (1972) Plate motions and deep mantle convection. Geol Soc Am Mem 132: 7–22

Mottl MJ (1983) Metabasalts, axial hot springs, and the structure of hydrothermal systems at mid-ocean ridges. Geol Soc Am Bull 94: 161–180

Muff R (1978) The Antimony deposits in the Murchison Range of the northeastern Transvaal, Republic of South Africa. Monogr Ser on Min Deposits 16, Gebrüder Borntraeger, Berlin, 1–90

Mulligan R (1971) Lithophile metals and the Cordilleran tin belt. Can Min Metall Bull 64: 714, 68–71

Mumpton FA, Thompson CS (1975) Mineralogy and origin of the Coalinga asbestos deposit. Clays and Clay Miner 23: 131–143

Munha J (1979) Blue amphiboles, metamorphic regime and plate tectonic modelling in the Iberian pyrite belt. Contrib Min Pet 69: 279–289

Naldrett AJ (1981) Nickel sulfide deposits: Classification, composition, and genesis. Econ Geol 75th Anniv Vol: 628–685

Naldrett AJ, Kullerud G (1967) A study of the Strathcona mine and its bearing on the origin of the nickel-copper ores of the Sudbury district, Ontario. J Petrol 8: 453–531

Naldrett AJ, MacDonald AJ (1980) Tectonic settings of some Ni-Cu sulfide ores: Their importance in genesis and exploration. In: Strangway DW (ed) The Continental Crust and Its Mineral Deposits. Geol Assoc Can Spec Pap 20: 633–657

Naldrett AJ, Hewins RH, Breenman L (1972) The main irruptive and the sublayer at Sudbury. Int Geol Congr 24th Montreal Proc sect 4: 206–214

Narayanaswami S, Zinuddin M, Ramachandra AV (1960) Structural control and localization of gold-bearing lodes, Kolar Gold Field, India. Econ Geol 55: 1429–1459

Nasseef AO, Bakor AR, Hashad AH (1980) Petrography of possible ophiolite rocks along the Qift-Quseir road, Eastern Desert, Egypt. In: Al-Shanti AMS (ed) Evolution and Mineralization of the Arabian-Nubian Shield. Pergamon Oxford 4: 157–168

Needham RS, Crick IH, Stuart-Smith PG (1980) Regional geology of the Pine Creek Geosyncline. In: Uranium in the Pine Creek Geosyncline. Int Atomic Energy Agency Vienna, 1–22

Neudert MK, Russell RE (1981) Shallow water and hypersaline features from the Middle Proterozoic Mt. Isa sequence. Nature 293: 284–286

Newberry RJ, Einaudi MT (1981) Tectonic and geochemical setting of tungsten skarn mineralization in the Cordillera. In: Dickinson WR, Payne WD (eds) Relations of Tectonics to Ore Deposits in the Southern Cordillera. Ariz Geol Soc Dig Vol. XIV: 99–111

Ney CS, Hollister VF (1976) Geologic setting of porphyry deposits of the Canadian Cordillera. In: Southerland Brown (ed) Porphyry Deposits of the Canadian Cordillera. Can Inst Min Metall Spec Vol 15: 21–29

Nicolas A, Violette JF (1982) Mantle flow at oceanic spreading centers: models derived from ophiolites. Tectonophysics 81: 319–339

Nielsen BL (1976) Geology of Greenland: Economic Minerals. Gron Geol Unders Den 461–486

Nilsen O (1978) Caledonian massive sulfide deposits and minor iron-formations from the southern Trondheim region, Norway. Norg Geol Unders 340: 35–85

Noble JA (1980) Two metallogenic maps for North America. Geol Rundsch 69: 594–609

Noe-Nygaard A, Pedersen AK (1974) Progressive chemical variation in a tholeiitic lava sequence at Kap Stosch, northern East Greenland. Bull Geol Soc Den 23: 175–190

Nokleberg WJ (1981) Geologic setting, petrology, and geochemistry of zoned tungsten-bearing skarns at the Strawberry Mine, central Sierra Nevada, Californa. Econ Geol 76: 111–133

Nolan TB (1933) Epithermal precious metal deposits. In: Ore Deposits of the Western States (Lindgren Volume) New York. Am Inst Min Metall Engineers 623–640

Norman DI (1977) Geology and geochemistry of Tribag Mine, Batchawana Bay, Ontario. Unpub PhD thesis Univ Minnesota, 257 p

Norman DI (1978) Ore deposits related to the Keweenawan Rift. In: Neumann ER, Ramberg IB (eds) Petrology and Geochemistry of Continental Rifts, Reidel, Dordrecht 245–254

Norman JW (1980) Causes of some old crustal failure zones interpreted from Landstat images and their significance in regional exploration. Trans Inst Min Metall 89: B63–B72

Normark WR, Morton JL, Koski RA, Clague DA, Delaney JR (1983) Active hydrothermal vents and sulfide deposits on the southern Juan de Fuca Ridge. Geology 11: 158–163

Northern Miner (1982) Major zinc-lead Alaska deposit now under study by Cominco. North Miner 67 no 49: A1, A6.

Northolt AJG (1979) The economic geology and development of igneous phosphate deposits in Europe and the USSR. Econ Geol 74: 339–350

Norton D (1978) Source-lines, source-regions, and pathlines for fluids in hydrothermal systems related to cooling plutons. Econ Geol 73: 21–28

Norton D (1979) Transport phenomena in hydrothermal systems - the redistribution of chemical components around cooling magmas. Bull Min 102: 471–486

Norton DL, Cathles LM (1973) Breccia pipes – products of exsolved vapor from magmas. Econ Geol 68: 540–546

Nunes PD, Pyke DR (1980) Geochronology of the Abitibi metavolcanic belt, Timmins-Matachewan area – progress report. Ont Geol Surv Misc Pap 92: 34–39

Oba N, Miyahisa M (1977) Relations between chemical composition of granitic rocks and metalization in the Outer Zone of southwest Japan. Bull Geol Soc Malaysia 9: 67–74

O'Driscoll EST (1981) A broad-scale structural characteristic of major nickel sulfide deposits of western Australia. Econ Geol 76: 1364–1372

Ohle EL (1980) Some considerations in determining the origin of ore deposits of the Mississippi Valley type – Part II. Econ Geol 75: 161–172

Ohmoto H (1978) Submarine calderas: A key to the formation of volcanogenic massive sulfide deposits. Min Geol 28: 219–231

Ohmoto H, Rye RO (1974) Hydrogen and oxygen isotopic compositions of fluid inclusions in the Kuroko deposits, Japan. Econ Geol 69: 947–953

Ohmoto H, Hart SR, Holland HD (1966) Studies of the Providencia area, Mexico, II, K-Ar and Rb-Sr ages of intrusive rocks and hydrothermal minerals. Econ Geol 61: 1205–1213

Olade MA (1980) Plate tectonics and metallogeny of intracontinental rifts and aulocogens, with special reference to Africa. Prof Fifth IAGOD Symp, Utah 91–112

O'Neil JR, Silberman ML (1974) Stable isotope relations in epithermal Au-Ag deposits. Econ Geol 69: 902–909

Palabora Mining Company Ltd Mine geological and mineralogical staff (1976) The geology and economic deposit of copper, iron, and vermiculite in the Palabora Igneous Complex: a brief review. Econ Geol 71: 177–192

Panayiotou A (1980) Cu-Ni-Co-Fe sulfide mineralization, Limassol Forest, Cyprus. In: Panayiotou A (ed) Ophiolites. Proc Int Ophiolite Symp Cyprus, 1979, 102–116

Pansze AJ (1975) Geology and ore deposits of the Silver City-Delamar-Flint region, Omyhee County, Idaho. Idaho Bur Mines Geol Pamphlet 161.

Park CF Jr (1961) A magnetite 'flow' in northern Chile. Econ Geol 56: 431–436

Park CF Jr (1972) The iron deposits of the Pacific basin. Econ Geol 67: 339–349

Paterson R (1976) Ardlethan tin mine. In: Ore deposits of the Lachlan fold belt, New South Wales. 25th Int Geol Congr Excursion Guide no 15C: 36–43

Pattison EF (1979) The Sudbury sublayer. Can Min 17: 257–274

Pearce JA (1980) Geochemical evidence for the genesis and eruptive setting of lavas from Tethyan ophiolites. In: Panayiotou A (ed) Ophiolites. Proc Int Ophiolite Symp Cyprus, 1979: 261–272

Pearson WN (1979) Copper metallogeny, North Shore region of Lake Huron, Ontario. Geol Surv Can Pap 79-1A: 289–303

Pedersen FD (1980) Remobilization of the massive sulfide ore of the Black Angel Mine, central west Greenland. Econ Geol 75: 1022–1041

Peredery WV, Geological Staff (1982) Geology and nickel sulfide deposits of the Thompson Belt, Manitoba. Geol Assoc Can Spec Pap 25: 165–209

Pereira J, Dixon CJ (1963) Evolutionary trends in ore deposition. Inst Min Metall Trans 74: 505–527

Perry VD (1961) The significance of mineralized breccia pipes. Min Engng 13: 367–376

Petersen U (1965) Regional geology and major ore deposits of central Peru. Econ Geol 60: 407–476

Petersen U (1970) Metallogenic provinces of South America. Geol Rundsch 59: 834–897

Petersen U, Noble DC, Arenas MJ, Goodell PC (1977) Geology of the Julcani district, Peru. Econ Geol 72: 931–949

Petersen JS Schonwandt HKr (1983) Porphyry-Mo occurrences in the Oslo Rift system. Tectonophysics 94:609–632

Petruk W (1973) The tungsten-bismuth-molybdenum deposit of Brunswick Tin Mines Ltd, its mode of occurrence, mineralogy, and amenability to mineral beneficiation. Can Inst Min Bull 66: 113–130

Pienaar PJ (1961) Mineralization in the Basement Complex. In: Mendelsohn F (ed) The Geology of the Northern Rhodesian Copperbelt. MacDonald, London, 30–41

Pilcher SH, McDougall JJ (1976) Characteristics of some Canadian porphyry prospects. Can Inst Min Metall Spec Vol 15: 79–82

Piper JDA (1982) The Precambrian paleomagnetic record. the case for the Proterozoic Supercontinent. Earth Planet Sci Lett 59: 61–89

Pipino G (1980) Gold in Ligurian ophiolites (Italy). In: Panayiotou A (ed) Ophiolites. Int Ophiolite Symp Proc Cyprus, 1979, 765–774

Pitcher WS (1979) The nature, ascent and emplacement of granitic magmas. J Geol Soc Lond 136: 627–662

Pitman WC III, Hayes JD (1973) Upper Cretaceous spreading rates and the great transgression. Abstr Progr Geol Soc Am 5: 768

Platt JW (1977) Volcanogenic mineralization at Avoca, Co. Wicklow, Ireland, and its regional implications. In: Volcanic Processes in Ore Genesis. Geol Soc Lond Inst Min Metall 163–170

Plimer IR (1978) Proximal and distal stratabound ore deposits. Min Deposita 13: 345–353

Porada H (1979) The Damara-Ribeira orogen of the Pan-African Brasiliano cycle in Namibia (Southwest Africa) and Brazil as interpreted in terms of continental collision. Tectonophysics 57: 237–265

Pouba Z (1971) Relations between iron and copper-lead-zinc mineralizations in submarine volcanic ore deposits in the Jeseniky Mts, Czechoslovakia. IAGOD vol Soc Min Geol Jpn Spec Issue 3: 186–192

Poulsen KH, Franklin JM (1981) Copper and gold mineralization in an Archean trondhjemitic intrusion, Sturgeon Lake, Ontario. Geol Surv Can Pap 81-1A: 9–14

Pretorius DA (1975) The depositional environment of the Witwatersrand goldfields: a chronological review of speculations and observations. Min Sci Engin 7: 18–47

Pretorius DA (1981a) Gold and uranium in quartz-pebble conglomerates. Econ Geol 75th Anniv Vol: 117–138

Pretorius DA (1981b) Gold, geld, gilt: Future supply and demand. Econ Geol Res Unit Univ Witwatersrand Inf Circ 152: 1–15

Priem HNA, Boelrijk NA, Hebeda EH, Verdurmen EA, Verschure RH, Bon EH (1971) Granitic complexes and associated tin mineralizations of 'Grenville' age in Rondonia, Western Brazil. Geol Soc Am Bull 82: 1095–1102

Prinz M (1967) Geochemistry of basaltic rocks: trace elements. Basalts, the Poldervaart treatise on rocks of basaltic composition I. Interscience, NY 271–323

Proffett JM Jr (1979) Ore deposits of the western United States – A summary. Nev Bur Mines Geol Rep 33: 13–32

Quade H (1976) Genetic problems and environmental features of volcanosedimentary iron-ore deposits of the Lahn-Dill type. In: Wolfe KH (ed) Handbook of Strata-bound and Stratiform Ore Deposits, Elsevier, Amsterdam 255–294

Radtke AS (1983) Geology of the Carlin gold deposit, Nevada. US Geol Surv Prof Pap (in press)

Radtke AS, Rye RO, Dickson FW (1980) Geology and stable isotope studies of the Carlin Gold Deposit. Econ Geol 75: 641–672.

Ransom PW (1977) Geology of the Sullivan orebody. Geol Assoc Canada Ann Mtg Vancouver B.C. Field Trip Guidebook No 1: 7–21

Raybould JG (1978) Tectonic controls on Proterozoic stratiform mineralization. Inst Min Metall Trans 87: B79–B86

Read HH (1957) The granite controversy. Murby, London, 1–430

Reid DL (1977) Geochemistry of Precambrian igneous rocks in the lower Orange River region. Precambrian Res Unit, Univ of Cape Town Bull 22: 1–397

Renfro AR (1974) Genesis of evaporite-associated stratiform metalliferous deposits – a Sabkha process. Econ Geol 69: 33–45

Rentzsch J (1974) The Kupferschiefer in comparison with the deposits of the Zambian copperbelt. In: Bartholome P (ed) Gisments stratiformes et Provinces cupriferes. Liége Soc Geol de Bélg 395–418

Rhodes RC (1975) New evidence for the impact origin of the Bushveld Igneous Complex. Geology 3: 549–554

Richards DNG (1980) Paleozoic granitoids of northeastern Australia. In: Henderson RA, Stephenson PJ (eds) The geology and geophysics of northeastern Australia. Brisbane Geol Soc Austr, Queensland Div 229–246

Richardson JMG, Spooner ETC, McAuslan DA (1982) The East Kemptville tin deposit, Nova Scotia: an example of a large tonnage, low grade, greisen-hosted deposit in the endocontact zone of a granite batholith. Current Research Part B Geol Surv Can Pap 82-1B: 27–32

Rickard DT, Zweifel H (1975) Genesis of Precambrian sulfide ores, Skellefte district, Sweden. Econ Geol 70: 255–274

Rickard DT, Willden MY, Marinder NE, Donnell TH (1979) Studies of the genesis of the Laisvall Sandstone lead-zinc deposit, Sweden. Econ Geol 74: 1255–1285

Ridler RH (1970) Relationship of mineralization to volcanic stratigraphy in the Kirkland-Larder Lakes area, Ontario. Geol Assoc Can 21: 33–42

Ripley EM, Lambert MW, Berendson P (1980) Mineralogy and paragenesis of red-bed copper mineralization in the Lower Permian of South central Kansas. Econ Geol 75: 722–729

Riverin G, Hodgson CJ (1980) Wall-rock alteration at the Millenbach Cu-Zn mine, Noranda, Quebec. Econ Geol 75: 424–444

Robbins EI (1983) Accumulation of fossil fuels and minerals in active and ancient rifts. Tectonophysics 94:633–658

Roberts DE, Hudson GRT (1983) The Olympic Dam copper-uranium-gold deposit, Roxby Downs, South Australia. Econ Geol 78: 779–823

Robertson AHF (1977) Tertiary uplift history of the Troodos Massif, Cyprus. Geol Soc Am Bull 88: 1763–1772

Robertson JM (1975) Geology and mineralogy of some copper sulfide deposits near Mount Bohemia, Keweenawan County, Michigan. Econ Geol 70: 1202–1224

Rodgers RK, Davis JM (1977) Geology of the Buick Mine, Viburnum Trend, southeast Missouri. Econ Geol 72: 372–380

Roedder E (1971) Fluid inclusion studies on the porphyry-type ore deposits at Bingham, Utah; Butte, Montana; and Climax, Colorado. Econ Geol 66: 98–120

Roedder E (1976) Fluid inclusion evidence in the genesis of ores in sedimentary and volcanic rocks. In: Wolf KH (ed) Handbook of stratabound and stratiform ore deposits. Elsevier, Amsterdam 4: 67–110

Roedder E (1977) Fluid inclusion studies of ore deposits in the Viburnum Trend, southeast Missouri. Econ Geol 72: 474–479

Rona PA (1978) Criteria for recognition of hydrothermal mineral deposits in oceanic crust. Econ Geol 73: 135–160

Rose AW, Burt DM (1979) Hydrothermal alteration. In: Barnes LH (ed) Geochemistry of Hydrothermal Ore Deposits. Wiley, NY 173–235

Ross JR, Travis GA (1981) The nickel sulfide deposits of Western Australia in global perspective. Econ Geol 76: 1291–1329

Rossiter AG, Ferguson J (1980) A Proterozoic tectonic model for northern Australia and its economic implications. In: Uranium in the Pine Creek Geosyncline. Int Atomic Energy Agency Vienna, 209–232

Routhier P, Aye F, Boyer C, Lecolle M, Moliere P, Picot P, Roger G (1979) La ceinture sud-iberique a amas sulfures dans sa partie espagnole mediane. Tableau geologique et metallogenique. Synthese sur le type amas sulfures volcano-sedimentaires. Mem Bur Res Geol Min 94: [1]-266

Rowlands NJ (1974) The gitology of some Adelaidean stratiform copper occurrences. In: Batholome P (ed) Gisements stratiformes et provinces cupriferes. Soc Geol Bélgique, Liége 419–427

Rowlands NJ (1980) Discussions and contributions: tectonic controls on Proterozoic stratiform mineralization. Trans Inst Min Metall 89: B167–B168

Rowlands NJ, Blight PG, Jarvius DM, von der Borch CC (1980) Sabkha and playa environments in late Proterozoic grabens, Willouran Ranges, South Australia. J Geol Soc Austr 27: 55–68

Royden L, Sclater JG (1981) The Neogene intra-Carpathian basins. Phil Trans R Soc Lond A300: 373–381

Rozendaal A (1980) The Gamsberg zinc deposit, South Africa: a banded stratiform base-metal sulfide deposit. Proc Fifth IAGOD Symp Vol: 619–633

Ruegg NR (1976) Characteristicas de distribuicao e teor de elementos tracos dosados em rochas basalticas de bacia do Parana. Naturalia 2: 23–45

Ruitenberg AA, Fyffe LR (1982) Mineral deposits associated with granitoid intrusions and related subvolcanic stocks in New Brunswick and their relationship to Appalachian tectonic evolution. Can Inst Min Bull 75 no 842: 83–97

Ruiz C, Aguilar A, Egert E, Espinoza W, Peebles F, Quezada R, Serrano M (1971) Strata-bound copper deposits of Chile. Third IAGOD Symp Vol, 252–260

Ruiz F and others (1965) Geologia y yacimientos metaliferos de Chile. Santiago Inst Invest Geol, 1–305

Russell MJ (1968) Structural controls of base metals mineralization in Ireland in relation to continental drift. Trans Inst Min Metall 77: B117–B128

Russell MJ (1975) Lithogeochemical environment of the Tynagh base-metal deposit, Ireland, and its bearing on ore deposition. Trans Inst Min Metal 84: B128–B133

Russell MJ (1978) Downward-excavating hydrothermal cells and Irish-type ore deposits: importance of an underlying thick Caledonian prism. Trans Inst Min Metal 87: B168–B171

Russel MJ (1983) Major sediment-hosted exhalative zinc + lead deposits: Formation from hydrothermal convection cells that deepen during crustal extension. In: Sangster DF (ed) Sediment-hosted stratiform lead-zinc deposits. Min Assoc Can, Short Course Handb 8: 251–282

Russell MJ, Smythe DK (1982) Metalliferous resources associated with rifting: the proto-North Atlantic example (360–280 Ma). (Abs) NASA Rifting Conf.

Russell N, Seaward M, Rivera J, McCurdy J, Kesler SE, Cloke PL (1981) Geology and geochemistry of the Pueblo Viejo gold-silver oxide ore deposit, Dominican Republic. Trans Inst Mining Metall 90: B178–B201

Ruzicka V (1971) Geological comparisons between East European and Canadian uranium deposits. Geol Surv Can Pap 70-48: 1–196

Ryan PJ, Lawrence AL, Lipson RD, Moore JM, Paterson A, Stedman DP, Van Zyl D (1982) The Aggenys base metal sulfide deposits, Namaqualand, South Africa. Econ Geol Res Unit, Univ Witwatersrand Info Circ 160: 1–33

Rye DM, Rye RO (1974) Homestake gold mine, South Dakota: I. Stable isotope studies. Econ Geol 69: 293–317

Rye RO (1966) The carbon, hydrogen, and oxygen isotopic composition of the hydrothermal fluids responsible for the lead-zinc deposits at Providencia, Zacatecas, Mexico. Econ Geol 61: 1399–1427

Rye RO (1974) A comparison of sphalerite-galena sulfur isotope temperatures with filling temperatures of fluid inclusions. Econ Geol 69: 26–32

Rye RO, O'Neil JR (1968) The O^{18} content of water in primary fluid inclusions from Providencia, north-central Mexico. Econ Geol 63: 232–238

Rye RO, Haffty J (1969) Chemical composition of the hydrothermal fluids responsible for the lead-zinc deposits at Providencia, Zacatecas, Mexico. Econ Geol 64: 629–643

Rye RO, Sawkins FJ (1974) Fluid inclusion and stable isotope studies on the Casapalca Ag-Pb-Zn-Cu deposit, Central Andes, Peru. Econ Geol 69: 181–205

Rye RO, Hall WE, Ohmoto H (1974) Carbon, hydrogen and sulfur isotope study of the Darwin lead-silver-zinc deposit, southern California. Econ Geol 69: 468–481

Rytuba JJ (1981) Relation of calderas to ore deposits in the western United States. Ariz Geol Soc Dig Vol XIV: 227–236

Saager R, Meyer M, Muff R (1982) Gold distribution in supracrustal rocks from Archean greenstone belts of Southern Africa and from Paleozoic ultramafic complexes of the European Alps: Metallogenic and geochemical implications. Econ Geol 77: 1–24

Sabir H (1979) Precambrian polymetallic sulfide deposits in Saudi Arabia and their metallogenic significance. In: Al-Shanti (ed) Evolution and Mineralization of the Arabian-Nubian Shield. Pergamon, Oxford 2: 83–92

Saito M, Sato E (1978) On the recent exploration at the Iwato gold mine. Min Geol 28: 191–202

Salas GP (1975) Carta y provincias metalogeneticas de la Republica Mexicana. Mexico, Consejo de Recursos Minerales Publ 21E 242 p

Samanov IZ, Pozharisky IF (1977) Deposits of copper. In: Smirnov VI (ed) Ore Deposits of the USSR. Pitman, London Vol 2: 106–181

Sangster DF (1969) The contact metasomatic magnetite deposits of southwestern British Columbia. Geol Surv Can Bull 172: 1–85

Sangster DF (1976) Carbonate-hosted lead-zinc deposits. In: Wolf KH (ed) Handbook of Stratabound and Stratiform Deposits 6: 447–456

Sangster DF (1979) Plate tectonics and mineral deposits: A view from two perspectives. Geosci Can 6: 185–188

Sangster DF (1980) Quantitative characteristics of volcanogenic massive sulfide deposits. Can Inst Min Bull 73: 74–81

Sangster DF (1981) Three potential sites for the occurrence of stratiform, shale-hosted lead-zinc deposits in the Canadian Arctic. Geol Surv Can Paper 81-A: 1–8.

Sangster DF ed (1983) Sediment-hosted stratiform lead-zinc deposits. Min Assoc Can, Short Course Handb 8: 1:309

Sangster DF, Brook WA (1977) Primitive lead in an Australian Zn-Pb-Ba deposit. Nature 270: 423

Sass-Gustkiewicz M, Dzulynski S, Ridge JD (1982) The emplacement of zinc-lead sulfide ores in the Upper Silesian District – A contribution to the understanding of Mississippi Valley-type deposits. Econ Geol 77: 392–412

Sato T (1974) Distribution and geological setting of the Kuroko deposits. Min Geol Spec Issue No 6 Soc Min Geol Jpn 1–9

Sato T (1975) Unilateral isotope variation of Miocene ore leads from Japan. Econ Geol 70: 800–805

Sato K, Sasaki A (1973) Lead isotopes of the Black Ore ("Kuroko") deposits of Japan. Ecol Geol 68: 547–552

Sato T, Tanimura S, Ohtagaki T (1974) Geology and ore deposits of the Hokuroko District, Akita Prefecture. In: Ishihara S (ed) Geology of Kuroko deposits. Min Geol Spec Issue 6: 11–18

Sawkins FJ (1964) Lead-zinc ore deposition in the light of fluid inclusion studies. Providencia Mine, Zacatecas, Mexico. Econ Geol 59: 883–919

Sawkins FJ (1966) Ore genesis in the north Pennine orefield, in the light of fluid inclusion studies. Econ Geol 61: 385–401

Sawkins FJ (1976a) Widespread continental rifting: some considerations of timing and mechanism. Geology 4: 427–430

Sawkins FJ (1976b) Metal deposits related to intracontinental hotspot and rifting environments. J Geol 80: 1028–1041.

Sawkins FJ (1976c) Massive sulfide deposits in relation to geotectonics. In: Strong DF (ed) Metallogeny and Plate Tectonics. Geol Assoc Can Spec Publ 14: 221–240

Sawkins FJ (1977) Fluid inclusion studies of the Messina copper deposits, Transvaal, South Africa. Econ Geol 72: 619–631

Sawkins FJ (1979) Fluid inclusion studies of copper-bearing breccia pipes, Inguaran Mine, Michoacan, Mexico. Econ Geol 74: 924–928

Sawkins FJ (1980) Single-stage versus two-stage or deposition in subduction-related volcano-plutonic ores. Proc Fifth Quadr IAGOD Symp E Schweizerbat'sche Verlagsbuchhandlung Germany, Stuttgart, 143–154

Sawkins FJ (1982a) Metallogenesis in relation to rifting. In: Palmason G (ed) Continental and Oceanic Rifts. Geodynamics Ser Vol 8: 259–270

Sawkins FJ (1982b) The formation of Kuroko-type deposits viewed within the broader context of ore genesis theory. Min Geol 32: 25–33

Sawkins FJ (1983) Tectonic controls of the time-space distribution of Proterozoic metal deposits. Geol Soc Am Spec Pap (in press)

Sawkins FJ, Burke K (1980) Extensional tectonics and mid-Paleozoic massive sulfide occurrences in Europe. Geol Rundsch 69: 349–360

Sawkins FJ, Kowalik J (1981) The source of ore metals at Buchans: Magmatic versus leaching models. Geol Assoc Can Spec Pap 22: 255–268

Sawkins FJ, Rye DM (1974) Relationship of Homestake-type gold deposits to iron-rich Precambrian sedimentary rocks. Trans Metall Inst Min Metall 83: B56–B60

Sawkins FJ, Rye RO (1976) Fluid inclusion and stable isotope studies of the Caudalosa Ag deposit: Evidence for the mixing of magmatic and meteoric fluids. Proc Fourth IAGOD Symp Varna Bulgaria, 110–116

Sawkins FJ, Rye RO (1979) Additional geochemical data on the Messina copper deposits, Transvaal, South Africa. Econ Geol 74: 684–689

Sawkins FJ, Scherkenbach D (1981) High copper contents of fluid inclusions in quartz from northern Sonora: implications for ore genesis theory. Geology 9: 37–40

Sawkins FJ, O'Neil JR, Thompson JM (1979) Fluid inclusion and geochemical studies of gold vein deposits, Baguio District, Philippines. Econ Geol 74: 1420–1434

Scherkenbach D, Sawkins FJ (1983) Studies of the mineralized breccias at Cumobabi, Sonora, Mexico: I. Geologic, mineralogic, and fluid inclusion data. Econ Geol (in press)

Schermerhorn LJG (1975) Spilites, regional metamorphism and subduction in the Iberian Pyrite Belt: Some comments. Geol Mijnbouw 54: 23–25

Schidlowski M (1976) Archaean atmosphere and evolution of the terrestrial oxygen budget. In: Windley BF (ed) The Early History of the Earth. Wiley, London 525–535

Sclater JG, Von Herzen RP, Williams DL, Anderson RN, Klitgord K (1974) The Galapagos spreading center: Heat flow on the north flank. R Astron Soc Geophys J 38: 609–626

Sclater JG, Jaupart C, Galson D (1980) The heat flow through oceanic and continental crust and the heat loss of the earth. Rev Geophys Space Phys 18: 269–311

Scott SD (1980) Geology and structural control of Kuroko-type massive sulphide deposits. In: Strangway DW (ed) The Continental Crust and Its Mineral Deposits. Geol Assoc Can Spec Pap 20: 705–722

Scott SD, Edmond J, Lonsdale P (1983) Modern analogue of a Besshi-type massive sulfide deposit on the sea floor, Guaymas Basin, Gulf of Californa (abst). Am Inst Min Eng Ann Mtg Atlanta Abstr Progr 84

Searle DL, Panayiotou A (1980) Structural implications in the evolution of the Troodos massif, Cyprus. In: Panayiotou A (ed) Ophiolites. Int Ophiolite Symp Cyprus, 1979, 50–60

Semenov EI (1974) Economic mineralogy of alkaline rocks. In: Sorenson H (ed) The Alkaline Rocks. Wiley, London 543–554

Sengor AMC, Burke K, Dewey JF (1978) Rifts at high angles to orogenic belts: tests for their origin and the upper Rhine graben as an example. Am J Sci 278: 24–40

Seyfried WE Jr, Bischoff JL (1979) Low temperature basalt alteration by seawater: an experimental study at 70 °C and 15 °C. Geochim Cosmochim Acta 43: 1937–1947

Seyfried WE Jr, Mottl MJ (1982) Hydrothermal alteration of basalt by seawater under seawater-dominated conditions. Geochim Cosmochim Acta 46: 985–1002

Shanks WC (1977) Massive sulfide deposits at divergent plate boundaries: origin and subsequent emplacement (abst) Geol Soc Am, Abstr with Progr 9: 1170

Shanks WC, Bischoff JL (1977) Ore transport and deposition in the Red Sea geothermal system: A geochemical model. Geochim Cosmochim Acta 41: 1507–1519

Shanks WC, Bischoff JL (1980) Geochemistry, sulfur isotope composition, and accumulation rate of Red Sea geothermal deposits. Econ Geol 75: 445–459

Sharp JE (1979) Cave Peak, a molybdenum-mineralized breccia pipe complex in Culberson County, Texas. Econ Geol 74: 517–534

Shatski NS (1947) Structural correlations of platforms and geosynclinal folded regions. Izv Akad Nauk SSSR Geol Ser 5: 37–56

Shcherba GN, Mukanov KM, Mitryayeva NM (1981) Ore-formation in Atasu-type deposits. Proc Fifth IAGOD Symp Utah 1980 337–345

Sheppard SMF, Gustafson LB (1976) Oxygen and hydrogen isotopes in the porphyry copper deposit at El Salvador, Chile. Econ Geol 71: 1549–1559

Sheppard SMF, Taylor HP Jr (1974) Hydrogen and oxygen evidence for the origin of water in the Boulder Batholith and the Butte ore deposit, Montana. Econ Geol 69: 926–946

Sheppard SMF, Nielsen RL, Taylor HP (1971) Hydrogen and oxygen isotope ratios in minerals from porphyry copper deposits. Econ Geol 66: 515–542

Shimazaki H (1980) Characteristics of skarn deposits and related acid magmatism in Japan. Econ Geol 75: 173–183

Shimazaki Y (1974) Ore minerals of the Kuroko-type deposits. Min Geol Spec Issue No 6 Soc Min Geol Jpn 311–322

Sibbald, TII, Munday RJC, Lewry JF (1977) Setting of uranium mineralization in northern Saskatchewan. Spec Publ Geol Soc Sask 3: 51–98

Sibson RH, Moore JM, Rankin AH (1975) Seismic pumping – a hydrothermal fluid transport mechanism. J Geol Soc Lond 131: 653–659

Silberman ML (1978) The volcanic and tectonic framework of hydrothermal precious metal deposits of the Great Basin of the western United States during Cenozoic time. (Abst) Fifth Symp Int Assoc Genesis of Ore Dep, 170

Silberman ML, McKee EH (1974) Ages of Tertiary volcanic rocks and hydrothermal precious-metal deposits in central and western Nevada. Nev Bur Mines Geol Rep 19: 67–72

Silberman ML, Stewart JH, McKee EH (1976) Igneous activity, tectonics, and hydrothermal precious-metal mineralization in the Great Basin during Cenozoic time. Soc Min Engnrs AIME Trans 260: 253–263

Silberman ML, MacKevett EM Jr, Connor CL, Mathews A (1981) Metallogenic and tectonic significance of whole-rock potassium-argon ages of the Nikolai Greenstone, McCarthy Quadrangle, Alaska. In: Silberman, Field, Berry (eds) Proc Symp Mineral Deposits of the Pacific Northwest. USGS Open-File Rep 81-355: 53–73

Sillitoe RH (1972a) A plate tectonic model for the origin of porphyry copper deposits. Econ Geol 67: 184–197

Sillitoe RH (1972b) Formation of certain massive sulfide deposits at sites of seafloor spreading. Inst Min Metall Trans 81: B141–B148

Sillitoe RH (1973) The tops and bottoms of porphyry copper deposits. Econ Geol 68: 799–815

Sillitoe RH (1974a) Tectonic segmentation of the Andes: Implications for magmatism and metallogeny. Nature 250: 542–545

Sillitoe RH (1974b) Tin mineralization above mantle hotspots. Nature 248: 497–499

Sillitoe RH (1976a) A reconnaissance of the Mexican porphyry copper belt. Inst Min Metall Trans 85: B170–B189

Sillitoe RH (1976b) Andean mineralization: a model for the metallogeny of convergent plate margins. In: Strong DF (ed) Metallogeny and Plate Tectonics. Geol Assoc Can Spec Pap 14: 59–100

Sillitoe RH (1977) Metallic mineralization affiliated to subaerial volcanism: a review. Geol Soc Lond Spec Publ No 7: 99–116

Sillitoe RH (1978) Metallogenic evolution of a collisional mountain belt in Pakistan: a preliminary analysis. J Geol Soc Lond 135: 377–387

Sillitoe RH (1979) Some thoughts on gold-rich porphyry copper deposits. Mineral Deposita 14: 161–174

Sillitoe RH (1980a) Types of porphyry molybdenum deposits. Min Mag 142: 550–553

Sillitoe RH (1980b) Are porphyry copper and Kuroko-type massive sulfide deposits incompatible? Geology 8: 11–14

Sillitoe RH (1980c) Cauldron subsidence as a possible inhibitor of porphyry copper formation. In: Granitic Magmatism and Related Mineralization. Min Geol Spec Issue No 8: 85–93

Sillitoe RH (1980d) Strata-bound ore deposits related to infraCambrian rifting along northern Gondwanaland. Proc Fifth IAGOD Symp, 163–172

Sillitoe RH (1981a) Ore deposits in Cordilleran and island-arc settings. Ariz Geol Soc Dig Vol XIV: 49–70

Sillitoe RH (1981b) Regional aspects of the Andean porphyry copper belt in Chile and Argentina. Inst Min Metall Trans 90: B15–B36

Sillitoe RH (1982a) Unconventional metals in porphyry deposits. Am Inst Min Eng Dallas Mtg Preprint No 82–63

Sillitoe RH (1982b) Extensional habits of rhyolite-hosted massive sulfide deposits. Geology 10: 403–407

Sillitoe RH, Sawkins FJ (1971) Geologic, mineralogic, and fluid inclusion studies relating to the origin of copper-bearing tourmaline breccia pipes, Chile. Econ Geol 66: 1028–1041

Sillitoe RH, Halls C, Grant NJ (1975) Porphyry tin deposits in Bolivia. Econ Geol 70: 913–927

Simmons S, Sawkins FJ (1983) Mineralogic and fluid inclusion studies of the Washington Cu-Mo-W breccia pipe, Sonora, Mexico. Econ Geol 78:521–526

Simpson ESW (1970) The anorthosite of southern Angola: a review of present data. In: Clifford J, Gass I (eds) African Magmatism and Tectonics. Oliver and Boyd, Edinburgh, 89–96

Sinclair AJ, Drummond AD, Carter NC, Dawson KM (1982) A preliminary analysis of gold and silver grades of porphyry-type deposits in western Canada. In: Levison AA (ed) Precious Metals in the Northern Cordillera. Assoc Explor Geochem 157–172

Skinner BF, White DE, Rose HJ, Mays RE (1967) Sulfides associated with the Salton Sea geothermal brine. Econ Geol 62: 316–330

Slack JF (1980) Multistage vein ores of the Lake City district, western San Juan Mountains, Colorado. Econ Geol 75: 963–991

Slaughter AL (1968) The Homestake Mine. In: Ridge JD (ed) Ore Deposits of the United States 1933-1967 (Graton-Sales Vol) New York. Am Inst Min Metall Petrol Engineers 1436–1459

Sleep NH, Snell NS (1976) Thermal contraction and flexure of mid-continent and Atlantic marginal basins. Geophys J R Astron Soc 45: 125–154

Sleep NH, Windley BF (1982) Archean plate tectonics: constraints and inferences. J Geol 40: 363–380

Smirnov VI (1970) Pyritic deposits, Parts 1 and 2. Int Geol Rev 12: 881–908, 1039–1058

Smirov VI (1977) Ore deposits of the USSR. Pitman, London

Smith DAM (1965) The geology of the area around the Khan and Swakop Rivers in South West Africa. S Afric Geol Surv Dep Mines Johannesburg, 1–113

Smith DM Jr, Albinson T, Sawkins FJ (1982) Geologic and fluid inclusion studies of the Tayoltita silver-gold vein deposits, Durango, Mexico. Econ Geol 77: 1120–1145

Smith RB, Christiansen RL (1980) Yellowstone Park as a window on the earth's interior. Sci Am 242: 84–95

Snyder WS, Dickinson WR, Silberman MC (1976) Tectonic implications of space-time patterns of Cenozoic magmatism in the western United States. Earth Planet Sci Lett 32: 91–106

Sohnge PG (1946) The geology of the Messina copper mines and surrounding country. S Afri Geol Surv Mem 40: 1–280

Sokolov GA, Grigorev VM (1977) Deposits of iron. In: Smirnov VI (ed) Ore Deposits of the USSR. Pittman, London 1: 7–113

Soler E (1973) L'association spilites-quartz keratophyres du sud-oest de la Peninsule Iberique. Geologie et Mijnbouw 52: 277–288

Solomon M (1976) "Volcanic" massive-sulfide deposits and their host rocks – a review and an explanation. In: Wolf KH (ed) Handbook of Stratabound and Stratiform Ore Deposits. Elsevier, Amsterdam 6: 21–54

Solomon M (1981) An introduction to the geology and metallic ore deposits of Tasmania. Econ Geol 76: 194–208

Souch BE, Podolsky, Geological Staff (1969) The sulfide ores of Sudbury: their particular relationship to a distinctive inclusion-bearing facies of the Nickel Irruptive. Econ Geol Monogr 4: 252–261

Spence CD, De Rozen-Spence AF (1975) The place of sulfide mineralization in the volcanic sequence at Noranda, Quebec. Econ Geol 70: 90–101

Spooner ETC, Bray CJ (1977) Hydrothermal fluids of seawater salinity in ophiolitic sulfide ore deposits in Cyprus. Nature 266: 808–812

Stemprok M (1981) Tin and tungsten deposits of the West Central European Variscides. Proc Fifth IAGOD Symp Utah 495–512

Steven TA, Ratte JC (1960) Geology and ore deposits of the Summitville district, San Juan Mountains, Colorado. US Geol Surv Prof Pap 343: 1–70

Steven TA, Laedke RG, Lipman PW (1974) Relation of mineralization to calderas in the San Juan volcanic field, southwestern Colorado. J Res US Geol Surv 2: 405–409

Stillman CJ, Williams CT (1978) Geochemistry and tectonic setting of some Upper Ordovician volcanic rocks in east and southeast Ireland. Earth Planet Sci Lett 41: 288–310

Stone JG (1959) Ore genesis in the Naica district, Chihuahua, Mexico. Econ Geol 54: 1002–1034

Stowe CW (1974) Alpine-type structures in the Rhodesian basement complex at Selukwe. J Geol Soc Lond 130: 411–426

Stumpfl EE, Clifford TN, Burger AJ, van Zyl D (1976) The copper deposits of the O'kiep District, South Africa. Min Deposita 11: 46–70

Sutherland Brown A (ed) (1976) Porphyry deposits of the Canadian Cordillera. Can Inst Min Metall Spec Vol 15

Sutherland Brown A, Cathro RJ, Panteleyev A, Ney CS (1971) Metallogeny of the Canadian Cordillera. Can Inst Min Metall Trans 74: 121–145

Sverjensky DA (1981) The origin of a Mississippi Valley-type deposit in the Viburnum Trend, Southeast Missouri. Econ Geol 76: 1848–1872

Swinden HS, Strong DF (1976) A comparison of plate tectonic models of metallogenesis in the Appalachians, the North America Cordillera, and the east Australian Paleozoic. In: Strong (DF) Metallogeny and Plate Tectonics. Geol Assoc Can Spec Pap 14: 443–471

Sykes LR (1978) Intraplate seismicity, reactivation of existing zones of weakness, alkaline magmatism, and other tectonism postdating continental fragmentation. Rev Geophys Space Phys 16: 621–688

Sykes LR (1980) Earthquakes and other processes within lithospheric plates and the reactivation of pre-existing zones of weakness. In: Strangway DW (ed) The Continental Crust and Its Mineral Deposits. Geol Assoc Can Spec Pap 20: 215–238

Takahashi M, Aramaki S, Ishihara S (1980) Magnetite-series/ilmenite series vs. I-type/S-type granitoids. In: Granitic Magmatism and Related Mineralization. Min Geol Spec Issue No 8: 13–28

Tamrazyn GP (1971) Siberian continental drift. Tectonophysics 11: 433-460.

Tankard AJ, Jackson MPA, Eriksson KA, Hobday DK, Hunter DR, Minter WEL (1982) Crustal evolution of Southern Africa. Springer, New York Heidelberg Berlin 523 p

Tankut A (1980) The Orhaneli massif, Turkey. In: Panayiotou A (ed) Ophiolites. Proc Int Ophiolite Symp Cyprus 702–713

Tapponnier P, Peltzer G, LeDain AY, Armijo R (1982) Propagating extrusion tectonics in Asia: New insights from simple experiments with plasticine. Geology 10: 611–617

Tarney J, Windley BF (1978) Chemistry, thermal gradients and evolution of the lower continental crust. J Geol Soc Lond 134: 153–172

Tarney J, Windley BF (1981) Marginal basins throughout geologic time. Philos Trans R Soc Lond A301: 217–231

Tarney J, Dalziel I, DeWit M (1976) Marginal basin 'Rocas Verdes' complex from S. Chile: a model for Archean greenstone belt formation. In: Windley BF (ed) The Early History of the Earth. Wiley, London 131–146

Taylor BE, O'Neil JR (1977) Stable isotope studies of metasomatic Ca-Fe-Al-Si skarns and associated metamorphic and igneous rocks, Osgood Mountains, Nevada. Contrib Min Petrol 63: 1–50

Taylor GR (1976) Styles of mineralization in the Solomon Islands – A review. In: Glasby GP, Katz HR (eds) Marine Geophysical Investigations in the Southwest Pacific and Adjacent Areas. ESCAP CCOP/SOPAC Tech Bull 2: 83–91

Taylor HP Jr (1973) O^{18}/O^{16} evidence for meteoric-hydrothermal alteration and ore deposition in the Tonapah, Comstock Lode, and Goldfield mining districts, Nevada. Econ Geol 68: 747–764

Taylor RG (1979) Geology of Tin Deposits. Elsevier Scientific Publishing Co. Amsterdam 543 p.

Templeman-Kluit D (1981) Geology and mineral deposits of the southern Yukon. In: Yukon Geology and Exploration 1979-80 Indian and Northern Affairs Canada, Whitehorse 7–31

Thacker JL, Anderson KH (1977) The geologic setting of the southeast Missouri Lead District – Regional geologic history, structure and stratigraphy. Econ Geol 72: 339–348

Thayer TP (1942) Chromite resources of Cuba. US Geol Surv Bull 935-A: 1–74

Thayer TP (1964) Principal features and origin of chromite deposits and some observations of the Guleman-Soridag district, Turkey. Econ Geol 59: 1497–1524

Thayer TP (1969) Gravity differentiation and magmatic re-emplacement of podiform chromite deposits. In: Wilson HDB (ed) Magmatic Ore Deposits. Econ Geol Monogr 4: 132–146

Thiessen R, Burke K, Kidd WSF (1979) African hotspots and their relation to the underlying mantle. Geology 7: 263–266

Thomas JA, Galey JT Jr (1982) Exploration and geology of the Mt. Emmons molybdenite deposits, Gunnison County, Colorado. Econ Geol 77: 1085–1104

Thurlow JG, Swanson EA (1981) Geology and ore deposits of the Buchans area, central Newfoundland. Geol Assoc Can Spec Pap 22: 113–142

Thurlow JG, Swanson EA, Strong DF (1975) Geology and lithogeochemistry of the Buchans polymetallic sulfide deposits, Newfoundland. Econ Geol 70: 130–144

Tischendorf G, Schust F, Lange H (1978) Relation between granites and tin deposits in the Erzegebirge, GDR. Metallization associated with Acid Magmatism IGCP 3: 123–138

Titley SR, Beane RE (1981) Porphyry copper deposits: Part 1 Geologic settings, petrology, and tectogenesis. Econ Geol 75th Anniv Vol, 214–234

Toens PD (1975) The geology of part of the southern foreland of the Damara Orogenic Belt in S.W.A. and Botswana. Geol Rundsch 64: 175–192

Tokunaga M, Houma H (1974) Fluid inclusions in the minerals from some Kuroko deposits. Mining Geology Spec Issue No 6. Soc Min Geol Jpn 385–388

Townend R, Ferreira PM, Franke ND (1980) Caraiba, new copper deposit in Brazil. Inst Min Metall Trans 89: B159–164

Trendall AF (1973) Iron-formations of the Hamersley Group in Western Australia: type examples of varved Precambrian evaporites. In: Genesis of Precambrian Iron and Manganese Deposits, Proc Kiev Symp 1970 Paris UNESCO, 25[7]-268

Trendall AF, Blockley JG (1970) The iron formatons of the Precambrian Hamersley Group, Western Australia. West Aust Geol Surv Bull 119: 366 p

Trettin HP (1979) Middle Oridvician to Lower Devonian deep-water succession at southeastern margin of Hazen Trough, Canon Fiord, Ellsemere Island. Geol Surv Can Bull 272: 1–84

Tu KC, Wang ZG, Yu XY (1980) Genesis of granitic rocks in South China and related mineralization. In: Granitic Magmatism and Related Mineralization. Min Geol Spec Issue No 8: 189–196

Tuach J, Kennedy MJ (1978) The geologic setting of the Ming and other sulfide deposits, Consolidated Rambler Mines, northeast Newfoundland. Econ Geol 73: 192–206

Tupper WM (1969) The geology of the Orvan Brook sulfide deposits, Restigouche County, New Brunswick. Geol Surv Can Pap 66-59: 1–11

Turcotte DL, Burke KCA (1978) Global sea-level changes and the thermal structure of the earth. Earth Planet Sci Lett 41: 341–346

Turneaure FS (1935) The tin deposits of Llallagua, Bolivia. Econ Geol 30: 14–60, 170–190

Turneaure FS (1971) The Bolivian tin-silver province. Econ Geol 66: 215–225

Turneaure FS, Walker KK (1947) The ore deposits of the Eastern Andes of Bolivia. The Cordillera Real. Econ Geol 42: 595–625

Turner DC, Webb PK (1974) The Daura igneous complex, N. Nigeria: a link between the Younger Granite district of Nigeria and S. Niger. J Geol Soc Lond 130: 71–77

Tweto O, Sims PK (1963) Precambrian ancestry of the Colorado mineral belt. Geol Soc Am Bull 74: 991–1014

Upadhyay HD, Strong DF (1973) Geological setting of the Betts Cove copper deposits, Newfoundland: an example of ophiolite sulfide mineralization. Econ Geol 68: 161–167

Urabe T, Sato T (1978) Kuroko deposits of the Kosaka Mine, northeast Honshu, Japan – Products of submarine hotsprings on Miocene sea floor. Econ Geol 73: 161–179

Uyeda S, Nishiwaki C (1980) Stress field, metallogenesis and mode of subduction. In: Strangway DW (ed) The Continental Crust and Its Mineral Deposits. Geol Assoc Can Spec Pap 20: 323–339

Vail JR (1977) Further data on the alignment of basic igneous intrusive complexes in Southern and Eastern Africa. Trans Geol Soc S Afr 80: 87–92

Valentine JW, Moores EM (1972) Global tectonics and the fossil-record. J Geol 80: 167–184

Van Alstine RE (1976) Continental rifts and lineaments associated with major fluorspar districts. Econ Geol 71: 977–987

Van Biljon WJ (1980) Plate-tectonics and the origin of the Witwatersrand basin. Proc Fifth IAGOD Symp Schweizerbart'sche Verlagsbuchhandlung, Stuttgart 217–226

VanEden JG (1978) Stratiform copper and zinc mineralization in the Cretaceous of Angola. Econ Geol 73: 1154–1160

Varentsov IM (1964) Sedimentary Manganese Ores. Elsevier, Amsterdam, 119 p

Vermaak CF (1976) The Merensky Reef – Thoughts on its environment and genesis. Econ Geol 71: 1270–1298

Vermaak CF (1981) Kunene Anorthosite complex. In: Hunter DR (ed) Precambrian of the Southern Hemisphere. Elsevier, Amsterdam, 578–598

Viljoen RP, Saager R, Viljoen MJ (1969) Metallogenesis and ore control in the Steynsdorp goldfield, Barberton Mountain Land, South Africa. Econ Geol 64: 778–797

Vine FJ (1966) Spreading of the ocean floor: new evidence. Science 154: 1405–1410

Vine FJ, Smith AG (1981) Extensional tectonics associated with convergent plate boundaries. Philos Trans R Soc Lond A 300: 217–442

Vineyard JD (1977) Preface to Viburnum Trend issue. Econ Geol 72: 337–338

Vokes FM (1968) Regional metamorphism of the Paleozoic geosynclinal sulphide ore deposits of Norway. Inst Min Metall Trans 77: 853–859

Vokes FM (1969) Regional metamorphism of the Paleozoic geosynclinal sulfide ore deposits of Norway. Inst Min Metall Trans 77: B53–B59

Vokes FM (1973) Metallogeny possibly related to continental breakup in southwest Scandinavia. In: Tarling DH, Runcorn SK (eds) Implications of Continental Drift to the Earth Sciences. Academic Press, London 1: 573–579

Vokes FM (1976) Caledonian massive sulfide deposits in Scandinavia: A comparative review. In: Wolf KH (ed) Handbook of Strata-bound and Stratiform Ore Deposits, Elsevier, Amsterdam 6: 79–127

Vokes FM, Gale GH (1976) Metallogeny relatable to global tectonics in southern Scandinavia. In: Strong DF (ed) Metallogeny and Plate Tectonics. Geol Assoc Can Spec Pap 14: 413–441

von der Borch CC (1980) Evolution of late Proterozoic to early Paleozoic Adelaide Foldbelt, Australia: Comparison with post-Permian rifts and passive margins. Tectonophysics 70: 115–134

Wagener J (1980) The Prieska zinc-copper deposit, Cape Province, South Africa. Proc Fifth IA-GOD Symp 635–651

Wakefield J (1978) Samba: a deformed porphyry-type copper deposit in the basement of the Zambian Copperbelt. Trans Inst Min Metall 87: B43–B52

Walker PN, Barbour DM (1981) Geology of the Buchans ore horizon breccias. Geol Assoc Can Spec Pap 22: 161–186

Walker RG (1970) Review of the geometry and facies organization of turbidites and turbidite-bearing basins. In: Lajoie J (ed) Flysch Sedimentology in North America. Geol Assoc Can Spec Pap 7: 219–252

Walker RN, Logan RG, Binnekamp JG (1977) Recent geological advances concerning the H.Y.C. and associated deposits, McArthur River, N.T. Geol Soc Aust J 24: 365–380

Walker RR, Matulich A, Amos AC, Watkins JJ, Mannard GW (1975) The geology of the Kidd Creek Mine. Econ Geol 70: 80–89

Wallace SR, Muncaster NK, Johnson DC, MacKenzie WB, Bookstrom AA, Surface VE (1968) Multiple intrusion and mineralization at Climax, Colorado. In: Ridge JD (ed) Ore Deposits of the United States, 1933-1967. AIME New York 606–640

Wallace SR, MacKenzie WB, Blair RG, Muncaster NK (1978) Geology of the Urad and Henderson molybdenite deposits, Clear Creek County, Colorado, with a section on a comparison of these deposits with those at Climax, Colorado. Econ Geol 73: 325–368

Warner LA (1978) The Colorado Lineament: a middle Precambrian wrench fault system. Geol Soc Am Bull 89: 161–171

Weiblen PW, Morey GB (1980) A summary of the stratigraphy, petrology, and structure of the Duluth Complex. Am J Sci 280-A: 88–133

Wellman P, McDougall I (1974) Cenozoic igneous activity in eastern Australia. Tectonophysics 23: 301–335

Wells PRA (1979) Chemical and thermal evolution of Archean sialic crust, southern West Greenland. J Petrol 20: 187–226

Westra G, Keith SB (1981) Classification and genesis of stockwork molybdenum deposits. Econ Geol 76: 844–873

White AJR (1979) Sources of granite magmas. Geol Soc Am Absts Progs 11: 539

White DE (1968) Environments of generation of some base-metal ore deposits. Econ Geol 63: 301–335

White DE (1974) Diverse origins of hydrothermal fluids. Econ Geol 69: 954–973

White DE, Anderson ET, Grubbs DK (1963) Geothermal brine well: Mile-deep drill hole may tap ore-forming magmatic water, rocks undergoing metamorphism. Science 139: 919–922

White WH, Bookstrom AA, Kamilli RJ, Ganster MW, Smith RP, Ranta DE, Steininger RC (1981) Character and origin of Climax-type molybdenum deposits. Econ Geol 75th Anniv Vol, 270–316

Whitehead RES, Goodfellow WD (1978) Geochemistry of volcanic rocks from the Tetagouche Group, Bathurst, New Brunswick, Canada. Can J Earth Sci 15: 207–219

Wiebe RA (1980) Anorthositic magmas and the origin of Proterozoic anorthosite massifs. Nature 286: 564–567

Willemse J (1964) A brief outline of the Bushveld igneous complex. In: Some Ore Deposits of Southern Africa. Geol Soc S Afr Publ 2: 19–28

Willemse J (1969) The geology of the Bushveld Igneous Complex, the largest repository of magmatic ore deposits in the world. Econ Geol Monogr 4: 1–22

Williams H, Hatcher RD Jr (1982) Suspect terranes and accretionary history of the Appalachian orogen. Geology 10: 530–536

Williams N (1978) Studies of the base metal sulfide deposits at McArthur River, Norther Territory, Australia: I. The Cooley and Ridge deposits. Econ Geol 73: 1005–1035

Wilse MA, McGlasson JA (1973) Prince William Sound, a volcanogenic massive sulfide province (Abstr) Geol Soc Am Ann Mtg Dallas 1973: 865

Wilson IF (1955) Geology and mineral deposits of the Boleo copper district Baja California, Mexico. US Geol Surv Prof Pap 273: 1–133

Wilson JT (1963) Evidence from islands on the spreading of ocean floors. Nature 197: 536–538

Wilson JT (1965) A new class of faults and their bearing on continental drift. Nature 207: 343–347

Windley BF (1978) The Evolving Continents. Wiley, New York 385 p

Wisser E (1966) The epithermal precious-metal province of northwest Mexico. Nev Bur Mines Geol Rep 13: 63–92

Wold RJ, Hinze WJ eds (1982) The geology and tectonics of the Lake Superior Basin – A Review. Geol Soc Am Mem 156: 278 p

Wolery TJ, Sleep NH (1976) Hydrothermal circulation and geochemical flux at midocean ridges. J Geol 84: 249–275

Wolfhard MR, Ney CS (1976) Metallogeny and plate tectonics in the Canadian Cordillera. In: Strong DF (ed) Metallogeny and Plate Tectonics. Geol Assoc Can Spec Pap 14: 361–392

Wu I, Petersen U (1977) Geochemistry of tetrahedrite and mineral zoning at Casapalca, Peru. Econ Geol 72: 993–1016

Wyllie PJ (1981) Magma sources in Cordilleran settings. In: Dickinson WK, Payne WD (eds) Relations of Tectonics to Ore Deposits in the Southern Cordillera. Ariz Geol Soc Dig XIV: 39–48

Wynne-Edwards HR (1976) Proterozoic ensialic orogensis: the millipede model of ductile plate tectonics. Am J Sci 276: 927–953

Yeates AN, Wyatt BW, Tucker DH (1982) Application of gamma-ray spectrometry to prospecting for tin and tungsten granites, particularly within the Lachlan Fold Belt, New South Wales. Econ Geol 77: 1725–1738

Young GM (ed) (1973) Huronian stratigraphy and sedimentation. Geol Assoc Can Spec Pap 12

Young GM (1976) Iron-formation and glaciogenic rocks of the Rapitan Group, Northwest Territories, Canada. Precambrian Res 3: 137–158

Ypma PJM, Fuzikawa K (1980) Fluid inclusion and oxygen isotope studies of the Nabarlek and Jabiluka deposits, Northern Territory, Australia. In: Uranium in the Pine Creek Geosyncline. Int Atomic Energy Agency Vienna, 375–396

Ypma PJM, Simons JH (1970) Genetical aspects of the tin mineralization in Durango, Mexico. In: Fox W (ed) A second technical conference on tin, Bangkok, 1969 London, Int Tin Council, 179–191

Zachos K (1969) The chromite mineralization of the Vourinos ophiolite complex, Northern Greece. In: Wilson HDB (ed) Magmatic Ore Deposits, Econ Geol Monogr 4: 147–153

Zachrisson E (1982) Spilitization, mineralization and vertical zonation at the Stekenjokk stratabound sulfide deposit, central Scandinavian Caledonides. Inst Min Metall Trans 91: B192–B199

Zaw UK (1976) The Cantung E-zone ore body, Tungsten, Northwest Territories – A major scheelite skarn deposit. Unpub MS thesis, Queens Univ Kingston Ont 327p

Ziegler PA (1978) North-western Europe: Tectonics and basin development. Geol Mijnbouw 57: 589–626

Zoback ML, Thompson GA (1978) Basin and Range rifting in northern Nevada: clues from a mid-Miocene rift and its subsequent offsets. Geology 6: 111–116

Zuffardi P (1977) Ore/mineral deposits related to the Mesozoic ophiolites in Italy. In: Klemm DD, Schneider HJ (eds) Time- and Strata-bound Ore Deposits, Springer, Berlin Heidelberg New York 314–323

Subject Index

Numbers in *italic* refer to tables or figures

Minerals and Rocks

Editor in Chief:
P.J.Wyllie

Editors:
**A.El Goresy,
W.v.Engelhardt,
T.Hahn**

Volume 15
J.B.Dawson

Kimberlites and Their Xenoliths

1980. 84 figures, 35 tables. XII, 252 pages
ISBN 3-540-10208-6

Contents: Introduction. – Distribution and Tectonic Setting of Kimberlites. – Geology of Kimberlite Intrusions. – Petrography of Kimberlite. – Geochemistry of Kimberlites. – Mineralogy of Kimberlites. – Xenoliths in Kimberlite. – The Megacryst Suite. – The Sub-Continental Mantle and Crust – Evidence from Kimberlite Xenoliths. – Kimberlite Genesis. – References. – Subject Index.

In the past two decades there has been a rapid growth of interest in kimberlite, not only as a source of diamonds, but also as a rock type that has sampled the uppermantle more thoroughly than any other type of igneous activity. Whereas earlier books published on the subject in recent years have concentrated on specific topics such as the geology of diamond or upper-mantle mineralogy, the present volume provides on overall coverage of the geology of kimberlite from which inferences on the nature of the earth's upper-mantle can be drawn. This synthesis of up-to-date results and opinions from the recent geological literature will be highly appreciated by reserchers in the field.

Springer-Verlag
Berlin
Heidelberg
New York
Tokyo

Minerals and Rocks

Editor in Chief:
P.J.Wyllie

Editors:
**A.El Goresy,
W.v.Engelhardt,
T.Hahn**

Springer-Verlag
Berlin
Heidelberg
New York
Tokyo

Volume 16
J.B.Gill

Orogenic Andesites and Plate Tectonics

1981. 109 figures. XIV, 390 pages
ISBN 3-540-10666-9

Contents: What is "Typical Calcalkaline Andesite"? – The Plate Tectonic Connection. – Geophysical Setting of Volcanism at Convergent Plate Boundaries. – Andesite Magmas, Ejecta, Eruptions, and Volcanoes. – Bulk Chemical Composition of Orogenic Andesites. – Mineralogy and Mineral Stabilities. – Spatial and Temporal Variations in the Composition of Orogenic Andesites. – The Role of Subducted Ocean Crust in the Genesis of Orogenic Andesites. – The Role of the Mantle Wedge. – The Role of the Crust. – The Role of Basalt Differentiation. – Conclusions. – Appendix. – References. – Subject Index.

The solution to the question of andesite genesis is a major, multi-disciplinary undertaking facing geoscientists in the 1980's. **Orogenic Andesites and Plate Tectonics** was written in response to the growing need of researchers in this area for a classification of the long-standing problem and identifications of profitable areas for future investigations.
This book critically summarizes the vast relevant literature on the tectonics, geophysics, volcanology, geology, geochemistry, and mineralogy of andesites and their volcanoes. The author cites over 1100 references in these specialities and includes information on the location and rock composition of more than 300 recently active volcanoes. In addition, he provides a systematic and original evaluation of genetic hypotheses. Numerous cross references enhance the integrated subject development which consistently emphasizes the implications of data for theories of magma genesis.
Orogenic Andesites and Plate Tectonics will prove an invaluable reference source researchers and graduate students in the geosciences seeking a careful evaluation of genetic hypotheses and keydata, arguments or gaps in this promising field.